# Semiconductors

# Semiconductors

Technical information and
characteristic data for students

Siemens Aktiengesellschaft

Deutsche Bibliothek Cataloguing-in-Publication Data

**Semiconductors:**
Explanatory technical information and characteristic data for students. —
Berlin ; Munich : Siemens-Aktienges., [Abt. Verl.], 1990
ISBN 3-8009-1567-7

ISBN 3-8009-1567-7

Published by Siemens Aktiengesellschaft, Berlin and Munich
© 1990 by Siemens Aktiengesellschaft, Berlin and Munich

Printed in the Federal Republic of Germany

# Foreword

Change is the only factor which is constant in the field of semiconductors. It is chiefly characterized by:

▷ rapid further development of semiconductor technology
▷ increasing product and application diversity
▷ increasing complexity of technology, products and applications
▷ increasing integration of systems on a chip.

A few years ago it was important to describe the basic principles and products in detail. Nowadays this is no longer possible in a work of this size. Consequently it is our aim to describe selected products and examples of applications to provide an insight into the various fields of development and the state of the art.

A key aspect of semiconductor manufacture is quality, so a separate chapter has been devoted to it.

Munich, October 1990

Siemens Aktiengesellschaft

# Contents

# 1  Integrated Circuits –
# Structure and Mode of Operation

On an integrated circuit (IC) all circuit components and their wiring are produced in a common manufacturing process on a monocrystalline semiconductor wafer (chip). The circuit components which are arranged close together on the chip must be mutually insulated electrically. The chip is incorporated in a package, and the chip terminals are linked to the package terminals by means of very thin wires which are welded on.

Silicon or gallium arsenide are suitable as semiconductor materials for the integrated circuits. Since gallium arsenide, both at present and in the foreseeable future, is of minor importance for integrated circuits, we shall restrict ourselves below entirely to silicon.

The important advantages of integrated circuits by comparison with circuits incorporating discrete components are low manufacturing costs for large quantities, high reliability, low space requirement and high operating speed. Owing to these advantages, there is an unbroken trend towards higher and higher integration levels and higher and higher packing densities, speed and complexity of the circuitry on the chip. This is achieved primarily by reducing the size of the structures on the chip. For reasons of economy, it is also attempted to produce larger and larger silicon wafers so as to be able to accommodate as many chips as possible on the silicon wafer. Fig. 1.1 shows how these trends have developed historically taking dynamic memories as an example.

Depending on the basic types of transistor, the bipolar transistor and the MOS transistor, we also distinguish between bipolar circuits and MOS circuits in the field of integrated circuits. In the following sections, we shall outline the technical structure and electrical operation of bipolar and MOS circuits.

## 1.1  Bipolar Integrated Circuits

### 1.1.1  The PN Junction

Pure silicon is a semiconductor with very low electrical conductivity at room temperature. But if only one silicon atom in a thousand is replaced by a doping atom (e.g. boron, phosphorus or arsenic), conductivity increases many times over. Consequently, depending on the doping atom concentration, a doped silicon region represents a resistor with a high or low resistance. See Fig. 1.2.

The second important semiconductor effect consists in the fact that the mobile charge carriers which are responsible for the conductivity are either negatively charged electrons or positively charged holes, dependent upon whether the silicon is doped with pentavalent atoms (phosphorus, arsenic or antimony) or with trivalent atoms (boron). The regions in which current flow is caused by the movement of electrons are termed N-regions and the regions in which current flow is caused by the effect movement of mobile holes are termed P-regions.

Both the N and P-regions are initially electrically neutral. In the N-regions for instance, the mobile electrons responsible for current flow are compensated for by the same number of stationary phosphorus, arsenic or antimony ions with positive charge (donors), located in the silicon lattice. The positively charged mobile holes in the P-regions are

11

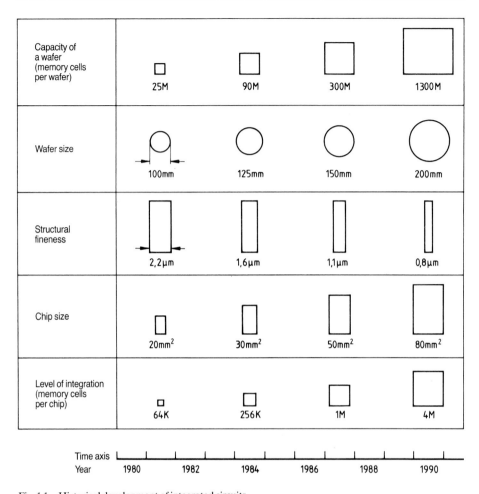

| | | | | |
|---|---|---|---|---|
| Capacity of a wafer (memory cells per wafer) | 25M | 90M | 300M | 1300M |
| Wafer size | 100mm | 125mm | 150mm | 200mm |
| Structural fineness | 2,2µm | 1,6µm | 1,1µm | 0,8µm |
| Chip size | 20mm² | 30mm² | 50mm² | 80mm² |
| Level of integration (memory cells per chip) | 64K | 256K | 1M | 4M |

Time axis
Year    1980    1982    1984    1986    1988    1990

Fig. 1.1    Historical development of integrated circuits

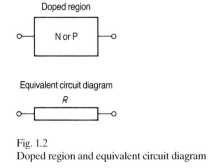

Doped region

N or P

Equivalent circuit diagram

R

Fig. 1.2
Doped region and equivalent circuit diagram

compensated for by the stationary, negative boron irons (acceptors).

A potential barrier is formed at the boundary layer between a P-region and an N-region (PN junction) since electrons diffuse from the N-region into the P-region and holes diffuse from the P-region into the N-region (Fig. 1.3). The electrons which have diffused into the P-region leave behind an electron-depleted layer in a thin layer at the PN junction, and the space charge of this layer results

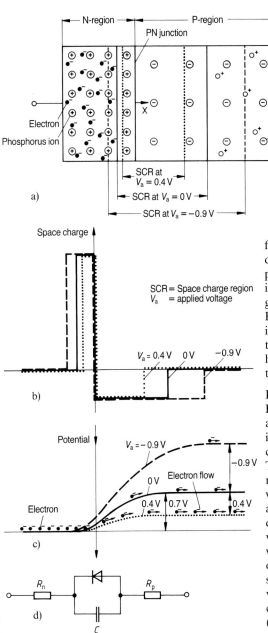

SCR = Space charge region
$V_a$ = applied voltage

Fig. 1.3
Boundary layer behavior in the semiconductor
a) and b) Charge distribution, c) Potential,
d) Equivalent circuit diagram

from the stationary, positively charged donors (Fig. 1.3a). Consequently, a hole-depleted negatively charged layer is produced in the P-region at the PN junction. The N-region thus assumes a higher potential than the P-region (Fig. 1.3c). The electrons diffusing into the P-region must now overcome this potential barrier. Diffusion of the electrons and holes stops at a specific magnitude of the potential barrier – approx. 0.7 V.

If a negative voltage is applied between the P-region and N-region, the potential barrier at the PN junction is increased (broken line in Fig. 1.3c). Only a few electrons or holes can overcome the higher potential barrier. This means that only a very low reverse current flows. Conversely, a high current flows with a positive voltage between the P-region and N-region. A PN junction thus functions electrically as a diode with a conducting-state voltage of 0.7 V. The space charge region which is depleted of mobile charge carriers on both sides of the PN junction acts in the same way as a capacitor. The electrical equivalent circuit diagram of a PN junction thus consists of a diode with parallel capacitor (Fig. 1.3d).

PN diodes break down (i.e. suddenly change from a high dynamic resistance to a much lower value) at a specific reverse voltage which lies between 5 V and over 100 V on the

PN junctions found in integrated circuits. On certain bipolar circuits, this breakdown voltage of the diodes (Zener diodes) is used to implement a defined voltage drop independently of the current.

Besides the PN diodes, many integrated circuits also use the so-called Schottky diode. It consists of a contact between aluminum and an N-region with a low doping level. The important difference with respect to the PN diode consists in the fact that the Schottky diode has a lower conducting-state voltage (around 0.4 V).

### 1.1.2 The Bipolar Transistor

The NPN bipolar transistor consists of two N-regions designated the emitter and collector, and a P-region in between, designated the base.

Fig. 1.4 shows the basic structure and mode of operation of such a bipolar transistor.

Without base voltage applied ($V_{BE} = 0$ V), the potential barrier between emitter and base is 0.7 V, and only very few electrons can overcome this barrier (cf. Fig. 1.3). The transistor is reverse-biased. With an applied voltage of $V_{BE} = 0.7$ V, the potential barrier has been reduced to such an extent that electrons can flow from the emitter region into the base region. If the base width, i.e. the distance between the PN junctions between emitter and base and base and collector, is only a few tenths of a μm, virtually all electrons diffuse as far as the base-collector junction, where they are accelerated and then dissipated via the collector contact after passing through the collector region. Only a few electrons unite (recombine) in the base region with the excess holes.

If the emitter-base junction is polarized in the forward direction, there is not only a flow of electrons from the emitter region to the base region, but also, conversely, a hole cur-

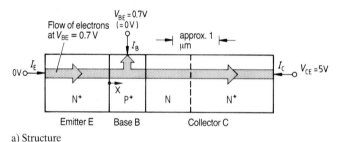

a) Structure

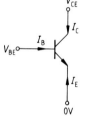

c) Graphic symbol

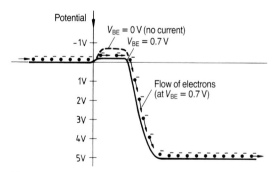

b) Potential distribution

Fig. 1.4 Structure and mode of operation of an NPN bipolar transistor

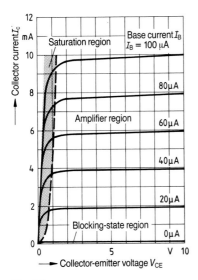

Fig. 1.5
Family of characteristics of an NPN bipolar

rent from the base region to the emitter region. However, this hole current is far lower than the flow of electrons if the doping atom concentration in the emitter is far higher ($N^+$-region) than in the base region (P-region). The hole current flowing from the base region into the emitter region is supplied externally as the base current, Fig. 1.4a.

Fig. 1.5 shows the typical family of characteristics of a bipolar transistor. The important feature is that a high collector current can be "controlled" with a low base current. The ratio of collector current to base current is termed the current gain. 100 is a typical value.

The bipolar transistor can also be operated inversely, i.e. the emitter and collector can be reversed. However, the current gain is lower (values of around 1) in this case, owing to the lower doping atom concentration of the emitter region.

### 1.1.3 Structure of Bipolar Circuits

An integrated bipolar circuit consists of a large number of bipolar transistors which are arranged adjacently on a silicon chip and interconnected with printed conductors dependent upon the required circuit function.

Fig. 1.6 shows a typical version of an NPN bipolar transistor with its direct environment in an integrated circuit. In this example, it has been assumed that the collector of the transistor is connected to the base region of a neighboring transistor by an aluminum printed conductor. The $P^+$-type isolating diffusions around the transistor act electrically in the same way as two diodes connected back-to-back (cf. Fig. 1.3) and thus guarantee mutual isolation of neighboring transistors.

The isolating diffusions and the P substrate connected to these diffusions are connected to the lowest potential occurring in the circuit.

In practice, NPN bipolar transistors are the main types since they have better electrical properties and can be manufactured more simply than PNP transistors.

The specific arrangement of the individual, doped regions in Fig. 1.6 results, amongst other things, from the marginal conditions relating to integration: the contacts can be attached only on the silicon surface and the transistors must be surrounded on all sides by a P-doped region for mutual isolation of the collector regions.

For instance, under these conditions one requires a highly doped buried $N^+$ subcollector in order to keep the collector series resistance low. These buried subcollectors in turn, mean that the monocrystaline silicon layer above, in which the emitter and base regions are embedded, has to be applied as an epitaxial layer after production of the buried subcollectors. The $P^+$ isolating diffusions extending through the epitaxial layer take up a relatively great deal of space. Thus, in integrated circuits, attempts are made to position the transistors whose collectors are connected in the circuit in a contiguous "resistor box".

An approx. 0.5 m thick SiO$_2$ layer which can be produced by thermal oxidation of the silicon surface serves as an insulating layer between the silicon surface and the printed conductors applied above them. Windows are etched into the SiO$_2$ layer using photolithographic masks at positions at which contacts are required. In general, each bipolar transistor in an integrated circuit requires 3 contacts with the pc-board level (high space requirement). One contact can be saved only if neighboring transistors have a common base region for instance.

The printed conductors essentially consist of aluminum. The resistance of a printed conductor of thickness $t$, width $w$ and length $l$ is as follows

$$R = \frac{\varrho \cdot l}{t \cdot w} \; ;$$

where $\varrho$ is the resistivity of aluminum. The ratio $l/w$ can be interpreted as the number of surface squares (□) with edge length $w$ of which the printed conductor is made up. Consequently, $\varrho/t$ is the resistance of a surface square of the printed conductor. This resistance is designated the sheet resistance, expressed in $\Omega/\square$. With 1 μm thickness, aluminium printed conductors have a sheet resistance of 30 m$\Omega/\square$. This means, that, for instance, a section of printed conductor with a width of 5 μm and a length of 50 μm (corresponding to 10 □), has a resistance of 0.3 $\Omega$.

More complex integrated bipolar circuits such as gate arrays or memories need more than one single printed conductor level. It is possible to implement multilayer wiring with the aid of deposited insulating layers between different printed conductor layers. The contact windows between the printed conductor levels are termed vias. They are produced in the same way as the contact windows to the silicon.

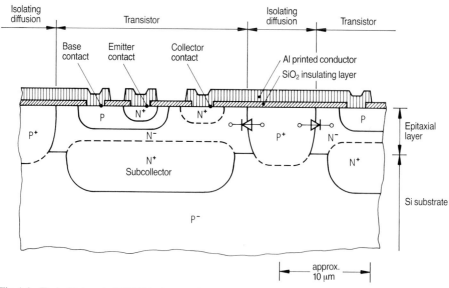

Fig. 1.6   Typical integrated NPN bipolar transistor

As compared with the structure shown in Fig. 1.6, modern bipolar circuits have two further developments, namely oxide isolation for electrically isolating neighboring bipolar transistors and polysilicon connections for the emitter and base contacts (Fig. 1.7). Both further developments lead to a major space saving and consequently lower parasitic capacitance and resistances, thus making faster circuits possible. Moreover, polysilicon emitter contacts achieve better transistor properties.

It is an obvious step to include not only the transistors in the integration, but also the doped regions individually or in other arrays in integrated bipolar circuits provided these arrays have the required electrical function. Thus, for instance, an emitter-base junction (if necessary with base-collector short-circuit in order to increase the conducting-state current) or an Al/N⁻ contact can function as diodes. Capacitors are implemented with the aid of reverse-biased PN junctions (see Fig.

1.3d) or with the aid of an $SiO_2$ layer (Fig. 1.6) as the dielectric between an $N^+$ region and an aluminum electrode. Resistors can be produced by appropriately rated, doped regions which are electrically isolated from their environment by a reverse-biased PN junction (see Fig. 1.2). Resistance values of between 2 and 40 $\Omega/\square$ can be achieved with the highly doped $N^+$ regions (see Fig. 1.6), whilst the resistance range between 100 and 300 $\Omega/\square$ can be achieved with typical base doping. If, in a bipolar transistor array (Fig. 1.6), the current is routed in the horizontal direction through the narrow base zone beneath the emitter, one obtains a resistor with a rating of around 5 k$\Omega/\square$ (pinch resistance), which, however, is non-linear and which has a low breakdown voltage (5 to 8 V). On the other hand, it is possible here to control the magnitude of the pinch resistance by a positive voltage at the $N^+$ emitter region (junction field effect transistor). High resistance values in the M$\Omega/\square$ region can be produced

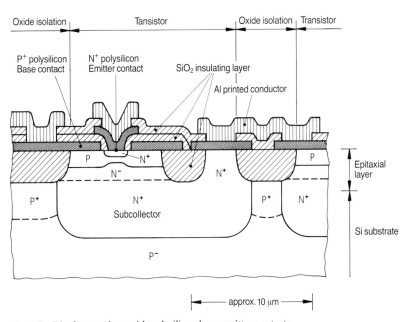

Fig. 1.7   Bipolar transistor with polysilicon base-emitter contacts

by polysilicon structures with a low doping level, applied to an $SiO_2$ substrate.

Finally, it should be mentioned that PNP bipolar transistors can also be implemented on the same chip with a different arrangement of the doped regions as compared with Fig. 1.6. If there are no subcollectors, one obtains a vertical PNP array (substrate PNP transistor). One other possibility is to arrange two P-doped regions a few micrometers apart in an N-doped environment (lateral PNP transistor). Admittedly, both types of PNP transistor are clearly inferior to the NPN transistors produced on the same chip as regards current gain and cut-off frequency, but, since the PNP transistors can be produced without additional process steps, they can also be integrated to advantage in certain applications (e.g. $I^2L$ = Integrated Injection Logic).

### 1.1.4 Bipolar Circuit Techniques

Bipolar circuits are used as analog circuits and as digital circuits. Whilst, in analog circuits, the bipolar transistors are operated in the amplifier region, they function as switches in digital circuits, whereby the two switch states lie in the blocking-state region and in the amplifier or saturation region respectively of the transistor.

Bipolar circuit techniques systematically utilize the following important advantages of the bipolar principle as compared with the MOS principle:

▷ The ability to drive high currents.
▷ The availability of an extremely stable and reproducible threshold voltage in the form of the emitter-base conducting-state voltage of 0.7 V and

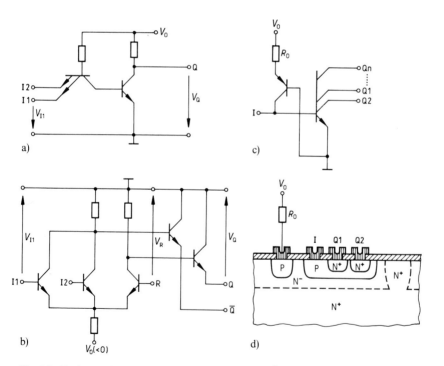

a)

b)

c)

d)

Fig. 1.8   Basic gates incorporating TTL (a), ECL (b) and $I^2L$ technique (c and d)

▷ The short switching time and the high cut-off frequency respectively of bipolar transistors.

Despite a broad variety of types with an extremely varied range of applications, analog circuits generally comprise relatively simple basic circuits, such as those with which the reader will probably already be familiar from circuit techniques with discrete components. However, basic circuits which benefit from the fact that the characteristics of the circuit elements and the temperature on a chip vary only slightly and the fact that area and resistance conditions on a chip can be observed very precisely are used frequently. In this respect, current-balancing circuits and difference amplifiers are worthy of mention, but we should also not forget multipliers and operational amplifiers. The amplifier output stages with low-impedance output can be integrated particularly well in bipolar circuits.

In the case of the digital circuits (logic and memory circuits) we distinguish between various families dependent on the style of the basic gates. The most important logic families are TTL (transistor-transistor logic), ECL (emitter coupled logic) and I²L (integrated injection logic).

Fig. 1.8 shows basic gates on the basis of the TTL, ECL and I²L techniques. Fig. 1.8a shoes a TTL-NAND gate, Fig. 1.8b shows an ECL-OR/NOR gate and Fig. 1.8c shows an I²L inverter. The ECL technique is characterized by particularly high speed. Gate propagation delays of around 100 picoseconds are possible. The I²L technique is space-saving and low-power, but is also slower than the ECL technique.

## 1.2 Integrated MOS Circuits

### 1.2.1 The MOS Transistor

The N-channel MOS transistor consists of two N-regions, designated the source and the drain, and a P doped channel region in be-

tween with a control electrode, the gate, mounted above this isolated.

Fig. 1.9 shows the basic structure and mode of operation of an MOS transistor. Fig. 1.9a shows the typical voltages applied, Fig. 1.9b shows the potential profile along the silicon surface and the flow of electrons from the source to the drain, and Fig. 1.9c shows the symbol of the MOS transistor. The $V_{BS}$ connection is generally omitted in the symbol. The letter N stands for N-channel. By analogy with the bipolar transistor, the current in the MOS transistor is controlled by lowering or increasing the potential barrier at the gate-side edge of the source. By contrast with the bipolar transistor however, the control voltage is applied to an insulated gate electrode above the P-region and not to the P-region itself. Fig. 1.10 shows a typical family of characteristics. The diagram is based upon an assumed gate oxide thickness of 20 nm, a channel length of 1 µm and a channel width of 10 µm. This different control mechanism is also responsible for the essential differences in electrical behavior of the MOS transistor by comparison with the bipolar transistor:

▷ Since the gate is isolated, no gate current flows. This means that it is possible to use the MOS transistor for wattless control.

▷ Since a positive voltage at the gate pulls the electrons which are responsible for current flow from the source to the drain region to the silicon surface, and on the other hand, pushes the excess holes in the P-region away from the surface (space charge region), the current channel, together with the source and drain N⁺ regions, is electrically isolated from the surrounding P-region (by the space-charge region at the bottom and at the sides, and by the gate insulating layer at the top). Since the gate is also isolated, the MOS transistor represents a self-isolating and, thus space-saving component which is eminently suitable for circuit integration.

▷ Since a part of the controlling gate voltage drops above the gate oxide, the current

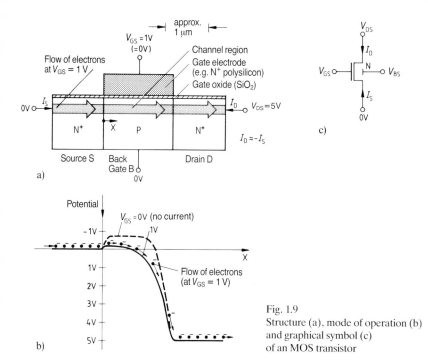

Fig. 1.9
Structure (a), mode of operation (b)
and graphical symbol (c)
of an MOS transistor

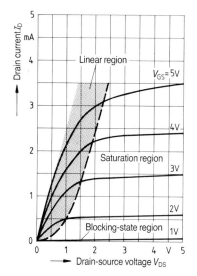

Fig. 1.10
Characteristics of an N-channel MOS transistor

threshold voltage which, in the case of the bipolar transistor, has a largely technology – independent value of 0.7 V, is technology-dependent on the MOS transistor. In the case of small dimensions, the threshold voltage even also depends upon the channel length and the channel width (disadvantage). On the other hand, the threshold voltage of the transistors can be varied specifically (advantage). For example, by a phosphorus implantation in channel region of N-channel transistors, it is possible to shift their threshold voltage into the negative region.

▷ For the same reason as above (voltage drop across the gate oxide), the transconductance $\Delta I_D / \Delta V_{GS}$ is lower under comparable conditions, than the transconductance $\Delta I_C / \Delta V_{BE}$ of the bipolar transistor. And the saturation resistance of an open MOS transistor is also higher than the saturation resistance

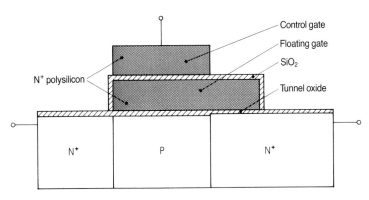

Fig. 1.11   E²PROM memory cell

of an open bipolar transistor (cf. the characteristics in Figs. 1.5 and 1.10). Consequently, MOS transistors are less suited for applications as current drivers.

▷ The MOS principle permits non-volatile memories to be implemented, i.e. memories which retain their memory contents when the supply voltage is switched off. The information can be erased either with ultraviolet light or electrically (EEPROM = electrically erasable programmable read-only memory). Fig. 1.11 shows the structure of an EEPROM memory cell (memory location).

The floating gate (Fig. 1.11) is insulated on all sides by an SiO₂ layer. Electrons can tunnel through the thin tunnel oxide to the floating gate owing to voltages in the region of 20 V. The electrons also remain there after the voltage is switched off. The threshold voltage of the N channel transistor with the control gate can thus be shifted by several volts.

### 1.2.2  MOS Circuits

An integrated MOS circuit consists of a large number of MOS transistors which are arranged adjacently on a silicon chip and interconnected by printed conductors dependent upon the required circuit function.

Fig. 1.12 shows a typical embodiment of an N-channel transistor with its direct environment in an integrated MOS circuit. The transistor is completely symmetrical electrically, the source and drain are reversible. In this example, it has been assumed that the drain region of the transistor is connected to a polysilicon "printed conductor" via an aluminum printed conductor.

As previously mentioned, the MOS transistor is a self-isolating circuit element. It is only necessary to make the oxide layer between neighboring transistors thicker than the gate oxide for the printed conductors running through the oxide layer not to act as gate electrodes and to induce a conductive channel between the transistors. This provides a space-saving array by comparison with the integrated bipolar transistor (Figs. 1.6 and 1.7). One other space-saving effect is achieved owing to the fact that it is not necessary to provide a contact with a printed conductor for each source, gate or drain connection. Rather, it is possible to implement electrical connections by extending the source or drain region or the gate electrode beyond the actual transistor region. However, the resistance of such printed conductors is approx. 1000 times higher than that of aluminum printed conductors (approx. 30 Ω/□). It is

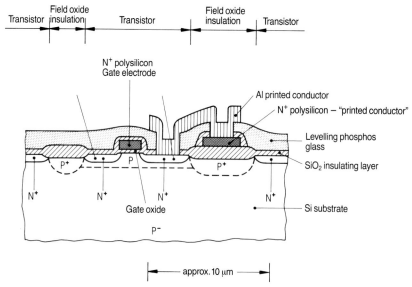

Fig. 1.12 Typical version of an N-channel MOS transistor

possible to reduce the sheet resistance by approximately 1 order of magnitude (approx. 3 $\Omega/\square$) with the aid of silicide layers (e.g. $TaSi_2$, $MoSi_2$, $TiSi_2$). Connection capabilities with the aid of $N^+$ doped silicon conductors or silicide conductors are utilized intensively in MOS circuits in order to save space. This results, for instance, in the fact that a large number of MOS circuits today can be implemented with only one single aluminum printed conductor level.

Dependent upon whether only N-channel transistors or only P-channel transistors or N-channel and P-channel transistors occur on the chip, one talks of NMOS or PMOS or CMOS circuits respectively (C = complementary). CMOS technology is the dominant technology today since it is a low-power technology and offers the circuit designer the most options.

If the N-channel transistors of a CMOS circuit are arranged in a P-doped substrate as shown in Fig. 1.13, the P-channel transistors must be accommodated in a "resistor box",

since P-channel transistors require an N-doped environment for self-isolation.

In order to always keep the substrate PN junctions reverse-biased, the lowest potential occurring in the circuit is applied to the P-type substrates (0 V in general) whilst N-type substrates are connected to the highest potential occurring (+5 V in general).

In order to avoid interference, e.g. latch-up effects, an epitaxial layer with a low doping level on a highly doped substrate should be given preference over a substrate with uniformly low doping level.

As is the case with the bipolar circuits, the MOS circuits also utilize the capabilities of implementing diodes, resistors and capacitors by a suitable arrangement of the doped regions and conductive and insulating structures occurring. The thin gate oxide permits relatively high capacitance values to be achieved per unit area, as required, for instance, in memories. The possibility of implementing EEPROMs with the aid of floating gates was already mentioned in the preceding section.

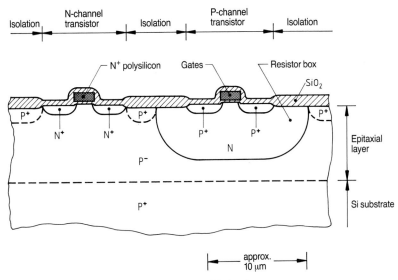

Fig. 1.13   N and P-channel transistors in a CMOS circuit

It is even possible to integrate MOS and bipolar transistors on one chip using certain additional process steps (BICMOS technology).

### 1.2.3 MOS Circuit Technique

MOS circuits are used primarily as digital circuits. But, to an increasing extent, analog functions are also being implemented with MOS techniques. Owing to the low space requirement of the MOS transistors, MOS circuits dominate the field of VLSI circuits (VLSI = very large scale integration) with over 1,000,000 transistors. CMOS technology dominates in this case owing to the low power requirement and the ease of design.

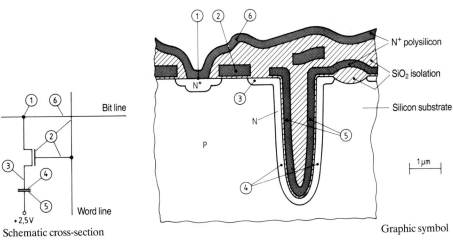

Fig. 1.14   Dynamic memory cell

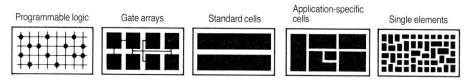

| Programmable logic | Gate arrays | Standard cells | Application-specific cells | Single elements |

Fig. 1.15 Design methods for application-specific circuits

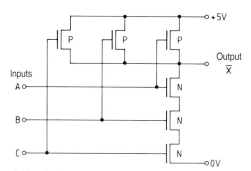

a) Circuit diagram

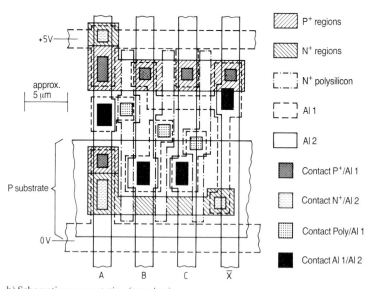

b) Schematic representation (top view)

Fig. 1.16 3-NAND gate as an example of a standard

As regards circuit design, we distinguish between standard integrated circuits and application-specific integrated circuits (ASICs). Whilst standard ICs such as memory chips (Fig. 1.14 dynamic memory cell) or microcomputer chips (microcontrollers, microprocessors and periphery chips) have been designed with the classic design methods on a transistor level, more rational design methods are used for ASICs and these methods take recourse to previously developed basic circuits with specific basic logic functions. Fig. 1.15 provides an overview of the various design methods conventional today for application-specific integrated circuits (ASICs). The larger the developed basic circuits with the standardized basic functions, the greater is the degree of rationalization during designing. The standard cells which are combined in cell libraries are of increasing importance. Fig. 1.16 shows a NAND gate as an example of a standard cell.

Fig. 1.16a shows the circuit diagram and 1.16b the schematic cross-section through the memory cell. In order to reduce the space required for the storage capacity, the capacitor extends approx. 4 m into the silicon substrate in the above example of the 4M DRAM.

# 2 Customized Integrated Circuits

By contrast with standard chips, customized integrated circuits are tailored to meet the needs of a customer and a specific application. Customized circuits are also abbreviated to ASCI (application specific integrated circuit).

In the case of customized integrated circuits, we distinguish between full-custom and semi-custom ICs. Full-custom ICs (IC stands for integrated circuit) are integrated circuits developed at the transistor level. Full-custom ICs are normally developed by the semiconductor manufacturer. Semi-custom IC are based upon gate arrays or cell ICs. Semi-custom ICs can be developed by the user himself with assistance from the semiconductor manufacturer.

Full-custom ICs require longer development times and have smaller chip areas than comparable semi-custom ICs. Since development times and chip sizes are essential factors which also determine the price of the chip, full-custom ICs are preferred for large quantities in cost-critical applications. One major advantage of semi-custom ICs lies in the shorter time in which such ICs can be implemented. The faster a new product comes onto the market, the greater will be the chances of success. This advantage may compensate for the disadvantage of the higher price under certain circumstances. The designer will always have to ask himself whether standard ICs, semi-custom ICs or full-custom ICs will provide the most economical system solution. The most important factors which must be taken into consideration in this case are system costs, development time, system reliability and flexibility.

## 2.1 Semi-Custom ICs

Semi-custom ICs are based upon gate arrays or cell ICs. Semi-custom ICs can be developed by the user himself with the assistance of the semiconductor manufacturer.

### 2.1.1 Gate Arrays

The structure of a gate array consists of so-called basic cells (gates) and wiring channels in between (channelled gate-array technique). Gates consist of 2 to 8 transistors. Nowadays, Siemens offers CMOS gate arrays with complexities of up to 20,000 equivalent gate functions. An equivalent gate function corresponds to four transistors. One more recent method offers the possibility of completely omitting the wiring channels and implementing the intercell wiring over the gate array cells (logic cells). This sea-of-gates technique substantially reduces the required silicon area (one factor determining costs).

The designer wires the gates together (symbolically on a workstation) so as to produce the required chip. The libraries of the CAD systems contain wiring specifications for higher-organised functions such as logic gates, counters and multiplexers etc. In the production department, the wafers are prefabricated with the gate arrays (master). The intra and inter-cell wiring personalizes the master.

The "personal" circuit is created from the universal master.

### 2.1.2 Cell Design

The method using a preset grid is abandoned in the case of cell design. Both the arrange-

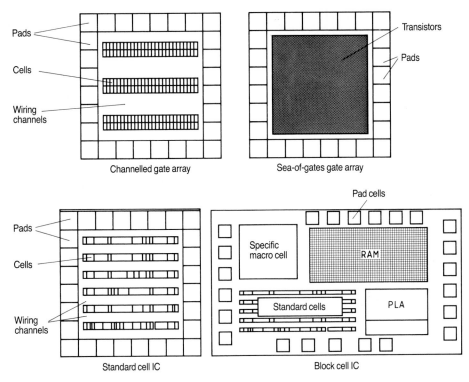

Fig. 2.1 The semi-custom types of IC

ment and the cell width can be selected individually. In addition, it is possible to call and integrate macros stored in the cell library (DRAM, SRAM, counters and multiplexers etc.).

Fig. 2.1 shows various semi-custom integrated circuit types.

### 2.1.3 Gate Array or Cell Design?

Feasibility permitting, this decision is essentially determined by two factors:

▷ by the time taken to make prototypes, allowing for any re-design if necessary.
▷ By the total costs of development and series production.

*The time factor*
Prototypes for gate arrays can be developed far faster than those for cell ICs.

In the case of gate arrays, the prefabricated master wafers only have to be connected by wiring layers. Cell ICs require a complete production run of the silicon wafers. Sample deliveries for gate arrays take 2 to 4 weeks, and sample deliveries for cell ICs take 6 to 10 weeks.

*The cost factor*
On a comparable project, development of a gate array costs approximately one third less than a cell design. The situation is different if we consider costs per unit. A cell IC is optimized for a specific function and thus contains only little redundancy. This results in smaller chip areas than is the case with gate arrays and, thus, lower production costs per unit.

27

## 2.2 Technologies

Apart from the logic, the selected technology largely determines the characteristics of the integrated circuit. Fig. 2.2 shows the assignment of the bipolar and CMOS technologies developed at Siemens to the gate arrays and cell ICs.

### 2.2.1 Bipolar Semicustom ICs

Bipolar (gate) arrays are suitable, in particular, for use at high frequencies or with short gate propagation delays in the order of magnitude of 150 to 200 ps.

Typical fields of application:

*Data systems engineering*
▷ CPUs of mainframes
▷ Peripheral processors

*Telecommunications engineering*
▷ Wideband communication
▷ Digital transmission systems

*Medical engineering*
▷ Digital signal processing in sonography and tomography

*Measurement systems*
▷ IC tester
▷ Logic analyzer

The maximum number of gates of the bipolar ASCIs available from Siemens is now around 10,000 gate functions in ECL technology and 13,000 in CMOS technology. Cell ICs incorporating bipolar technology are available only in exceptional cases.

### 2.2.2 CMOS Semicustom ICs

In the case of CMOS semicustom ICs both gate arrays and cell ICs are available. Products incorporating 2 m and 1.5 m technology (and smaller) are state of the art today. The smaller the structure width, the higher is the possible integration density and the higher is also the possible operating frequency. The trend is towards 1 µm structures. Every

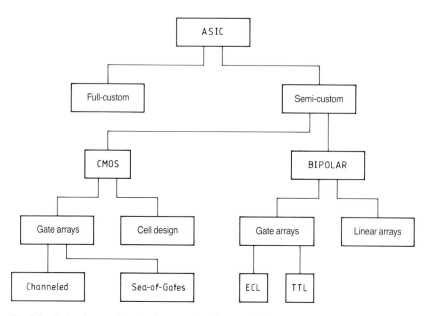

Fig. 2.2   Technology variants in the case of semi-custom ICs

semicustom design can be developed only with perfect CAD tools. The user interface plays an important role in this respect. The flexibility during the circuit implementation phase must be emphasized in particular in the case of cell design. Software generators may create RAM, ROM, PLA and processor structures incorporating individual architecture. Structures with analog functions and microprocessor kernels can also be integrated. Hierarchical design techniques make it possible to generate, simulate and debug subcircuits.

CAD tools also support artwork design (placement and intercell wiring), whereby existing placement and wiring requirements of the circuit designer can be taken into consideration.

### 2.2.3 Bipolar Gate Arrays

Gate propagation delays of approx. 50 ps will be attainable for the OXIS V bipolar technology manufactured today. This corresponds to a maximum frequency of 20 GHz.

The SH100E gate array family offers the possibility of combining ultra-fast gate propagation delays (130 ps) or maximum clock frequencies with circuit sections which are less fast but which do, however, involve less power dissipation (speed power programming). The circuit designer can decide on the required ratio between short gate propagation delay and low power dissipation (trade off) individual for each individual cell. Fig. 2.3 shows typical speed and power dissipation values for the three possible stages: low power, standard and high speed.

The flexibility is also supported by the fact that the designer can opt between the technologies ECL (emitter coupled logic) and CML (current mode logic). The difference between ECL and CML technology is essentially that an emitter follower is used in ECL technology. Fig. 2.4 shows the circuitry differences between ECL and CML.

| | | Low Power | | High Speed |
|---|---|---|---|---|
| Propagation delay | OR/NOR gate | | | |
| Typical propagation delay (F0 1) | [ps] | 190 | 140 | 130 |
| Increase per load unit | [ps] | 60 | 30 | 15 |
| Increase per mm lead | [ps] | 300 | 150 | 75 |
| Power | | | | |
| a) OR/NOR gate | | | | |
| 1 core cell (slice) at $V_{EE} = -3.3$ V | | 1.35 mW | 2.7 mW | 5.4 mW |
| 1 core cell (slice) at $V_{EE} = -4.5$ V | | 1.85 mW | 3.7 mW | 7.4 mW |
| b) Macro cells with series gating | | | | |
| ø power/core cell $V_{EE} = -3.3$ V | | 1.25 mW | 2.5 mW | 5.0 mW |
| ø power/core cell $V_{EE} = -4.5$ V | | 1.70 mW | 3.4 mW | 6.8 mW |

Fig. 2.3
Speed power programming with the ECL gate array family SH100E: Speed and power dissipation values of the three possible stages: low power, standard and high speed

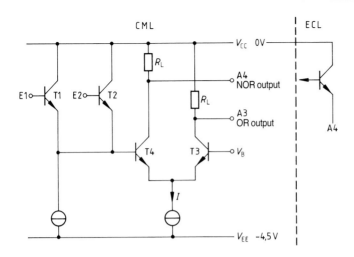

Fig. 2.4
Circuitry differences
between ECL
and CLM

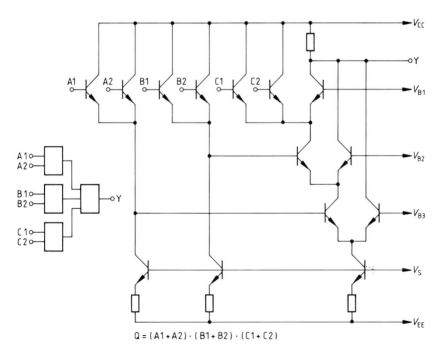

$$Q = (A1+A2) \cdot (B1+B2) \cdot (C1+C2)$$

Fig. 2.5
Implementing the Boolean function $Q = (A1 + A2) \cdot (B1 + B2) \cdot (C1 + C2)$ with series gating

The advantages and disadvantages of these technologies are as follows:

|      | Advantages | Disadvantages |
| ---- | ---------- | ------------- |
| ECL  | High drive capability | More transistors High power dissipation |
| CML  | Greater freedom from jitter | Lower drive capability |

The performance features can be enhanced with the series gating principle. More complex cells can be configured from a large number of simple OR, NOR, AND and NAND gates which does, however, have a disadvantageous effect on the circuit speed and power dissipation. It is possible to minimize the space required by the logic gates and the power dissipation and to achieve major reductions in propagation delay by multiple utilization of the transverse current I (up to 3 difference amplifier stages).

Fig. 2.5 shows the circuit configuration of a cell which represents the Boolean function

$$Q = (A1 + A2) \cdot (B1 + B2) \cdot (C1 + C2)$$

The following macro cells are available for integration on the gate array in order to support development work:

SRAM 0.75 k
Dual port RAM 0.5 k
Multiplier
Ripple carry adder
Cross point matrix

The master range covers gate arrays with complexities from 1000 to 13000 gate equivalents. The library is expanded continually.

### 2.2.4 Bipolar Transistor Arrays (Linear Arrays)

The cell structure of transistor arrays is already prefabricated, i.e. CAD cell library

support is no longer required. The SH807E transistor array has

236 NPN transistors
320 resistors
8 capacitors
19 ESD protective structures
1 bias driver

This transistor array is suitable for configuring digital and analog circuits in the frequency range up to 2.4 GHz. The prefabricated array is personalized by individual 3-layer wiring. The first two layers wire the existing discrete elements (transistors and resistors...) for the relevant, required function. The topmost wiring plane serves to configure the power supply.

## 2.3 Package Variants

A broad range of packages is available for semi-custom ICs. The correct package must be selected, dependent upon the number of pins, power consumption and installation requirements. Here is a list of current packages:

DIP packages up to 48 pins
PLCC packages up to 84 pins
PGA packages up to 280 pins
Flatpack packages up to 196 pins
SO packages

The micropack is suitable for very large numbers of pins with compact dimensions. Fig. 2.6 provides an overview of all important package designs.

Fig. 2.6 Packages for semicustom ICs

## 2.4 Cooperation between Customer and Supplier

This cooperation may occur at various levels, dependent upon customer requirements. This can be illustrated most clearly by way of example of the development sequence for gate arrays and cell ICs (Fig. 2.7).

The starting point for every project is the individual circuit diagram (logic diagram) of the customer. The following steps are taken on the basis of this:

▷ Converting the circuit on the basis of the cell library of the semiconductor manufacturer
▷ Entering the circuit in the CAD system
▷ Logic simulation of the circuit

Placement and wiring are carried out after logic simulation. The following steps are required for this:

▷ Placement and wiring: automatic layout generation
▷ Logic simulation with wiring influences
▷ Generating the control tape for mask production
▷ Generating the control tape for the test department

This is followed by sample production. It consists of the following steps:

▷ Producing the set of masks
▷ Wafer production
▷ Mounting the chip in the package
▷ Testing the integrated circuit

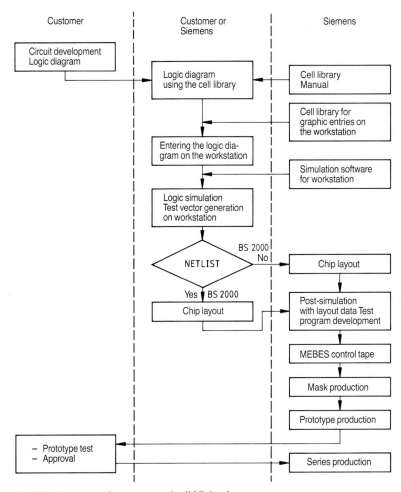

Fig. 2.7    Sequence of gate array and cell IC development

Which of these work steps is performed by whom is stipulated in detail with the customer. There are two tried-and-tested possibilities for this:

*Submitting the individual circuit diagram (logic diagram)*

The customers use a design center. The manufacturer performs all other work for the customer. Siemens has set up such design centres at the parent company (Munich), at branch offices and in the national Siemens companies.

*Transfer of the simulated netlist*

Customers who have appropriate CAD systems and experience themselves receive the cell library on a suitable data medium from the semiconductor manufacturer. After entering the circuit and simulation, the customer returns the results on a suitable data medium. The semiconductor manufacturer use this information to make samples.

# 3 Discrete Semiconductors

The fields of discrete semiconductors and integrated circuits can no longer be separated as precisely as was possible a few years ago. More and more logic circuits are being integrated with power transistors, opto-electronic semiconductors or sensors on a chip or in a package. One should be aware of this trend when reading this chapter.

The chapter is subdivided into sections on radio frequency semiconductors, power semiconductors and sensors. You can find applications for radio frequency transistors in Chapter 8, Consumer Electronics.

## 3.1 Transistors

During the last few years, little has changed as regards the basic application of transistors and diodes. Rapid advances have occurred only in relation to details, e.g. as regards the

performance of the GaAs field-effect transistors.

Since the fundamentals of this subject are now a fixed part of the curricula, we shall restrict ourselves in this chapter to an application for radio frequency transistors, an 11 to 13 GHz converter for satellite reception.

This section describes input stages, mixers, oscillator and intermediate frequency amplifier of the satellite converter. Fig. 3.1 shows the block diagram of the converter and Fig. 3.2 shows the circuit implemented with the individual components. The illustrations which follow outline the individual stages of the converter with their mechanical and electrical characteristics. The circuits are manufactured using the microstrip technique and all components are SMDs. Glass fibre or ceramic-filled teflon and aluminum oxide $Al_2O_3$ is suitable as the strip line substrate.

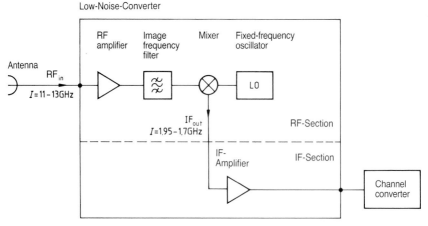

Fig. 3.1   Block diagram of the 11 to 13 GHz tuner

LNC RF-Section

Substrate:
RT−Duroid 6010
Size: 75×16 mm

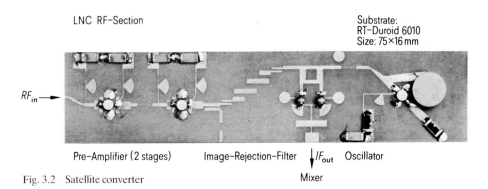

$RF_{in}$ →

Pre-Amplifier (2 stages)    Image−Rejection−Filter   $IF_{out}$   Oscillator

Mixer

Fig. 3.2   Satellite converter

Fig. 3.3 shows the preamplifier, Fig. 3.4 the image frequency filter, Fig. 3.5 the mixer, Fig. 3.6 the oscillator with frequency-determining dielectric resonator and Fig. 3.7 the magnetic coupling of the dielectric resonator to the strip line.

The first stage of the preamplifier is crucial to the overall coverage noise figure of the converter. The GaAs field-effect transistor is adapted here with the input circuit to minimum noise and with the output circuit to maximum power gain. Open-ended stub lines or $\lambda/4$ transformers which transform the transistor impedances to the value of 50 conventional in microwave systems are used as matching elements. The second or possibly third preamplifier stage is then matched to maximum power gain.

The strip line filter consists of coupled $\lambda/4$ resonators whose filter characteristic represents that of a band-pass filter. The image frequency filter suppresses the unwanted image

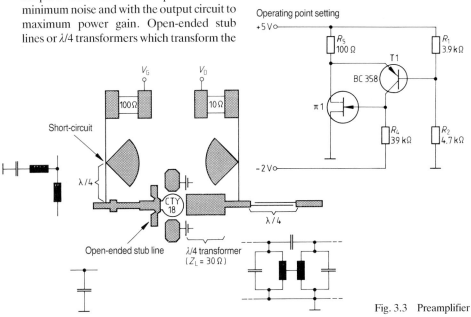

Fig. 3.3   Preamplifier

35

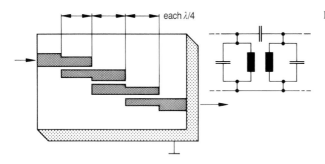

Fig. 3.4 Image frequency filter

frequencies and reduces the emission of the oscillator at the input.

The mixer is designed as a balanced mixer. The 3 dB coupler splits the oscillator and signal power in half for the diodes which are connected in a push-pull circuit. The short circuit for the oscillator and the signal at the IF side are intended to prevent reconversion.

Fig. 3.6a shows a dielectric resonator (material ceramic, $\varepsilon_r = 38$) between two microstrip lines. The resonator acts in this case as a resonant circuit which overcouples the power within a narrow band between the strip lines. In Fig. 3.6b, this resonant circuit is incorpo-

rated in the feedback path between gate and drain of a GaAs FET, and, under corresponding amplitude and phase conditions, the system oscillates with the dielectric resonator as the frequency-determining element.

The block diagram and the circuit of the IF amplifier are shown in Figs. 3.8 and 3.9. The

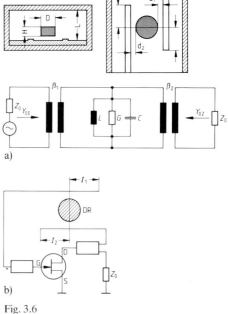

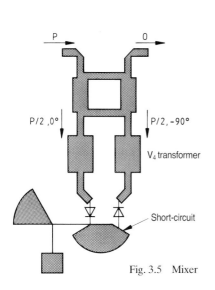

P/2 ,0°    P/2 ,-90°

$V_4$ transformer

Short-circuit

Fig. 3.5    Mixer

Fig. 3.6
Oscillator with frequency-determining dielectric resonator

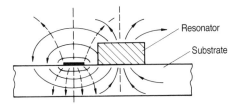

Fig. 3.7
Magnetic coupling of the dielectric resonator
with the strip line

IF amplifier must compensate for subsequent cable losses and make available an adequate signal level to the satellite receiver. The gain is 10 dB per stage, and the frequency response has a band-pass filter character in order to filter off possible out-of-band sources of radio noise.

## 3.2 Power Semiconductors

Without the work on power semiconductors during the 50s and 60s, development of microelectronics would hardly have advanced as quickly because silicon production-technology is based upon the development of powerful static converters. Nowadays, developments are oriented less towards IC technology and more towards power semiconductors.

As early as 1956, two years after starting with silicon power rectifiers at Siemens, the first stage of development was completed, 1000 V blocking ability and 300 A current carrying capacity. Such components were the key to the further development of modern electric locomotives. The next stage of development was the component which not only rectifies current but also switches it. The importance

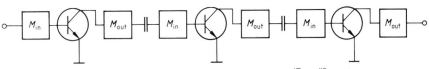

Fig. 3.8   Block diagram of the IF amplifier

IF amplifier
3 stages, silicon bipolar,
transistors Gain ≈ 10 dB/stage AF ≈ 2.5 dB
M = Matching network

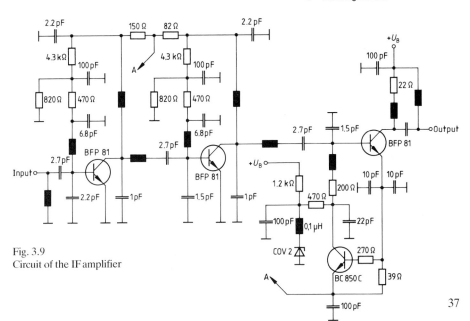

Fig. 3.9
Circuit of the IF amplifier

37

of the development of switchable power semiconductors on the basis of junction transistors started in 1955, was, however restricted to special cases since the thyristor which was produced soon afterwards, as a logical further development is clearly superior to such switchable power semiconductors as regards the limit rating range.

The thyristor not only permitted new solutions for the previously mentioned locomotives, but it also permitted a large number of concepts which had long been wanted in power engineering to be implemented: From electronic control for drives through to converters and compensators for mains systems. Thus, thyristors were the key components for the Cabora Bassa power station. We must also mention the most recent example: the Gezouba-Shanghai HVDCT system (China) for which Siemens supplied approx. 3000 thyristors with 5500 V off-state voltage. This is the thyristor with the highest off-state voltage manufactured on a series basis today.

The development of integrated circuits provided materials and technologies for development of new power semiconductors. The SIPMOS® was a completely new product family. SIPMOS transistors are switching elements for high electric currents and voltages which can be controlled directly by microelectronic components and which thus permit a smooth transition from control electronics to power electronics. A SIPMOS power transistor for example contains several thousand parallel-connected transistor functions over an area of 16 mm², thus permitting it to switch a total electrical power of a few kilowatts.

One noteworthy advantage for users of SIPMOS transistors is that power converters can be manufactured with operating frequencies of well over 100 kHz.

FREDFET-SIPMOS transistors on which the required free-wheeling diode is integrated in the transistor were developed as special components for simple-construction, regulated three-phase drives in the kilowatt range.

SIPMOS technology permits further impetus from various applications to be integrated in innovative products for power electronics. In the case of a number of circuits in industrial and automotive electronics, the circuit state of power transistors must be monitored, and they must be protected against any malfunction which could occur, e.g. a short-circuit.

Figs. 3.10 and 3.11 show fields of application of various power semiconductors and the maximum current density as a function of the switching frequency.

If functions of this type are integrated in a power semiconductor element, we speak of intelligent power semiconductors. An extension of SIPMOS technology − Smart-SIPMOS − permits products of this type to be manufactured reliably and at low cost. It comprises SIPMOS transistors and CMOS circuits for voltages up to 100 V, has integrated overload protection in TEMPFET® products and also permits feedback to the control logic in PROFET® products.

Electronic load-disconnecting relays isolate a sensitive control circuit from an output circuit electrically and with high-voltage strength (in the case of 220 V mains voltages). SIPMOS technology has provided a solution for the core functions in a component for this task also, to date in circuits with many components: the SITAC®.

A dramatic battle between semiconductor concepts is currently under way in the field of power modules. It was triggered by the requirements of turn-off capability, which is not met by the thyristor concept, and the higher operating frequency, in particular for low-noise, closed-loop-controlled three-phase drives. The framework for the necessary further developments of the components is exceedingly narrow: The switching losses must be low and the new product must not be substantially more expensive.

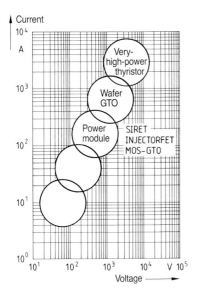

Fig. 3.10
Fields of application of various power semiconductors

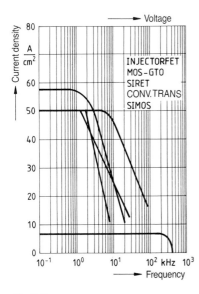

Fig. 3.11
Maximum current density and switching frequency

In the related voltage range of 500 to 1200 V, the bipolar transistor principle is superior to the unipolar MOS principle as regards current density and, thus, also costs. Conventional bipolar transistors achieve their high current carrying capacity at the expense of long switching times and thus switch with high losses. One is thus faced by the requirement for a fast bipolar transistor. The Siemens ring-emitter transistor SIRET® was developed for this purpose. Its switching frequency exceeds that of conventional bipolar power transistors by a factor of 10, and it has the same high current carrying capacity as these conventional bipolar power transistors. The SIRET thus permits construction of static converters in the power range of several hundred kilowatts at frequencies above 10 kHz, as required for low-noise drives.

Other principles in the module sector which will compete with SIRET in future use the MOS principle in combination with injection effects on which the thyristor is based for instance: the class of injector FETs; the MOS-GTO is still the front runner.

The thyristor principle is still irreplaceable today for switching currents of more than 1000 A and, at the same time voltages of several thousand volts. But this technologically relatively simple component does have a disadvantage: once it is turned on, it can only be turned off if the current flowing through the thyristor is interrupted for approx. 100 μs by a complex circuit. In order to solve this problem, developments are being aimed at power semiconductors with turn-off capability. The most well-known representative of this type is the gate-turn-off thyristor (GTO). This thyristor is turned off by a negative gate current which is approximately one fifth of the load current. Siemens is the first European manufacturer currently introducing a family of wafer GTOs for a voltage range of 1.8 to 4.5 kV and currents up to 3000 A. The first electric-powered suburban public transport vehicles with Siemens GTOs have already been in operation since 1986.

And developments are continuing even in the very high high-power sector which is served with the classical thyristor principle: Higher voltages, higher making and breaking capacities and integrated functions such as overvoltage protection and light pulse firing permit construction of better static converters and compensators for modern power supply networks. The chain of new power semiconductor types demonstrates that, even in an area such as that of power semiconductors which have had a long and steady history, there is virtually no niche which is not being occupied with new components, using ultra-modern microelectronics. They provide the user with greater benefits, and, in some cases, they even permit new equipment concepts.

### 3.2.1 SIPMOS Transistors

Now that we have described the technological fundamentals, the possible circuitry and an example application, we shall now discuss the members of the SIPMOS family FRED-FET, TEMPFET®, PROFET®, SITAC® and SIRET®.

SIPMOS power transistors permit the production of switched-mode power supply units with operating frequencies extending through to the range of well over 100 kHz. FREDFET-SIPMOS transistors on which the required free-wheeling diode is integrated in the transistor have been developed for simple-design, closed-loop-controlled three-phase drives in the kilowatt range. Monitoring circuits are integrated in the smart FET.

SIPMOS transistors are self-blocking field-effect transistors with gate, source and drain connections. The channel resistance between drain and source is controlled by applying a voltage across the gate and source. We distinguish between N-channel and P-channel transistors. N-channel types are controlled with a positive gate-source voltage and block positive drain-source voltages. In the case of P-channel doping, the voltage polarities are

the reverse. SIPMOS transistors have an asymmetrical reverse behavior, i.e. an N-channel transistor can be rendered reverse-biased only in the drain-source direction. The inverse diode is forward-biased in the opposite direction.

The range of types of N-channel transistors is more extensive than that of the P-channel transistors. This is because of the better conductivity of the N-channel, owing to physical reasons. In the case of MOS transistors with the same reverse voltage and chip area, the drain-source-on resistance $R_{DS(on)}$ of a P-channel transistor is more than twice as high. In addition, the production effort and expense increases, so that the price-performance ratio shifts in favour of the N-channel transistor. Every N-channel transistor can be used in place of a P-channel transistor if driven appropriately.

The most important characteristics of the SIPMOS transistors are as follows:

▷ Voltage-controlled
▷ High making and breaking capacity
▷ Simple parallel connection
▷ Short switching times
▷ Adjustable switching time
▷ No carrier storage time
▷ High cut-off frequency
▷ High current carrying capacity and dielectric strength
▷ Overload protection (no "second break down")
▷ Linear characteristic

The most important possible applications are as follows:

▷ Switched-mode power supply units
▷ Motor control units
▷ DC converters
▷ Inverters
▷ Proximity switches
▷ Wide-band amplifiers
▷ AF amplifiers
▷ Ultrasonic generators
▷ No-break power supply
▷ Flicker-free monitors
▷ Automotive electronics

## Technology

*Structure of the SIPMOS power transistor*

SIPMOS transistors are vertically structured and have a double-implanted channel structure. We thus also speak of a DIMOS process (Fig. 3.12). In the case of an N-channel transistor, the $N^+$ substrate, with the drain plating below it, serves as the carrier. A $N^-$ epitaxy layer whose thickness varies and which is doped appropriately dependent upon the reverse voltage follows over the $N^+$ substrate. The gate above this, comprising $N^+$ polysilicon, is embedded in insulating silicon dioxide. The source plating covers the entire structure and connects the chip's individual transistor cells in parallel.

The source plating thus forms a reliable short-circuit between the $N^+$ and $N^-$ source region (Fig. 3.13). This shorts the base-emitter junction of the parasitic, vertical $N^+PN^-$ bipolar transistor. This is necessary in order to avoid the transistor turning on when subject to dynamic processes. Even as the result of high rates of voltage rise between the drain and source, the parasitic NPN transistors are not turned on in the case of pure

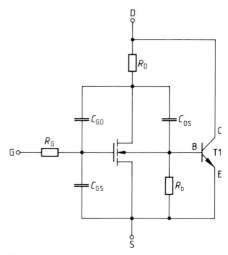

Fig. 3.13
Parasitic bipolar transistor in the N-channel SIPMOS

transistor operation by currents resulting from the drain-source capacitance. However, this effect must be noted if high rates of commutation voltage rise occur in the inverse diode. The base-collector diode ($PN^-$

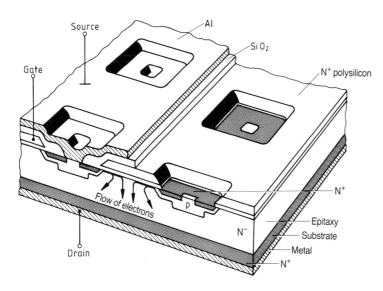

Fig. 3.12
Structure of an N-channel SIPMOS transistor

41

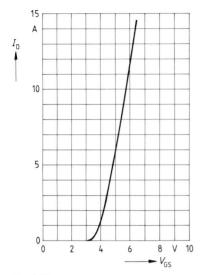

Fig. 3.14
Typical transfer characteristic by way of example
of the BUZ 45

junction) then corresponds to the SIPMOS
inverse diode.

The vertical transistor structure mentioned
above guarantees both optimum utilization
of the chip area and good heat dissipation,
and also permits high reverse voltages. Double implantation with the extremely short
channel lengths permits very high rates of
current rise. The source and gate are bonded
on the chip upper side by ultrasonic bonding
with aluminum wires.

*Family of characteristics*
If positive drain-source voltage is applied to
an N-channel transistor with control voltage
$V_{GS} = 0$ V, this causes a temperature and vol-
tage-dependent reverse current to flow. This
reverse current limit value is specified in the
data sheets and is typically a few nA. If the
gate-source control voltage is increased, the
transistor remains reverse-bias until the gate-
source threshold voltage $(V_{GS}(T))$ is
reached. The threshold voltage $V_{GS}(T)$ lies
between 2.1 and 4.0 V at $I_D = 10$ mA in the

case of power FETs, whilst it lies between
0.8 and 2.8 V at $I_D = 1$ mA in the case of
small-signal FETs.

The temperature coefficient is $-5$ mV/°C in
the case of power FETs and $-3$ mV/°C in the
case of small-signal FETs. If the control voltage is increased beyond the threshold voltage, the drain current increases in accordance with the transfer characteristic ($I_D =$
$f[V_{GS}]$, Fig. 3.14). The rate of rise is non-
linear, lies in a range between 1 S and 20 S
and is dependent upon the type of transistor.

The transistor is completely reverse-biased
in the case of a gate-source voltage below the
threshold voltage. A negative gate-source
voltage does not increase the blocking ability, i.e. the entire family of characteristics can
be obtained with control voltages of one polarity.

The maximum value of the gate-source voltage is 20 V. This value must not be exceeded,
even briefly, since, otherwise, the transistor
may be destroyed. If the drain current is measured as a function of the drain-source voltage with the parameter gate-source control
voltage, we obtain the family of output
characteristics (Fig. 3.15).

In ON state, the transistor behaves in the
same way as an ohmic resistance, i.e. positive and negative drain currents flow. In the
third quadrant of the family of characteristics, an ohmic behavior does, of course,
occur only inasmuch as the inverse diode
threshold voltage has not yet been exceeded
(Fig. 3.16). This behavior is important particularly if rectifier circuits with extremely
low conducting-state voltages are to be implemented or if the inverse diode reverse recovery time is to be shortened by biasing the
transistor.

*Switching operations*
SIPMOS transistors require no control current in stationary operating state since they
are voltage-controlled. Each change in
operating state however causes charge-rever-

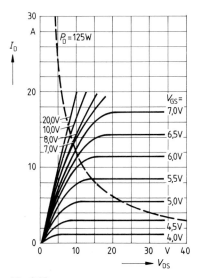

Fig. 3.15
Typical output characteristic using the BUZ 45
as an example

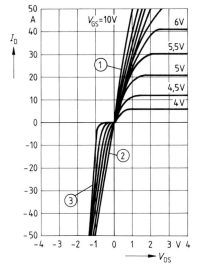

① Transistor output characteristics
② Inverse transistor output characteristics
③ Inverse diode forward characteristic

Fig. 3.16
Output characteristic of the BUZ 45 with inverse
diode behavior

sal currents of the input capacitances. Whilst these currents are hardly important in the VF range (analog operation), they must be noted in the case of RF applications and when switching. Since SIPMOS transistors are primarily used as switches, we shall thus give a special explanation of the switching behavior.

The switching time of a SIPMOS transistor is determined only by charge reversal of the input capacitance. By freely selecting the internal resistance $R_i$ of the drive circuit, it is possible to set the switching time of SIPMOS transistors in a board range. The limit for a high internal resistance is determined by the thermal load rating owing to higher switching losses occurring. In the case of a low internal resistance, the charge-reversal current of the input capacitance is limited by the gate bulk resistance and the inductance of the control circuit.

*Switching resistive load*
Measurement is conducted with a drive generator with defined internal resistance $R_i$ which supplies a square-wave output voltage (cf. measurement circuit for switching times in the data book).

*Turn-on*
The transistor is triggered at instant to (Fig. 3.17). The gate-source voltage $V_{GS}$ rises cor-

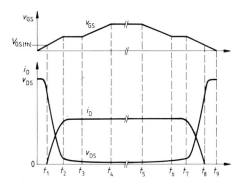

Fig. 3.17
Switching operation of a SIPMOS transistor
with resistive load

responding to the charging process which results from the input capacitance $C_{ipp}$ and the internal resistance $R_i$ of the control circuit. As soon as the threshold voltage is reached at instant $t_1$, the transistor starts to conduct current. The drain-source voltage drops corresponding to the increasing voltage drop at the load resistor. The drain current increases in time segment $t_1$ to $t_2$. The Miller capacitance which is low at this instant is discharged with the drain-source voltage excursion, and, simultaneously, the gate-source voltage increases in accordance with the transfer characteristic (Fig. 3.14).

At instant $t_2$ the drain-source voltage $V_{DS}$ is equal to the gate-source voltage $V_{GS}$. The greatly increased Miller capacitance now comes into effect. In time segment $t_2$ to $t_3$, the transistor operates as a Miller integrator, i.e. the gate-source voltage remains constant whilst the gate charging current flows through the Miller capacitance and leads to a further reduction in the drain-source voltage. At instant $t_3$, the drain-source voltage has reached the end of the analog range of the family of output characteristics and the Miller capacitance has reached its maximum value. In time segment $t_3$ to $t_4$, the input capacitance $C_{ipp}$ is charged to the level of the applied control voltage. In this case, the channel resistance continues to drop. This can be seen in the family of characteristics by the family of curves in the ohmic region. At instant $t_4$, the transistor has reached its lowest forward resistance (turn-on resistance $R_{DS}(on)$) (corresponding to the drain-source residual voltage divided by the drain current).

*Turn-off*

Turn-off is initiated at instant $t_5$ by switching off the control voltage. The highest input capacitance $C_{ipp}$ at this instant is discharged via the internal resistance $R_1$ of the drive generator. The gate-source voltage drops to a value at which the instantaneous drain current can still be kept in the ohmic region of the family of characteristics. This is reached

at instant $t_6$ at which time the forward resistance has increased slightly. In time segment $t_6$ to $t_7$, the transistor, in turn, acts as a Miller integrator, i.e. the gate-source voltage remains constant whilst the gate control current flows completely via the Miller capacitance which is still increased and leads to a drain-source voltage rise. At instant $t_7$, there is voltage equilibrium between the instantaneous gate-source voltage and the drain-source voltage, i.e. the Miller capacitance drops to a low value. In time segment $t_7$ to $t_8$, the Miller capacitance which is now lower is charged, corresponding to the rapidly increasing drain-source voltage. At instant $t_8$, the threshold voltage is reached and the transistor is completely reverse-bias. The input capacitance is then discharged to the control voltage level in time segment $t_8$ to $t_9$.

*Switching a clocked inductive load*

In steady state, a current which does not change for the duration of the ON state flows through the inductive load and through the free-wheeling diode (Fig. 3.18).

*Turn-on*

The SIPMOS transistor is reverse-biased and is controlled at instant $t_0$ with a square-wave voltage (Fig. 3.19). The gate-source voltage $V_{GS}$ rises, corresponding to the charging process resulting from the input capacitance $C_{ipp}$ of the transistor and the internal resistance $R_i$ of the control circuit. The threshold voltage is reached at instant $t_1$.

In time segment $t_1$ to $t_2$, the drain current rises proportionally with the gate-source voltage, whilst the drain-source voltage remains unchanged at the level of the operating voltage. At instant $t_2$, the transistor assumes the load current completely. In the following time segment $t_2$ to $t_3$, the drain current increases further since the diode reverse current is added to the load current. The maximum drain current occurs at instant $t_3$, the diode reverse current reversal point. Up to this instant, the drain-source voltage is unchanged and is equal to the operating phase,

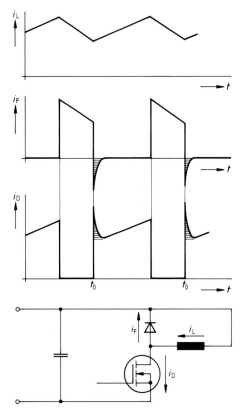

Fig. 3.18
Switching behavior of a SIPMOS transistor
with inductive load

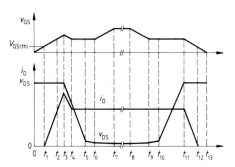

Fig. 3.19
Switching operation of a SIPMOS transistor
with inductive load and free-wheeling diode

the gate-source voltage remains constant (Miller integrator), as is the case in the following time segment $t_4$ to $t_5$.

However, in time segment $t_3$ to $t_4$, the drain current change which is caused by the dropping diode reverse current also influences the switching operation. With dropping drain current, the gate-source capacitance is discharged via the Miller capacitance. The gate-source voltage drops to such an extent that the instantaneous drain current can flow. Consequently, there is a far steeper drain-source voltage edge in this time segment. The operations which lead to the voltage characteristic at the drain-source junction in time segment $t_3$ to $t_4$ must always be noted. Low-resistance driving of a SIPMOS transistor produces a high rate of rise of the drain current and thus, simultaneously, too high a rate of commutation current rise of the free-wheeling diode current. The consequence is a high diode reverse current which drops abruptly after reaching its maximum. The rate of current variation of the decaying diode reverse current causes voltage overshoots in the circuit and, together with the SIPMOS capacitances, causes extremely steep drain-source current edges.

Since the free-wheeling diode is replaced in bridge circuits by the inverse diode of the other SIPMOS transistor, it must be mentioned that this operating case in particular is critical as regards turning on the parasitic transistor. The SIPMOS-FREDFET (fast-recovery-epitaxial-diode-field-effect-transistor) was developed in order to prevent this. The inverse diode of this transistor has an extremely short reverse recovery time. This means that the reverse currents drop during commutation to such an extent that the parasitic transistor can no longer be turned on and no longer have a second breakdown.

At instant $t_5$, the drain-source voltage is equal to the gate-source voltage; the Miller capacitance increases greatly. In time segment $t_5$ to $t_6$, a reduction in the drain-source

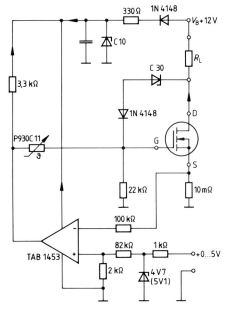

Fig. 3.20
Driving a SIPMOS transistor
in the analog region

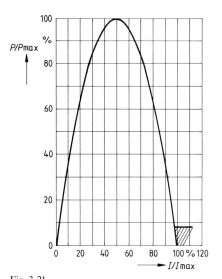

Fig. 3.21
Analog power loss characteristic
of a SIPMOS transistor

voltage occurs, whereby the transistor now acts as an integrator with the increased Miller capacitance. In time segment $t_6$ to $t_7$, the gate-source voltage rises to the level of the applied control voltage.

*Turn-off*
Turn-off starts at instant $t_8$. At instant $t_9$, the gate-source voltage has reached a value at which the transistor can just still keep the instantaneous drain current in the ohmic region of the family of the characteristics. In time segment $t_9$ to $t_{10}$, the transistor acts as a Miller integrator with increased Miller capacitance. At instant $t_{11}$, the free-wheeling diode is rendered forward-biased, whilst the drain-source voltage $V_{DS}$ remains constant. The drain current now drops proportionally to the gate-source voltage $V_{DS}$ and drops to zero at instant $t_{12}$ when the gate-source voltage has dropped to the threshold voltage. The input capacitance is discharged to zero in time segment $t_{12}$ to $t_{13}$.

*Control in the analog region*
In analog applications, it is practical to connect an operational amplifier in series (Fig. 3.20) owing to the tolerance $V_{GS}(T)$ (gate threshold voltage). The setpoint (0 ... 5 V) is applied to the non-inverting input of the operational amplifier via a 40:1 voltage divider. A voltage which is derived from a shunt in the source circuit (10 mV) is applied to the input. The operational amplifier controls the current flowing through the transistors in such a way that there is always equilibrium between the voltage injected and the voltage fed back, i.e. the circuit simultaneously acts as a current limiter. The high loop gain of the servo loop means that tolerances of the transistor are virtually unimportant. The maximum load rating of this circuit is shown by the power loss parabola in Fig. 3.21.

**Avalanche resistance**

The SIPMOS transistors of the new generation are avalanche-resistant. Consequently, they require no external components for limiting overvoltage peaks over a defined power loss range. Moreover, the user can base his calculations upon far lower safety clearances than previously. This permits cheaper types (same $R_{DS}(on)$ or lower $V_{DS}$) or lower losses (lower $R_{DS}(on)$, lower $V_{DS}$).

*Calculation*
Losses occur owing to operation of a transistor in the avalanche region. They may never exceed the maximum permitted power loss ($P_D$) of the transistor. Consequently, avalanche losses must be added to the switching losses ($P_S$) and the forward power losses ($P_V$).

The maximum permitted avalanche energy $E_{(AS)}$ is specified in every SIPMOS data sheet of the new SIPMOS generation (see Table 3.1). This value may never be exceeded. It must be noted that this value, in the same way as all data sheet specifications, refers to defined states. The operating temperature must be included in the individual calculation. For this purpose, the SIPMOS

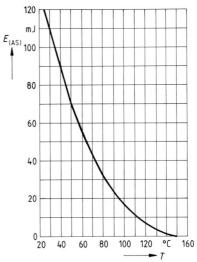

Fig. 3.22
Maximum avalanche energy as a function of chip temperature

data sheets contain a diagram (Fig. 3.22). It shows the reliable avalanche energy as a function of chip temperature.

Table 3.1    Data of the BUZ 73

|  |  |  | Conditions |
|---|---|---|---|
| DC drain current | $I_D$ | 7 A | $T = 30\,°C$ |
| Drain current, pulsed | $I_{Dpulse}$ | 28 A | $T = 25\,°C$ |
| Gate-source voltage | $V_{GS}$ | $\pm20$ V | |
| Power loss, max. | $P_D$ | 75 W | |
| Avalanche energy, single pulse | $E_{AS}$ | 120 mJ | $R_{GS} = 7\,A: V_{DD} = 50V$ $R_{GS} = 25\,\Omega: L = 3.67\,mH$ |
| Avalanche current, periodic and non-periodic | $I_{AR}$ | 7 A | Limited by $T_j$ max. |
| Avalanche energy, periodic | $E_{AR}$ | 6.5 mJ | Limited by $T_j$ max. |
| Operating temperature | $T_i$ | $-55$ to $+150$ °C | |
| Storage temperature | $T_{AR}$ | $-55$ to $+150$ °C | |
| Humidity rating | | E | DIN 400440 |
| Climatic category | | 55/150/56 | DIN IEC 68 Part 1 |

Thermal resistance

| Thermal resistance, chip package | $R_{thJC}$ | $<3.1$ K/W | |
|---|---|---|---|
| Thermal resistance, chip environment | $R_{thJC}$ | $<75$ K/W | |

The energy $E$ is calculated as follows

$E = V \cdot I \cdot t$ (joules)

Our example is based on the BUZ 73.

Since the avalanche current is non-linear, the following applies in our case

$E = V_{DS(BR)} \cdot I \, dt$

where

$V_{DS(BR)}$ = breakdown voltage. Since the avalanche current has an approximately delta wave form, the following applies

$E = V_{DS(BR)} \cdot 0.5 \, I \cdot t$

with an avalanche peak of $I_D = 7$ mA and a duration of $t = 0.4$ μs.

The following applies until the current decays:

$E = 220 \, V \cdot 7 \, A \cdot 0.5 \cdot 0.4 \, \mu s = 0.3 \, mJ.$

6.5 mJ is permitted in accordance with Table 3.1.

If we multiply the energy by the switching frequency (e.g. 50 kHz), we obtain the power loss for avalanche operation ($P_{VA}$):

$P_{VA} = E \cdot f,$
$P_{VA} = 0.3 \, mJ \cdot 50 \, kHz = 15 \, W.$

These losses $P_{VA}$, the switching losses $P_S$ and the forward power losses $P_V$ must be equal to or less than the maximum power loss $P_D$. If this is the case, the SIPMOS transistor can be used with no problems.

We recommend the following equation for estimation $P_{VA-} \leqq 0.2 \, (P_V + P_S)$.

**Circuit**

SIPMOS transistors can be simply connected in parallel in order to increase the power. It must be noted that oscillations may occur owing to the high switching rate and owing to the high transconductance. These oscillations are suppressed by decoupling resistors in each gate line (Fig. 3.23) or by separate drivers (Fig. 3.24). Incorrect transistor current distributions may occur owing to component tolerances and an asymmetrical circuit structure. Reducing the drain current by a factor of 0.8 is thus advisable in order to avoid overloading the individual transistor.

$I_{Dtot} = 0.8 \cdot I_D \cdot n$ ($n$: Number of transistors to be connected in parallel.)

The following aspects must always be observed:

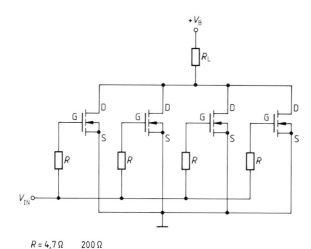

$R = 4,7 \, \Omega \qquad 200 \, \Omega$

Fig. 3.23
Parallel connection of SIPMOS transistors with gate resistors

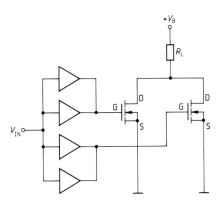

Fig. 3.24
Parallel connection of SIPMOS transistors
with separate drivers

▷ Designing the circuit structure with as low
  an induction as possible,
▷ laying load current leads symmetrically,
▷ avoiding earth loops,
▷ mutually decoupling control leads,
▷ reducing the total drain current,

▷ blocking the power supply with capacitor
  and
▷ operating with as high a switching rate as
  possible.

Particular attention must be paid to the tolerance of the threshold voltage and the very
high transconductance of the transistors if
connecting in parallel in the analog region.

*Push-pull and bridge circuit*
Push-pull circuits may be driven with DC voltage coupling or with a transformer. In the
case of transformer drive, both source connections are connected to ground via a low-
impedance shunt (Fig. 3.25). The other
push-pull circuit is a so-called half-bridge circuit (Fig. 3.26). In this case, the two transistors are connected in series. A full-bridge circuit (Fig. 3.27) can be implemented with two
half-bridge circuits).

*Driving with CMOS gate*
The CMOS standard six-fold inverter 4049
(Fig. 3.28) provides a low-cost solution to the
problem of fast charging and discharging of
the input and Miller capacitance. Each inver-

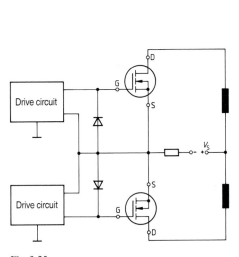

Fig. 3.25
Transformer push-pull drive

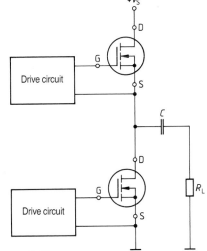

Fig. 3.26
Driving a half-bridge circuit

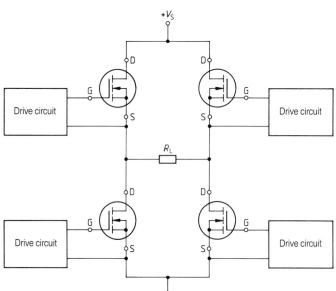

Fig. 3.27
Driving a fullbridge circuit

ter output supplies approx. −40 or +20 mA. Four inverters connected in parallel supply adequate gate current for rapidly switching through the SIPMOS transistors.

*Driving via optocoupler*
Fig. 3.29 shows a floating drive circuit with optocoupler. The insulation resistance of op-

tocouplers lies between approx. 0.5 and 5.2 kV. Switch-on and switch-off peak times can be reduced by connecting a complementary push-pull stage in between (between the optocoupler and SIPMOS transistor). This achieves a turn-on time of 1.2 μs and a turn-off time of 7 μs.

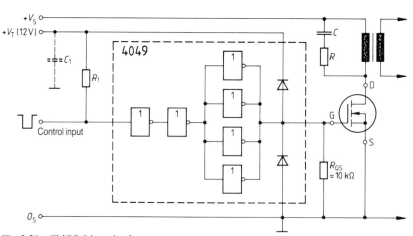

Fig. 3.28   CMOS driver circuit

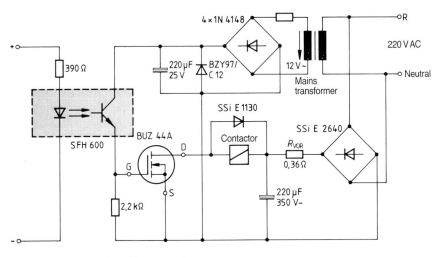

Fig. 3.29    Floating drive with optocoupler

**250 W switched-mode power supply unit**

The switched-mode power supply unit described below supplies 5 V/20 A DC voltage at 117/220 V primary AC voltage.

Switched-mode power supply units of power class 50 to 250 W and output currents >5 A are usually designed as forward converters. This method of connection makes do with low component complexity and has a problem-free operating behavior. A 50 kHz switched-mode power supply unit operating on the basis of the single-ended forward converter principle is described in this circuit example. The circuit operates with the SNT control IC TDA 4718, the MOSFET BUZ 80 as the power circuit breaker and the Schottky double diode BSY 28.

*Power section primary circuit*
After the RFI suppression filter, the AC input voltage (220 V or 117 V), rectified by the bridge-connected rectifier, charges the electrolytic filter capacitors $2 \times 1000$ µF whose voltage is applied by the BUZ 80 to the primary winding of the transformer. In the case of 117 V operation, this potential is generated by voltage doubling (Fig. 3.30).

The electrolytic filter capacitors ($2 \times 1000$ µF) are overrated in order to bridge mains voltage failures over 2 to 3 half-cycles. If the full current drain is not required, the rating of the electrolytic capacitors must be selected appropriately lower. The TDA 4718 sets the drive pulse duty factor of the BUZ 80. Since only one output is required for driving the BUZ 80, the pulse duty factor is limited to >50 %. This ensures that the transformer core is fully demagnetized in the interpulse period via windings $n_1$ and $n_3$, whereby the magnetic energy is fed back to the electrolytic filter capacitors in order to improve the efficiency with a fast switching diode. The windings $n_1$ and $n_3$, together, have the same number of turns as $n_2$. The shielding winding $n_4$ consisting of copper foil damps the disturbing capacitive crosstalk to the secondary side between the primary and secondary side of the transformer.

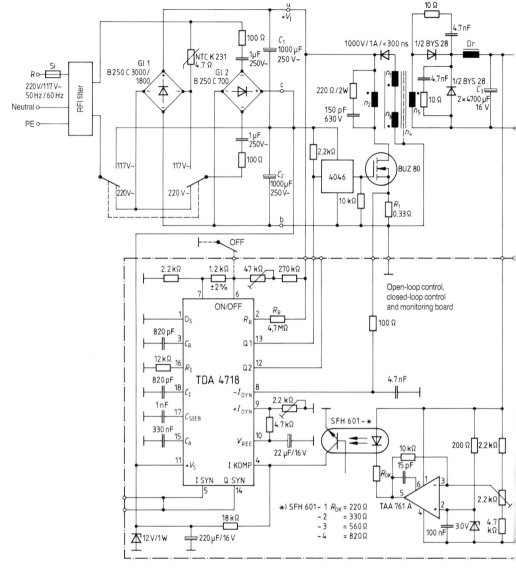

Fig. 3.30   Switched-mode power supply unit 50 to 250 W

## Switching behavior

The BUZ 80 is clocked with 50 kHz. It is driven via a CMOS driver module (4049). The switching edge lasts 50 ns when switching on and switching off.

There is no snubber circuit for the transistors to protect against high pulsed power load during the switching edges since SIPMOS transistors do not have a second breakdown. An $RC$ circuit of the transformer's primary winding is required to damp the backfire voltage caused by the leakage inductance. A pulse-resistant 63 V polypropylene capacitor is provided for this purpose.

## Open-loop control, closed-loop control and monitoring circuit

The TDA 4718 generates the synchronization of the switching frequency, the interpulse modulation and various monitoring and protection functions. The TDA 4718 is powered with low loss by rectification of the mains voltage and Zener diode stabilization with capacitive dropping resistor.

The TDA 4718 has the following protection functions:

▷ Short-circuit-proof reference voltage
▷ Smooth start
▷ Double pulse suppression

The following limit values are monitored

▷ Dynamic current limiting
▷ Overvoltage and undervoltage monitoring
▷ Supply voltage monitoring

The module blocks the two switching outputs $Q_1/Q_2$ if one of the specified limit values is exceeded. When the actual value drops below the limit value, the module resumes operation with a smooth start. One exception to this rule is dynamic current limiting. It does not cause a smooth start.

## Synchronization of the switching frequency

The $R_T/C_T$ combination determines the 50 kHz switching frequency. A square-wave voltage for synchronizing the internal oscillator can be injected at input 5. The frequency capture range is 30 %. If terminals 14 and 5 are connected, the oscillator oscillates at its nominal frequency.

## Biasing

The input voltage $V_i$ is applied to input 2 via resistor $R_R$ for suppression of system hum. This measure controls the output pulse duty factor in phase opposition to the input voltage hum. This largely compensates for it.

## Monitoring of the input voltage

The input voltage $V_i$ is monitored for the upper and lower limit value with the overvoltage and undervoltage switch-off circuit respectively (inputs 7 and 6). The 47 kΩ trimmer is set so that overvoltage switch-off cuts in at approx. 242 V and undervoltage switch-off cuts in at approx. 187 V for 220 V operation.

## Dynamic current limiting

The source current of the BUZ 80 is detected via the shunt $R_1$. The cut-in threshold can be adjusted by means of a trimmer in order to compensate for variations of the reference voltage $V_{ref}$ and the tolerance of $R_i$. This permits the cut-in point of the current limiting facility to be set precisely, e.g. to 21 A. Since SIPMOS transistors do not have carrier storage times, the dynamic current limiting circuit operates virtually with no delay. The source current is switched off exactly when the set limit value is exceeded.

## Siemens power transistors

### Smart SIPMOS transistors

The transistors of the smart SIPMOS family are combinations of power transistor and logic. They are essentially switching transistors which protect themselves against short-circuit, overvoltage and overtemperature by means of integrated sensors and thus guarantee a higher reliability. The term "Smart SIPMOS transistors" includes TEMPFET and PROFET.

The TEMPFET protects itself against over-temperature, against overload and with a suitable auxiliary circuit, also against short-circuit. It switches with respect to ground (N-channel) or with respect to battery (P-channel).

The PROFET protects itself against short-circuit and overtemperature. It detects load interruptions and can turn off in the case of undervoltage. It is TTL-/5-V-CMOS-compatible and switches ground-circuit loads. The switch status is signalled.

FREDFETs are SIPMOS transistors with the integrated free-wheeling diode: They were developed for simple-structure, closed-loop-controlled three-phase drives in the kilowatt range.

SIRETs are high-speed 1000 V transistors.

SITACs are optocoupled triacs for separating the control circuit from the output circuit electrically and with high voltage strength (in the case of mains voltages of 220 V).

*FREDFETs with free-wheeling diode*
The free-wheeling power diodes are integrated in the FREDFET. This dispenses with the need for external snubber circuits when operating reactive loads.

*TEMPFETs with temperature monitoring*
The TEMPFET is an overtemperature-safe and short-circuit-proof SIPMOS power transistor with thermally coupled temperature sensor. The sensor switches on at temperatures >155 °C and connects the gate and source terminals. This causes fast turn-off of the transistor owing to discharge of the input capacitance.

*PROFETs with monitoring circuit*
The PROFET is a CMOS and TTL-compatible SIPMOS power transistor with integrated protection functions to protect against destruction owing to short-circuit, overtemperature, overload and ESD etc. for switching ground-circuit loads. It indicates system faults via its status output. The status level is HIGH in volt-free state, provided a voltage

is applied to $V_{BB}$ (Fig. 3.31). The figure shows a circuit for fault simulation of the PROFET. Dependant upon the type of fault occurring, the status signal changes to LOW in on or off state. In cases of critical faults, the PROFET itself switches off the load current.

The following faults act on the status output:

▷ Discontinuity in the load circuit
▷ Short-circuit in the load circuit
▷ Overtemperature in the transistor (overload)
▷ External overtemperature
▷ Excessively low operating voltage

Table 3.2 shows the fault states of the PROFET.

*SIRET – fast bipolar transistor*
SIRETs are Siemens-ring-emitter-transistors for high switching rates in the voltage range 500 to 1200 V. They permit construction of static converters in the power range of several hundred kilowatts at frequencies over 10 kHz as required for low-noise drives.

*SITAC, an optically coupled triac*
The SITAC is a high-noise-immunity linking element between logic and load.

The SITAC BTR 12 is TTL/CMOS compatible and achieves a high interference immunity of the output circuit with sensitive input circuit (2 mA gate trigger current). The critical rate of rise of off-state voltage of 10000 V/s during static operation and commutation dispenses with the need for an *RC* circuit when switching inductive loads. This means lower losses, higher reliability, less space required and, thus lower costs.

Technical data of the SITAC:

Peak off-state voltage
   600 V
rms limit current
   300 mA
Gate trigger current
   2 mA
Critical rate of rise of off-state voltage
   10000 V/s

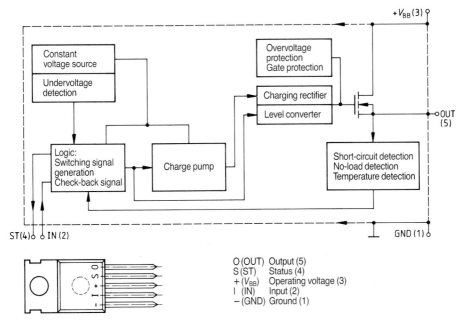

Fig. 3.31 Fault simulation of the PROFET

O (OUT)  Output (5)
S (ST)  Status (4)
+ ($V_{BB}$)  Operating voltage (3)
I (IN)  Input (2)
– (GND)  Ground (1)

Plastic package
20A6 in accordance with DIN 41 866 or DIP6 in accordance with JEDEC

Its advantages are as follows:

▷ the broad safe operating range for 220 V AC applications,
▷ it can be driven by microprocessors/microcontrollers without repeater,
▷ the broad safety range for load peak currents,
▷ no additional power triac is required for many low-load applications, – it is insensitive to external interference.

Fig. 3.32 shows the graphic symbol and pin assignment of the SITAC BRT 12.

The BRT 12 is particularly suitable for direct control of synchronous motors, valves, relays, solenoid actuators and drivers of high-power triacs and thyristors. Besides industrial controls, the preferred fields of application include office machines and domestic appliances.

Table 3.2   Fault states of the PROFET

|  | Input voltage | Status | Output voltage |
|---|---|---|---|
| Normal function | L | H | L |
|  | H | H | H |
| Load, interrupted | L | L | H |
|  | H | H | H |
| Short-circuit | L | H | L |
|  | H | L | L |
| Overtemperature | L | L | L |
|  | H | L | L |
| Undervoltage | L | H | L |
|  | H | L | L |

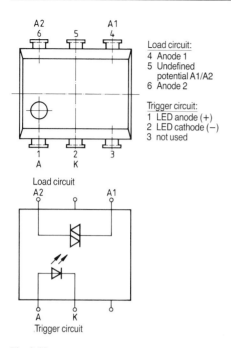

Load circuit:
4 Anode 1
5 Undefined
  potential A1/A2
6 Anode 2

Trigger circuit:
1 LED anode (+)
2 LED cathode (−)
3 not used

Fig. 3.32
Graphic symbol and pin assignment
of the SITAC BRT 12

### 3.2.2 High-Power Semiconductors

The following diagrams show the limit rating range (on-state current as a function of off-state voltage) of mains diodes, high-speed diodes, symmetrical and asymmetrical thyristors and mains thyristors (Figs. 3.33 to 3.37). We shall now discuss GTO thyristors in further detail.

*GTO thyristors*
Gate-turn-off thyristors have been used in drive engineering to an increasing extent wherever the size and weight of the static converter were crucial criteria, for example in traction. Owing to dropping prices and reduced turn-off complexity, the device costs become so favorable that they are also used, to an ever-increasing extent, in stationary industrial drives. GTOs are particularly attractive in applications in which the performance

of modern power transistor modules is inadequate, i.e. for off-state voltages over 2000 V and gate turn-off currents over 1000 A.

The main field of application is currently drive engineering with operating frequencies up to 1 kHz and intermediate voltages up to 3 kV. GTOs can be used for higher frequencies only in special applications (e.g. in resonant parallel-tuned converters) owing to excessively long carrier storage times and excessively high turn-off losses.

Fig. 3.38 shows a chopper circuit.

The maximum gate turn-off current $I_{TGQM}$ is a limit value at which the GTO still turns off under defined secondary conditions. This means that the protection system must be designed such that this current is not exceeded even under worst-case conditions. GTOs are generally operated at approx. 50% of the maximum on-state current which can be turned off.

The losses comprise on-state power losses and switching losses. The turn-off losses dominate in this case.

In the GTO, the product of current density and off-state voltage must not exceed a specific limit value (Fig. 3.39).

The loss concentration reaches critical values in the turn-off phase since this is when high current densities occur inside the semiconductor owing to current constrictions despite decreasing load current.

This results in important operating information:

▷ The voltage rise in the critical turn-off phase must be damped by a snubber capacitor ($C$ in Fig. 3.38). Owing to the line inductance in the snubber circuit, a spike voltage occurs at turn-off resulting from the rate of current rise before the snubber capacitor can have a damping effect. If this spike voltage is too high, the GTO is destroyed. Fig.

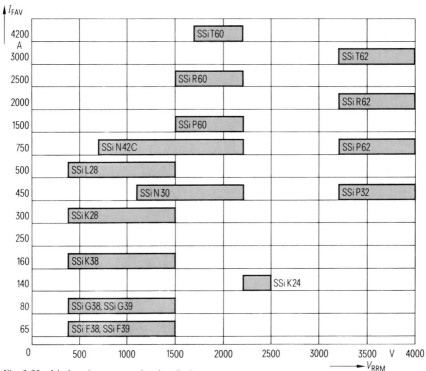

Fig. 3.33   Limit rating ranges of mains diodes

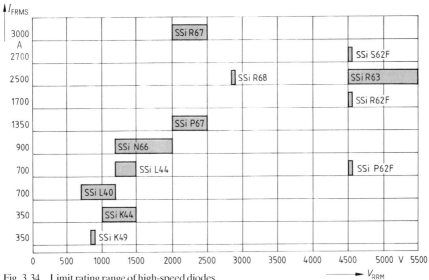

Fig. 3.34   Limit rating range of high-speed diodes

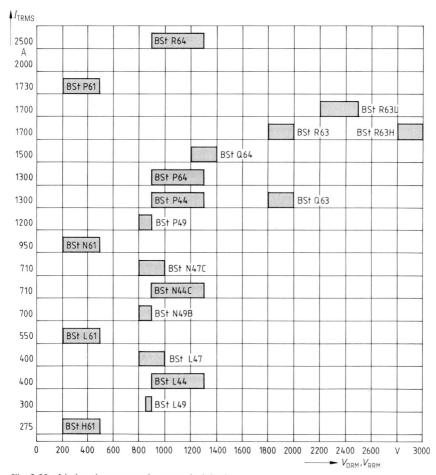

Fig. 3.35   Limit rating ranges of symmetrical thyristors

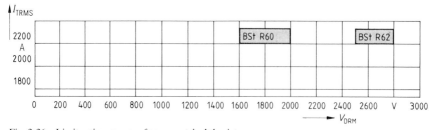

Fig. 3.36   Limit rating ranges of asymmetrical thyristors

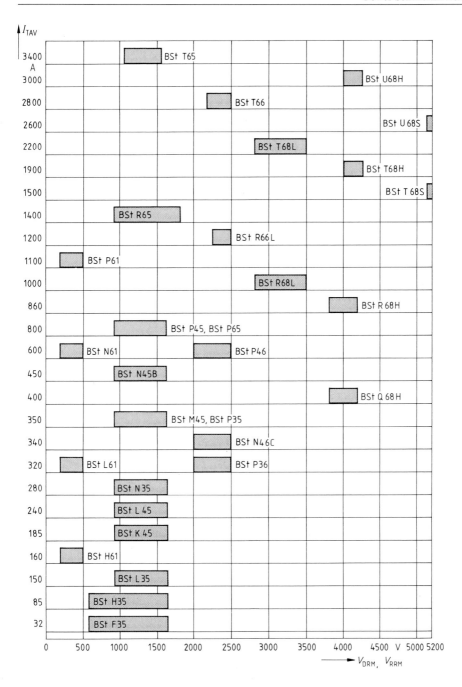

Fig. 3.37    Limit rating ranges of mains thyristors

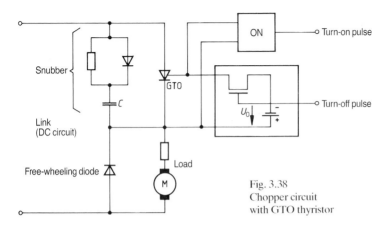

Snubber

Link
(DC circuit)

Free-wheeling diode

Load

ON — Turn-on pulse

$U_0$ — Turn-off pulse

M

Fig. 3.38
Chopper circuit
with GTO thyristor

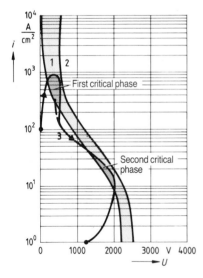

1 SOA curve for conventional design
2 Improved SOA curve owing to new doping profile
3 Approximate $i$-$V$ characteristic in the GTO
  thyristor with current constriction effect

——— with
– – – without     inductance of the snupper lead

Fig. 3.39
Current density-voltage diagram of the turn-off
process of GTO thyristors

3.39 shows the current and voltage characteristics in the mains circuit and gate circuit.

▷ High-speed turn-off reduces the turn-off
losses. For this purpose, the charge stored in
the thyristor must be extracted in the gate circuit by a negative gate pulse. The impedance
of the gate circuit must be very low. Low-
threshold high-current MOS power transistors are particularly well suited for this. The
required and desired range of rate of gate current rise is dependent upon type and is thus
defined in the data.

Fig. 3.40   GTO thyristor BGT S2000 A25

▷ Selecting the correct operating voltage $V_0$ for turn-off of the gate is important (Fig. 3.38). If the battery voltage is near to the gate breakdown voltage $V_{GRM}$, this results in a short carrier storage time but a long avalanche time which may endanger the GTO. If $V_{GRM}$ is around 20 V, this achieves optimum switching times with 12 to 15 V.

Fig. 3.40 shows the GTO thyristor BGT S2000 A25 with exposed pellet, showing the electrode structure.

## 3.3 Sensors

### 3.3.1 Magnetic Field-Dependent Semiconductors

The magnetic field-dependent semiconductors include Hall generators and magnetoresistors which are based upon utilization of the Hall effect.

On the Hall generator, a so-called Hall voltage is tapped at two opposite sides of a thin slice of semiconductor material with an electric current flowing through it and if it is permeated by a magnetic field perpendicular to the wafer. This Hall voltage is dependent upon magnetic field and current. In the case of magnetoresistors, the resistance of the current-carrying wafer is changed under the action of a magnetic field.

The interaction of magnetic field and current produces a voltage so that we can talk of a voltage being generated, hence a Hall generator.

**Hall generators**

Technically applying the Hall effect was not made possible until the discovery of the unusually high electron mobility of specific semiconductive III-V compounds, e.g. indium antimonide $In_5Sb_3$. In these materials, current flow is not the result of a large number of extremely slow moving electrons but, rather is the result of a few very quickly moving electrons. Consequently, the Hall voltage is several orders of magnitude higher than in the case with metals and lies in the range of up to a few 100 mV, a voltage which can be evaluated simply with state-of-the-art electronics.

*Structure of Hall generators*
A current $I_{con}$ (control current) flows through a long wafer made of a suitable material, thickness $d$ (Fig. 3.41), and the wafer is permeated by a magnetic field $B_z$ (control field) perpendicular to its surface. Simultaneous action of these two control variables produces a potential difference between the points (open circuit Hall voltage $V_H$), the magnitude of which is defined as follows:

$$V_H = \frac{R_h}{d} \cdot I_{con} \cdot B_z.$$

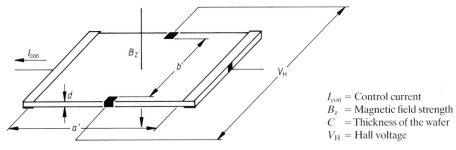

$I_{con}$ = Control current
$B_z$ = Magnetic field strength
$C$ = Thickness of the wafer
$V_H$ = Hall voltage

Fig. 3.41   Basic structure of a Hall generator

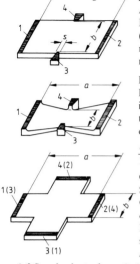

Rectangular shape:
$R_{LL}/R_{20} \approx 3$
High Hall power
($R_{LL}$ terminating
resistor for linear
matching)

Butterfly shape:
High flux sensitivity $R_0$ with concentration of the flux
on the central area

$$\frac{a}{2} \cdot b$$

Cross shape:
Symmetrical:
Control and Hall
electrodes reversible;
high induction
sensitivity
$b = s; R_{LL}/R_{20} > 10$

1, 2 Supply electrodes    3, 4 Hall electrodes
$a$ Length in control current direction
$b$ Effective width of the Hall plate
$s$ Hall electrode width

Fig. 3.42    Shapes of Hall plate

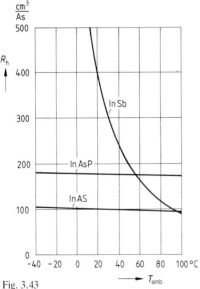

Fig. 3.43
Dependence of the Hall constant upon
temperature

The formula shows the most important feature of the Hall effect in relation to application, mainly representing the product of two electrical variables (current and magnetic conduction) again as an electrical variable.

$R_h$ is the material constant (Hall constant).

The arrows in Fig. 3.41 show the direction for N-semiconductors.

The semiconductor layer can be manufactured using the following technology:

The semiconductor body is obtained from molten semiconductor rods by sawing, grinding and etching: thicknesses 5 to 100 μm. The carrier plate and semiconductor layer are connected with a 1 to 2 m thick epoxy resin layer.

The Hall generator can be optimized for the scheduled measurement task by shaping the semiconductor wafer (Fig. 3.42).

*Definitions and general data*
The characteristic data and ratings specified in the data sheets refer to an ambient temperature of 25 °C.

*Ratings of the control current $I_{1n}$*

The rated current is selected such that the semiconductor layer assumes a temperature rise of 10 to 15 °C when operating the Hall generator in stationary air. The change in the Hall constant resulting with this temperature increase and, thus, the open circuit Hall voltage are shown in Fig. 3.43 and by the temperature coefficient $\beta$ specified in the data sheets.

The Hall coefficient $R_h$ is a temperature-dependent material constant. $R_h$ is independent upon the magnetic field in the case of indium arsenide (InAs) up to inductions of 15 T($= 150$ kG), and in the case of indium antimonide (InSb) of approx. 5 T($= 50$ kG).

*Control field B*
The control field range must be delimited in order to permit quantitative statements on the proportionality between Hall voltage

and control field. The control field range to which all linearization specifications refer to is given in the relevant data sheets. The Hall generator will not be damaged if this specified range is exceeded. It must be noted that the control-circuit internal resistance increases with increasing magnetic induction. In the case of inductions exceeding 2 Tesla (1 Tesla = $10^4$ Gauss) in particular, the magnitude of the control current must be selected such that the maximum permitted temperature of the semiconductor layer (120 °C) is not exceeded.

*Rated magnetic control flux $\Theta_n$*
The rated control flux is specified in the case of Hall generators with ferromagnetic material. The control flux specified as the rated control flux lies below the saturation bend of the enclosure material. The specified linearity and multiplication error refers to the rated magnetic control flux and applies in the range between positive and negative rating of the magnetic control flux. Exceeding the rating will not damage the Hall generator.

*Rated magnetomotive force (field excitation) n*
A rated magnetomotive force ($I_F \cdot n$) is specified in the data sheets for modulators and multipliers. At this magnetomotive force, the flux density of the magnetic material used remains below the saturation bend. All linearization specifications refer to the range between positive and negative rating of the magnetic magnetomotive force. Exceeding the rated magnetomotive force will not damage the Hall generator.

*Open circuit Hall voltage $V_{20}$*
In the data sheets, the voltage which the unloaded Hall generator generates at the nominal control current $I_{1n}$ and the specified control field B is specified as the open circuit Hall voltage $V_{20}$. In the case of Hall generators with ferromagnetic enclosure, the no-load voltage refers to the rated control current $I_{1n}$ and the rated magnetic control flux $\Theta_n$. In the case of modulators and mul-

tipliers, the open circuit voltage refers to the rated control current $I_{1n}$ and the rating $\Theta_n$.

The values of the open circuit voltage specified in the data sheets are lower limits. Maximum values may be 1.5 times higher.

*Induction sensitivity at open circuit $H_{a0}$*
The induction sensitivity at open circuit load is defined by the following equation

$$H_{a0} = \frac{V_{20}}{I_{1n} \cdot B}.$$

*Terminating resistance $R_L$ for linear matching in the relevant, specified control field range of B=0 to B=1 T*
Fig. 3.44 shows the dependence of the Hall voltage upon the control field B for various terminating resistance values $R_L$ on the Hall generator FA 24. The Hall voltage referred to the control current unit is plotted on the ordinate. As can be seen, the best linearity between the Hall voltage, referred to the control current unit, and the control field is achieved only for a specific terminating resistance $R_{LL}$.

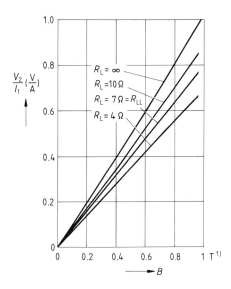

Fig. 3.44   Standardized Hall voltage

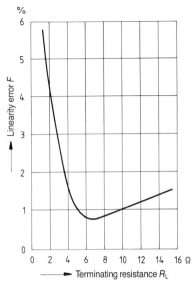

Fig. 3.45
Linearity error of the Hall generator FA24

The terminating resistance $R_{LL}$ for optimum linearity must be determined experimentally for every Hall generator. The approximate value of $R_{LL}$ is specified in the data sheet.

Fig. 3.45 shows the linearity error for the Hall generator FA 24 as a function of the load resistance in the control range of 0 to 1 Tesla.

Table 3.3 shows types and characteristic data of measurement Hall generators and Table 3.4 shows ferrite Hall generators and signal Hall generators from Siemens.

*Applications*
It is possible to categorize the Hall generators in the following types, dependent upon the design for various fields of application:

▷ Field measurement
▷ Measurement of tangential and axial fields
▷ Field measurement at low temperatures

Table 3.3   Type overview and characteristic data of measurement Hall generators

| Type | Material | Open circuit sensitivity referred to 1 T $K_{BO}$ (B/A·T) | Open circuit Hall voltage at $I_{ln}$ and 1 T $V_{20}$ (mV) | Zero resistance $R_0$ (mV/A) | Control current rating $I_{ln}$ (mA) | Internal resistance control-circuit $R_{10}$ (Ω) |
|---|---|---|---|---|---|---|
| EA 218 | InAs | ≥ 0.85 | ≥ 85 | < 5 | 100 | 3 |
| FA 22e | InAs | ≥ 0.85 | ≥ 120 | < 2 | 150 | 2 |
| FA 24 | InAs | ≥ 0.75 | ≥ 300 | < 2.5 | 400 | 1.4 |
| FC 32 | InAsP | ≥ 1.3 | ≥ 130 | < 1.5 | 100 | 6.5 |
| FC 33 | InAsP | ≥ 1.45 | ≥ 145 | < 1 | 100 | 5 |
| FC 34 | InAsP | ≥ 1.45 | ≥ 290 | < 1 | 200 | 5 |
| SBV 603 | InSb | ≥ 4·2 | ≥ 210 | < 2 | 50 | ~6 |
| SBV 604 | InSb | ≥ 4·2 | ≥ 210 | < 2 | 50 | ~6 |
| SBV 613 | InSb | ≥ 0·4$^8$ | ≥ 120 | < 0,4 | 250 | ~1 |
| SBV 620 | InSb | ≥ 8 | ≥ 600 | < 75 | 50 | ~6 |
| SVB 525 | InAs | ≥ 0.97 | ≥ 97 | < 2.5 | 100 | 2.2 |
| SV 210 | InAs | ≥ 6 | ≥ 300 | < 33 | 60 | 30 |
| SV 230S | InAs | ≥ 6.5 | ≥ 650 | < 100 | 100 | 30 |
| TC 21 | InAs | ≥ 0.60 | ≥ 90 | < 2 | 150 | 1.2 |
| RHY 10 | InAs | ≥ 0.7 | ≥ 70 | < 2.5 | 100 | 2 |
| RHY 11 | InAs | ≥ 0.7 | ≥ 105 | < 2 | 150 | 3 |
| RHY 17 | InAs | ≥ 6 | ≥ 300 | < 33,3 | 60 | 30 |
| RHY 18 | InAs | ≥ 6 | ≥ 150 | < 57.1 | 35 | 30 |

Operating temperature range −20 °C to +90 °C unless otherwise specified in the data sheet.

Table 3.4    Type overview and characteristic data of ferrite Hall generators and signal Hall generators

| Type | Material | Open circuit sensitivity referred to 1 T $K_{BO}$ (B/A·T) | Open circuit Hall voltage at $I_{1n}$ and 1 T $V_{20}$ (mV) | Zero resistance $R_0$ (mV/A) | Control current rating $I_{1n}$ (mA) | Internal resistance control-circuit $R_{10}F$ (Ω) |
|---|---|---|---|---|---|---|
| RHY 15 | InSb | – | ≥ 120 | < 10 | 50 | 30 |
| RHY 20 | InSb | – | ≥ 120 | < 10 | 50 | 30 |
| SBV 566 | InSb | – | ≥ 130 | < 1000 | 35 | 30 |

▷ Signaling
▷ Multiplication
▷ Magnetogram scanning

The types within the groups also differ as regards their suitability for the relevant application and as regards accuracy.

Hall generators for field measurements are designed for measuring the strength of magnetic fields. If a constant control current is passed through the Hall generator, the magnitude of the Hall voltage is proportional to the strength of the magnetic field. Consequently, the Hall generators are required to provide a high constancy of the sensitivity and zero voltage.

The designs extend from relatively large-area precision probes through probes with a small sensitive area for punctiform field measurement and universal applications to particularly thin probes which make it possible to measure fields in narrow air gaps.

In the case of the ferrite Hall generators for non-contact and "solid-state" signaling, importance is attached primarily to a high sensitivity. This is achieved by concentrating the magnetic flux onto the Hall element with the aid of flux-concentrating ferrite segments.

Since the application is generally digital, the temperature dependence of the sensitivity is of less importance than a high signal amplitude.

*Field measurement*

For gauging the strength of magnetic fields, the Hall generator is terminated with the matching linearization resistor and powered from a constant current source. Powering from a constant current source with dropping resistor cannot be used since the control-circuit internal resistance increases in the case of high fields, thus reducing the control current. Fig. 3.46 shows the in-

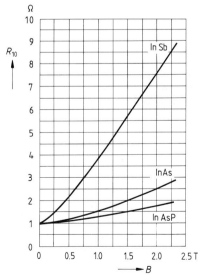

Fig. 3.46
Increase in the control resistance of Hall generators

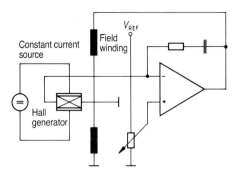

Fig. 3.47
Block diagram of a field control system

current to be measured through the winding of a magnet yoke and to measure the magnetic field in the air gap.

*Scanning magnetizable foils*
The Hall generator KSM 2 which is encapsulated in a mechanically sturdy package, screened against stray fields is particularly suitable for scanning adjacently arranged tracks.

Magnetic rubber and magnetic PVC, but also magnetically hard alloys, are suitable as the storage surface.

crease in resistance in the magnetic field of 3 Hall generators made of different semiconductor materials.

One further aspect must be noted particularly in the case of low Hall voltages: The Hall voltage terminals are connected to the semiconductor material by two soldered connections whose thermal e.m.f.s normally cancel each other out. If the Hall generator is subjected to heating on one side, the thermal e.m.f.s no longer correspond and may lead to substantial measuring errors.

Magnetic fields can be controlled and stabilized in such a way that the output voltage of a Hall generator arranged in the field is used to control the coil current. It is best to mount the Hall generator in the air gap on a pole shoe beneath a non-magnetic cover, whereby it may never be subjected to mechanical strain. The closed loop must be damped with an *RC* network on the control amplifier in order to eliminate the tendency to oscillate which always occurs in this case (cf. Fig. 3.47).

*Current measurement in an isolated circuit*
Using Hall generators in a magnet yoke permits direct currents to be measured with full electrical isolation between the circuits. The simplest method is to pass the

**Magnetoresistors**

Magnetoresistors are magnetically controllable resistors made of InSb/NiSb which can be influenced owing to the Hall effect or Gauss effect. The charge carriers passing through the semiconductor are deflected to the side owing to the action of a transversal magnetic field.

The angle by which the current direction changes when a magnetic field is applied is called the Hall angle. This may be approximately 80° with an induction of 1 Tesla. By contrast with the Hall generator, low-impedance needles made of NiSb incorporated in the magnetoresistor crystal maintain the uniform distribution of the charge carriers over the cross-section of the semiconductor transverse to the current direction of the magnetoresistor which is not subjected to a magnetic field. Fig. 3.48 shows the configuration of the conducting paths in a rectangular semiconductor wafer with conductive needles made of NiSb as shorting strips, a) without magnetic field and b) with magnetic field. The extension of the path of the charge carriers with increasing magnetic field results in an increase in the resistance of the magnetoresistor, but with no distinction in the field polarity.

The resistance dependence of the magnetic field is shown qualitatively in Fig. 3.49.

a) Without magnetic field

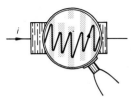

b) With magnetic field

Fig. 3.48
Conductive paths in a rectangular
semiconductor wafer

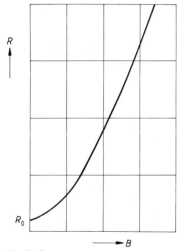

Fig. 3.49
Dependence of the magnetoresistor
resistance upon the magnetic field

*Magnetoresistive system*
Indium antimonide-nickel antimonide
InSb-NiSb is produced as semiconductor
ingots by fusion. The required doping D, L
or N is achieved by adding tellurium. In a
special fibre-drawing process, nickel antimonide solidifies in the form of needles in-

side the indium antimonide, and these needles are aligned in parallel over the entire
length of the ingot.

In the component, these needles form the
shorting needles which produce the
geometry-dependent resistance effect. The
conductivity of the material is relatively
high. $\sigma = 200$ $(\Omega$ cm$)^{-1}$ for D material,
$\sigma = 550$ $(\Omega$ cm$)^{-1}$ for L material and
$\sigma = 800$ $(\Omega$cm$)^{-1}$ applies to N material.

In order to produce resistances in the range
10 to 500, the semiconductor must be adjusted for as low a current-flow cross-section as possible. In addition, the component is designed with a meandering configuration in order to obtain high basic resistances by as long semiconductor strips as
possible. For physical reasons (geometrical
effect of the change in resistance), the
width of the strip must not be less than approx. 80 $\Omega$m. Thus, the influencing capability of the basic resistance is restricted to varying length and thickness of the meandering strips.

The ingot is sawn into slices of 16 mm x 18
mm and cemented onto auxiliary carriers.
Semiconductor wafers which are approx.
25 μm thick are produced by grinding and
etch-polishing.

Conventional photographic techniques
then permit contour-etching of the individual meanders. The following resistance
values can be implemented, referred to the
meandering surface: D-material 100 $\Omega$/mm$^2$,
L-material 40 $\Omega$/mm$^2$ and N-material 25
$\Omega$/mm$^2$.

*Magnetoresistors*
The contour-etched semiconductor systems are cut out of the multi-element
semiconductor wafer with a laser and
bonded onto insulated substrates. In most
cases, they are bonded onto insulated ferrous substrates (Fig. 3.50). Permenorm
5000 H2 (saturation induction 1.5 T, static
coercive field strength 0.04 A/cm,

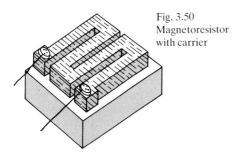

Fig. 3.50
Magnetoresistor
with carrier

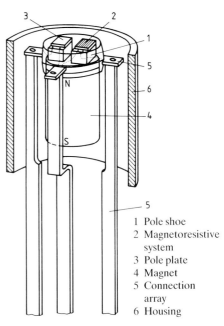

5

1 Pole shoe
2 Magnetoresistive
  system
3 Pole plate
4 Magnet
5 Connection
  array
6 Housing

Fig. 3.51
Structure of the magnetoresistive sensor FP210

maximum permeability 60 000 to 80 000) serves as the substrate material of these magnetoresistors which are designated E-types.

Besides this, it is also possible to bond substrates onto ferrite. The semiconductor surface is covered with a lacquer coat to protect against mechanical damage.

*Magnetoresistive sensors*
The magnetoresistive sensors FP 210/211/212 are designed as an open, magnetic circuit. The sensor consists of the components pole shoe (1), magnetoresistive system (2), pole plate (3), magnet (4), connection array (5) and housing (6). The structure is shown in Fig. 3.51.

The magnetoresistive system (2) is bonded onto the insulated surface of a ferrous pole shoe (1) with distinctive humps. The system is soldered with Cu or Ag wire. Since the soldered joints project beyond the system surface, soft iron pole plates (3) with a thickness of 0.2 mm are bonded onto the active semiconductor surfaces in order to protect the systems against mechanical damage and in order to bridge the soldered joint height through to the surface of the enclosure by a highly permeable material.

On the sensor FP 211 which has a single-hump pole shoe, a pole plate has not been used, owing to the narrow active zones of the bonded differential magnetoresistor. In this case, the system is covered by an approximately 0.25 mm thick plastic coating.

*Definitions and general data*
The basic resistance $R_0$ of the magnetoresistor is the resistance of the semiconductor system not subject to a magnetic field. It is determined by:

▷ The conductivity of the InSb-NiSb; we distinguish between three degrees of doping:
D-material: $\sigma = 200 \ (\Omega \ cm)^{-1}$ (non-doped)
L-material: $\sigma = 550 \ (\Omega \ cm)^{-1}$
N-material: $\sigma = 800 \ (\Omega \ cm)^{-1}$;

▷ The width of the meandering strip; this is generally approx. 80 μm;

▷ The meander thickness; it is approx. 25 μm;

▷ The overall length of the active, i.e. magnetic field-sensitive meandering strips.

The tolerance of the basic resistance is dependent upon the homogeneity of the base material and the reproducibility of the geometrical dimension of the magnetoresistive system. The current state of the art in production permits the required basic resistance $R_0$ to be observed to within 20 %.

*Resistance $R_0$ in magnetic field*
The resistance of a magnetoresistor under the action of a magnetic field is designated the resistance $R_B$. It is determined by:

▷ The basic resistance $R_0$
▷ The magnitude of the perpendicularly acting magnetic field, whereby the polarity is of no importance
▷ The degree of doping

Fig. 3.53a shows a graph on which the relative change in resistance $R_B/R_0$ at 25 °C has been plotted for three base materials as a function of the magnetic field. Up to approx. 0.3 T, the characteristics run approximately on the basis of the square law. In the direction of higher fields, they asymptotically approximate a straight line.

The tolerance of the relative resistance dependence is primarily dependent upon the uniform distribution of the nickel antimonide needles incorporated in the material and upon the variation in doping. Increasing doping of the base material weakens the magnetic field dependence of the magnetoresistor's resistance as a result of a reduction in electron mobility.

Since only the vertical component of the field is decisive as regards the increase in resistance, the effective component of the field is reduced with the cosine of the angle of inclination with respect to the vertical if the field direction is inclined. By way of example, Fig. 3.52b shows the resistance ratio $R_B/R_0$ as a function of the magnetic induction B for the various semiconductor materials ($T_{amb.} = 25$ °C). Fig. 3.52b shows

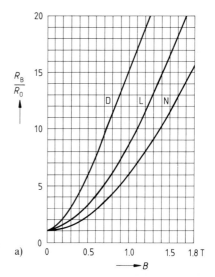

a)

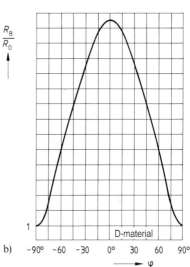

b)

Fig. 3.52
Resistance characteristics of magnetoresistors

the dependence of the resistance ratio $R_B/R_0$ upon the angle of inclination of the magnetic field.

Table 3.5 shows an overview of magnetoresistor types.

Table 3.5 Overview of magnetoresistor types

Magnetoresistors on ferrous substrates

| Type | Basic resistance at $T = 25\,°C$ | | Relative change in resistance at $T = 25\,°C$ and induction $B =$ | | Temperature coefficient | | | Coefficient of thermal conductivity in |  |
|---|---|---|---|---|---|---|---|---|---|
| | $R_{tol} = \pm 20\%$ | | 0,3 T | 1 T | 0 T | 0.3 T | 1 T | mW/K | |
| | $R_0\ (\Omega)$ | | $R/R_0$ | | $TK_{25}\ (\%/K)$ | | | $G_{thU}$ | $G_{thG}$ |
| FP 30D 250E | 250 | | 3 (>2.8) | 15 (>12) | −1.8 | −2.7 | −2.9 | 10 | 0.8 |
| FP 30L 100E | 100 | | 1.85 (>1.7) | 8.5 (>7) | −0.16 | −0.38 | −0.54 | 10 | 0.8 |

Differential magnetoresistors on ferrous substrates

| Type | Basic resistance at $T = 25\,°C$ $R_{tol} = \pm 20\%$ | Center symmetry at $T = 25\,°C$ $\dfrac{R_1 - R_2}{R_1} \cdot 100\%$ $(R_1 > R_2)$ | Relative change in resistance at $T = 25\,°C$ and induction $B =$ | | Temperature coefficient | | | Coefficient of thermal conductivity in mW/K | |
|---|---|---|---|---|---|---|---|---|---|
| | | | 0,3 T | 1 T | 0 T | 0,3 T | 1 T | | |
| | $R_0\ (\Omega)$ | $M\ (\%)$ | $R_B/R_0$ | | $TK_{22}\ (\%/K)$ | | | $G_{thU}$ | $G_{thG}$ |
| FP 110 D155 | $2 \times 155$ | 2 (<5) | 3 (>2.8) | 15 (>12) | −1.8 | −2.7 | −2.9 | 10 | 0.8 |

Magnetoresistive differential sensors

| Type | Overall resistance of the sensor system at $T = 25\,°C$ [1] | Tolerance value $T = 25\,°C$ | Center symmetry at $T = 25\,°C$ $\dfrac{R_1 - R_2}{R_1} \cdot 100\%$ $(R_1 > R_2)$ | No-load voltage at $T = 25\,°C$ [2] | | maximum permitted operating voltage at $T_G = 25\,°C$ |
|---|---|---|---|---|---|---|
| | $R_{1-3}$ $(\Omega)$ | $R_{1-3\,TOL}$ $(\Omega)$ | $M$ $(\%)$ | $V_{A0}$ $(mV)$ [1] | $V_{ASS}$ $(mV)$ | $V_{Bmax}$ $(V)$ |
| FP 210 D250 | 1000 | ± 300 | ≤ 10 | ≤ 132.5 | 850 | 7.5 |
| FP 210 L100 | 300 | ± 80 | ≤ 10 | ≤ 132.5 | 850 | 7.5 |
| FP 211 D155 | 400 | ± 120 | ≤ 5 | ≤ 64 | 400 | 5.5 |
| FP 212 L100 | 300 | ± 80 | ≤ 10 | ≤ 132.5 | 850 | 10 |

[1] Air gap $\delta = \infty$
[2] $V_B = 5\,V$
[3] Air gap 0.5 mm; end face flux of the control magnet $\phi_{St} = 2\,\mu Wb$
[4] Air gap 0.2 mm

## ICs for Hall sensors

*Double Hall sensor cell*
Minimal mechanical straining of the silicon is inevitable when the chips are fitted in the various packages. This non-uniform strain results in piezoelectric effects which, in turn, generate differing output voltages even without a magnetic field. A double version of the sensor cell can compensate for this effect.

*Integrated protection structures*
Integrated Zener diodes protect both the input and the output against the noise and overvoltage peaks occurring generally in industry and, in particular, also in the automobile. This improves the functional reliability of the components even under difficult ambient operating conditions.

*Close magnetic switching thresholds with good long-term stability*
The TLE 49xx family is optimized for low switching thresholds. These remain constant during the entire service life. Cobalt-samarium (CoSm) with its good long-term stability is particularly suitable as the magnet material.

*Thermal behavior*
By virtue of their very nature, the magnetic switching thresholds are dependent upon temperature. The required intensity of the magnetic field for reliable response of the Hall-effect switch in the relevant temperature range can be seen from the information in the data sheets.

*Packages*
The available flat plastic packages (P-SSO-3) have compact dimensions (4.65 mm x 4.65 mm x 1.5 mm). This means that close spacings between magnet and the active sensor surface are possible. The TNB package with a thickness of only 0.6 mm is suitable for extremely small air gaps.

## Magnets, materials

With the exception of measuring currents in an isolated circuit, a permanent magnet is always required for Hall IC applications. This magnet either moves itself or its magnetic field is influenced by a magnetically permeable component such as on a magnetic barrier.

The characteristic data and properties of various permanent magnet materials are important when selecting a permanent magnet suitable for the application. The characteristic data are remanence $B_R$, coercive field strength $H_C$ and electromagnetic energy density $BH_{max}$.

Fig. 3.53 shows the hysteresis loops of a permanent magnet.

Other important characteristic data are maximum application temperature, reversible temperature coefficient of the remanence, thermal coefficient of expansion (parallel and perpendicular to the prefer-

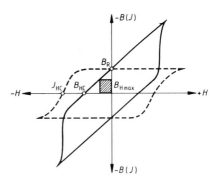

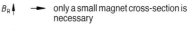

$B_R \uparrow$ → only a small magnet cross-section is necessary

$H_C \uparrow$ → permits the use of a relatively short magnet

$B_{Hmax} \uparrow$ → only a small volume of the magnet is required

Fig. 3.53
Hysteresis loops of a permanent magnet

red direction), density, flexural strength, compressive strength, Vickers hardness HV and electrical resistivity.

*Properties of permanent magnet materials*

*Al/Ni/Co alloys*

Advantages:
▷ very good thermal properties
▷ easy to work or machine (before magnetizing)
▷ good mechanical stability

Disadvantages:
▷ low coercive field strength
▷ moderate long-term stability

*Rare-earth cobalt sintered material*
Most conventional form: $SmCo_5$ and $Sm_2Co_{17}$

Advantages:
▷ relatively high temperature range, up to approx. 150 °C in the case of $SmCo_5$, up to approx. 300 °C in the case of $Sm_2Co_{17}$
▷ high magnetic field strength – good long-term stability

Disadvantages:
▷ high price owing to high cobalt content
▷ brittle material, thus cannot be worked or machined and is easy to damage
▷ difficult to demagnetize

*Sintered composite material comprising neodymium, iron and boron ($Nd_2Fe_{14}B$)*

*Advantages:*
▷ high energy value
▷ very high field strengths can be achieved
▷ good mechanical resistance

Disadvantages:
▷ low temperature range
▷ relatively high reversible temperature coefficient of the remanence – Susceptible to corrosion

*Barium and strontium ferrites*

Advantages:
▷ high coercive field strength
▷ not subject to attack by oxidation
▷ favorable price

Disadvantages:
▷ low remanence
▷ high reversible temperature coefficient

### 3.3.2 Pressure Sensors

Siemens manufactures piezoresistive pressure sensors from 2 kPa to 40 MPa. They are suitable for absolute, relative and differential pressure measurements at low pressure (2, 4 and 10 kPa), moderate pressure (25, 50, 200, 400 and 1000 kPa) and high pressure (6, 16 and 40 MPa). Computer-aided designs have made possible accurately measuring and sensitive sensors. The applications of these sensors include hydraulic systems ($>100$ kPA), barometers and liquid-level meters, in addition to measurement of slight atmospheric pressure fluctuations ($<10$ kPa).

*Principle of the pressure sensor*
Fig. 3.54 shows the basic structure of a pressure sensor. Resistive tracks are produced in a silicon diaphragm by ion implantation. If a pressure acts on the diaphragm so that it deflects, this results in a change in resistance on the basis of the piezoresistive effect. The scheduled measuring range and the quality requirements determine the design, technology and structure of the chip.

Computer-aided designs permit a high sensitivity with low linear deviation and given overload safety. The variations in zero voltage, sensitivity, temperature dependence and stability are dependent upon the technology used. Other effects such as long-term drift, pressure hysteresis and temperature hysteresis which deviate from the required ideal and good seal-tightness are chiefly influenced by mounting.

The wanted signal which is dependent upon the size of the sensor design is typically 70 mV at 25 °C (at 5 V supply voltage). Whilst the sum of most interference parameters is less than 1% of the final value, there still remain the zero voltage,

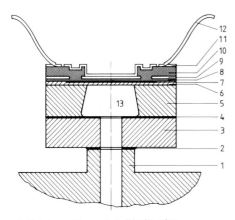

1 Metal mounting socket of the housing
2 Au-Sn solder
3 Silicon substrate
4 Metallic connecting layer
5 Silicon substrate
6 Silicon epitaxy layer
  (corresponds to a pressure-sensitive diaphragm)
7 Implanted resistances
8 Silicon oxide
9 Silicon nitride
10 Plating
11 CVD nitride
12 Aluminum strip leads
13 Cavity, equalizing the pressure with respect to
  the rear of the housing

Fig. 3.54
Basic structure of the pressure sensor

sensitivity variations and their temperature coefficients. These may need to be compensated for if required by an external circuit.

Table 3.6 summarizes the definitions and the most important characteristic parameters of a pressure sensor. Table 3.7 contains the characteristic data of the piezoresistive elementary pressure sensor compared with alternative principles.

**Media-compatibility**

Unprotected pressure sensors are suitable only for use in dry, non-aggressive atmospheres. There are two possible ways of protecting the sensor chip against fluids or aggressive gases:

▷ The pressure acts on the insensitive rear side of the diaphragm. This method can be used only for differential or relative pressure sensors.

▷ The best protection is guaranteed by a flexible, metallic separating diaphragm, whereby the space between the chip and separating diaphragm is filled with an inert fluid, e.g. silicone fluid.

*Temperature compensation*

Three relevant temperature-dependent variables must be noted: Temperature hysteresis and the temperature coefficients of the zero voltage and of the sensitivity.

Whilst the temperature hysteresis can be kept negligibly low with skillful mechanical installation in the housing ($\leq 0.5$ % of the final value), this is not the case with the other two variables dependent upon the temperature range. Typical values of the temperature coefficients are as follows:

Temperature coefficient of zero suppression = $\pm 2 \cdot 10^{-4}\,H^{-1}$
Temperature coefficient of the sensitivity = $-2 \cdot 10^{-3}\,H^{-1}$.

For instance, the characteristics shown in Fig. 3.56 results for a temperature range of 100 K. The physical mechanisms which lead to these temperature responses are strains of the thin silicon diaphragm owing to installation influences, slightly differing doping-dependent thermal coefficients of expansion of the individual resistances and the temperature dependence of the piezoelectric effect itself. Temperature compensation will be required if a pressure sensor is to operate as precisely as possible over a broad temperature range.

The temperature dependencies of the bridge sensitivity and of the zero voltage should always be adjusted mutually inde-

73

**Table 3.6** Definition of the most important characteristic parameters of a silicon pressure sensor

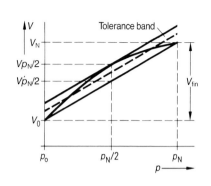

1. Output signal $V$:
   $V = V(p, T)$
   Zero voltage $\quad V_0 = V(p_0)$
   Output voltage at rated pressure $\quad V_N = V(p_N)$

2. Sensitivity $e$:

$$e = \frac{V_N - V_0}{(p_N - p_0)\, V_{cc}} \qquad \frac{mV}{V\, 10^5\, Pa}$$

3. Span signal $V_{fin}$:

   $V_{fin} = V_N - V_0$ (bei $V_{cc} = 5$ V und $p = p_N$) $\qquad$ mV

   or

   $V_{fin} = e \cdot (p_N - p_0) \cdot V_{cc}$

4. Temperature coefficient of the zero voltage $TK_{V0}$:
   $(T_0 = 25\,°C,\ T = 125\,°C)$

$$TK_{V0} = \left( \frac{V_0(T) - V_0(T_0)}{V_{fin}(T_0)} \cdot \frac{1}{T - T_0} \right) \times 100\ \frac{\%}{K}$$

5. Temperature coefficient of the span signal $TK_{Vfin}$

$$TK_{Vfin} = \left( \frac{V_{fin}(T) - V_{fin}(T_0)}{V_{fin}(T_0)} \cdot \frac{1}{T - T_0} \right) \times 100\ \frac{\%}{K}$$

6. Linearity error $L_F$:

$$L_F = \pm \frac{1}{2} \left( \frac{V p_N/2 - V' p_N/2}{V_{fin}} \right) \times 100\%$$

   where

   $V'_p = \dfrac{V_N - V_0}{p_N - p_0} \cdot p + V_0$

   $V'_p = V_{cc} \cdot e \cdot p + V_0$

**Table 3.7** Characteristic data of various pressure sensors

| Characteristic data | Piezo-resistive | Metal strain gauge | Ceramic strain gauge | Capacitive (silicon) | Capacitive (ceramic) |
|---|---|---|---|---|---|
| | | | (standardized to values of the piezoresistive sensor) | | |
| Gauge factor | 1 | 0.02 | 0.2 | — | — |
| Pressure sensitivity | 1 | 0.002 | 0.2 | 10 | 10 |
| Linearity error | 1 | 0.5 | 1 | 5 | 1 |
| Zero voltage | 1 | 1 | — | 10 | 10 |
| Temperature coefficient | | | | | |
|     Zero point | 1 | 1 | — | 1 | 1 |
|     Sensitivity | 1 | 0.05 | 0.1 | 0.05 | 0.05 |
| Temperature hysteresis | 1 | 1 | 1 | 0.25 | 0.25 |
| Long-term stability | 1 | 0.5 | 1 | 0.5 | 0.5 |
| Size of the elementary sensor | 1 | 10 | 10 | 1 | 10 |
| Price | 1 | 10 | 5 | — | — |

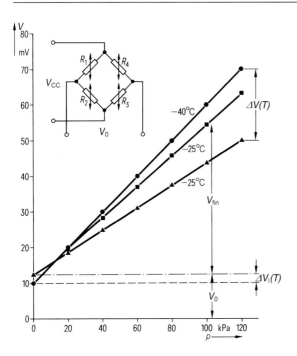

Fig. 3.55
Typical characteristic of a
piezoresistive pressure
sensor

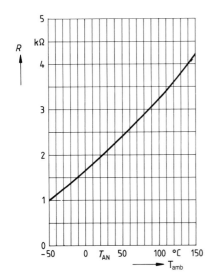

Fig. 3.56
Temperature dependence of the resistance of a
pressure sensor

pendently. Unfortunately, this is possible only conditionally in practice and largely determines the complexity and result of compensation. In the case of only slight temperature variations, so-called passive compensation with resistors and temperature sensors will suffice. Fig. 3.57 shows a simple passive compensation circuit. The output signal $V_{out}$ drops with increasing temperature. A temperature-dependent

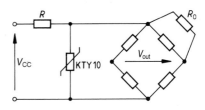

Fig. 3.57
Temperature compensation circuit

75

metal-film resistor $R$ is connected in series and a silicon temperature sensor KTY 10 is connected in parallel with the bridge for compensation. The pressure-dependent signal voltage can be set dependent upon temperature by selecting a suitable dropping resistor $R$.

The rating of the dropping resistor $R$ is calculated from the change in sensitivity of the signal voltage at two different temperatures and pressures. A temperature-dependent resistor $R_0$ is connected in parallel with one of the bridge arm resistances. This permits both the zero voltage and the temperature coefficient of the zero voltage to be influenced.

Dependent upon the rating of resistor $R_0$ (in the range 500 kΩ to 2.5 MΩ), there is a shift in the zero point up to 20 mV and a change in the zero point temperature coefficient up to 0.5 mV/25 K. If it is intended to change the zero point temperature coefficient with this measure, the zero point voltage must be compensated with the following circuit. Fig. 3.58 shows a diagram in which the temperature dependence $V_{out}$ of the output signal (referred to the signal at $-25\,°C$) of 5 sensors in each case is plotted. On the one hand, with passive compensation circuit as shown in Fig. 3.57 and, on the other hand, without temperature compensation.

Fig. 3.59 shows the percentage temperature error of adjusted sensors. The two error bands identify the temperature dependence of the sensitivity (span) and of the zero voltage. These measurement data were determined from approx. 1000 sensors. The temperature coefficient of the span is compensated to 0.5% in the temperature interval 25 to 125 °C and the temperature coefficient of the zero voltage is even compenseted to ±0.5% in the temperature interval 25 to 125 °C and the temperature coefficient of the zero voltage is even compensated to 0.2%.

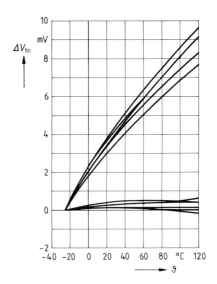

Fig. 3.58
Temperature compensation curves

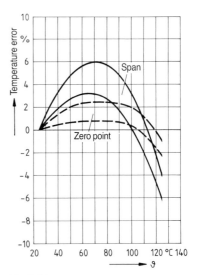

Fig. 3.59
Compensated percentage temperature error

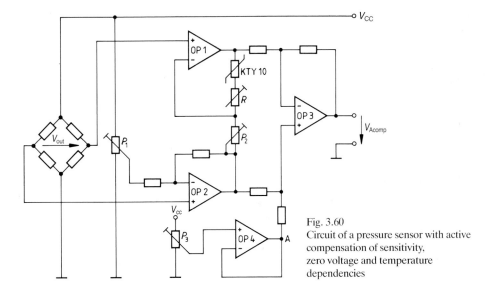

Fig. 3.60
Circuit of a pressure sensor with active
compensation of sensitivity,
zero voltage and temperature
dependencies

This simple type of passive compensation thus compensates the sensors to ±1%.

For precision measurements, circuits with active components are used, for example operational amplifiers.

Fig. 3.60 shows a complete circuit of a pressure sensor with active compensation of sensitivity, zero voltage and their temperature dependencies: Two operational amplifiers are connected as non-inverting amplifiers. The gain factor of operational amplifier OP1 is set dependent upon temperature with the temperature sensor KTY10. With increasing temperature, the output voltage $V_{out}$ drops. If the temperature sensor and the resistor $R$ are suitably designed, it is possible to boost the gain of operational amplifier OP1 thus compensating for the drop in the bridge voltage. Operational amplifier OP4 can be used to shift the output level as required. P1 is used to set the zero voltage to zero and P2 is used to set the system gain, within broad limits.

**Pressure sensor applications**

The ranges of application of piezoresistive pressure sensors can be subdivided into three sectors in relation to the media compatibility:

▷ Non-critical applications (non-aggressive gases or fluids). This group includes digital altimeters, barometers, sphygmomanometers, scales for weighing persons and various medical applications.

▷ Critical applications (non-aggressive but damp media). This sector includes media which come into contact with condensation for instance, such as vacuum systems, pneumatics, packaging and beverage bottling and canning machines (automatic coffee makers).

▷ Applications with media separation (aggressive gases and fluids). Industrial pressure gauges and flow meters, pumps and compressors in the fields of sewage treatment, air conditioning and refrigeration are typical applications.

Large numbers of piezoresistive pressure sensors are used in the field of automotive engineering for controlling the fuel-air mixture and for energy-saving ignition timing. They are also used in engine diagnostic equipment.

### 3.3.3 Temperature Sensors

Metallic resistors made of nickel or platinum have been the preferred element for measuring temperatures to date. They are reliable and can be used in a broad temperature range. The only disadvantage is their low sensitivity and the relatively high price.

Semiconductor thermistors are more sensitive and achieve virtually the close tolerances and the reproducible characteristic of the metallic temperature sensors.

The silicon sensor has the following data.

Temperature range
−50 °C to 150 °C

Resistance at 25 °C
2 kΩ ±2%

Long-term stability
±0.2%

Resistance ratio

$$\frac{R\,(100\,°C)}{R\,(25\,°C)} = 1.67 \pm 1.2\%$$

Within the resistance tolerance of ±2%, subgroups are obtainable, gauged to within an accuracy of ±0.5%, so as to permit measuring accuracies of 1 °C without additional gauging of the components.

The dependence of the resistance value upon the current direction, frequently a disturbing aspect of semiconductor temperature sensors, has been reduced to values <2 kΩ by technological means.

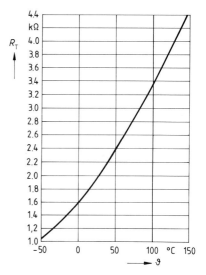

Fig. 3.61   Typical characteristic of the KTY10-6

Thus, if a sensor is to measure within a broad temperature range and if a measuring accuracy of a few tenths of a °C is adequate for this, the silicon temperature sensor of the KTY series can be used at favorable cost. The sensor elements are manufactured in various package designs (KTY10 to KTY16) and resistance groups (KTY10-3 to KTY10-9). Owing to the yield distribution, the ratings of the resistance groups lie at intervals of 30 about the mean values of 2000 Ω. Tolerance classes 0.5, 1, 2, 5 and 10% are available for the rating of the sensor resistance at the rated temperature $T_{amb} = 25\,°C$.

Fig. 3.61 shows the typical resistance-temperature characteristic of the KTY10-6.

Example applications of temperature sensors can be found in the chapter on automotive and industrial electronics.

### 3.3.4 Detectors
### for α, β and γ radiation

The basic mode of operation of semiconductor detectors is similar to that of ionization chambers. High-energy radiation releases positive charge carriers (holes) and negative charge carriers (electrons) in the crystal owing to the internal photoelectric effect. These charge carriers are separated by an electric field and produce a charge pulse at the electrodes. The pulse amplitude is proportional to the quantity of charge carriers produced. Since the quantity of these charge carriers is proportional to the energy of the ionizing particles, this permits the energy to be measured.

Semiconductor detectors afford the following advantages over ionization chambers (Geiger counters):

▷ Small sizes of the semiconductors mean shorter charge collecting times (fast pulse rise).

▷ Higher energies can be measured (shorter range in the solid).

▷ Semiconductor detectors are far smaller and less mechanically sensitive. This makes possible more compact devices.

▷ The spectral resolution is far higher since a pair of charge carriers can be generated with an energy lower by a factor of 10 (3.6 eV on the semiconductor as compared with 30 eV on an ionization chamber).

*Activity*
Activity is the number of disintegrations per unit of time. The activity unit in the SI system is the becquerel (Bq), $1 \text{ Bq} = 1 \text{ s}^{-1}$.

*α Sources*
α rays (helium nuclei) of natural radioactive substances have energies of approx. 4 to 10 MeV. Owing to the short range of these rays, surface junction silicon detectors (Schottky contacts) are particularly suitable as detectors. These afford the advantage that the sensitive volume starts directly beneath the entrance window. Junction detectors can also be used.

*β Sources*
β rays (electrons) can also be detected with semiconductor detectors. However, activity measurements are more difficult than is the case with α rays since backscattering effects and a continuous emission spectrum occur.

*γ Sources*
Owing to the higher atomic number and the associated higher absorption cross-section, germanium is better suited than silicon for detection of gamma rays (photons). Germanium detectors must, however, be cooled to −50 °C to 70 °C owing to the higher dark currents, thus offsetting the advantage to a certain extent. Fig. 3.62 shows the penetration depth of α, β and γ rays in silicon. Fig. 3.63 shows the penetration depth in germanium.

Semiconductor detectors are particularly suitable for good spectral resolution (low energy per electron-hole pair). The measure of energy resolution is the half-width value of a spectral line. The following factors influence this variable:

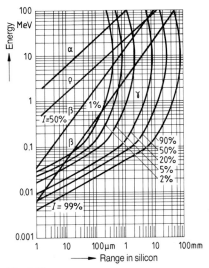

Fig. 3.62
Penetration depth of α, β and γ rays in silicon

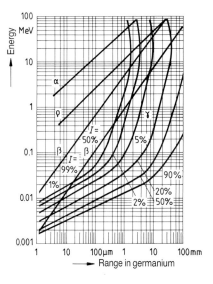

$I_a$  Absorbed intensity
$I_o$  Radiant intensity received
$\alpha$  Helium nucleus
$\beta$  Electrons
p  Protons
$\gamma$  Gamma radiation
%  Absorbed energy, referred to total energy

Fig. 3.63
Penetration depth of $\alpha$, $\beta$ and $\gamma$ rays in germanium

▷ Fluctuation of the charge carriers pro-
  duced per event
▷ Fluctuation of the detection efficiency
▷ Noise of the detector current in the vol-
  ume
▷ Surface noise of the detector
▷ Noise of the amplifier circuitry

A high bias of the detector increases the col-
lection effectiveness for electron-hole pairs
and reduces the junction capacitance. This is
generally crucial to the noise limit of the subsequent amplifier circuitry. The dark current
noise is, by contrast, frequently negligible.
An optimum must be determined experimentally for each application.

### 3.3.5 Infrared Detectors

The sensitive infrared sensor PID 11 is particularly well suited to the following applications:

▷ Automatic switch-on and switch-off sys-
  tems for lighting
▷ Stairwell lighting
▷ Switches for water fittings
▷ Hand dryers
▷ Person or animal counters
▷ Access control
▷ Automatic opening and closing of doors
  and garage doors etc.
▷ Installation security
▷ Detecting persons in front of elevator
  doors
▷ Personnel safety (in the case of robots for
  instance)

The advantages of the pyroelectric PID 11 in
these applications are low circuit complexity
and current consumption, "monocular"
mounting, no licence required, no mutual interference and reverse-voltage protection.

The most important data are as follows:

Current consumption 0.4 mA at 4.5 V
Operating voltage range 4 to 12 V
Output impedance 2.2 k$\Omega$ at 4.5 V

Range approx. 7 meters if the body is 5 °C
hotter or colder than the environment
Response time 500 ms
Wanted output signal dependent upon temperature, distance and operating voltage approx. 0.5 to 1.8 V
Operating temperature range $-20$ to $+70$ °C

Fig. 3.64 shows the internal circuit of the PID
11 and two example connection circuits.

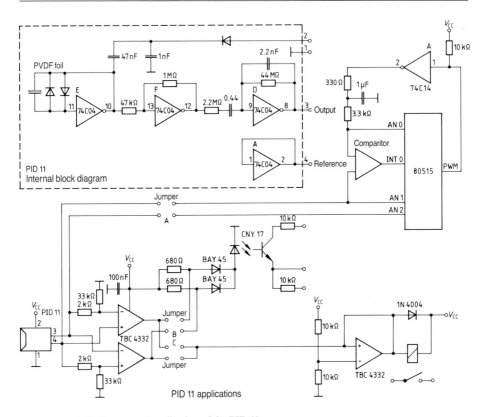

Fig. 3.64   Block diagram and application of the PID 11

# 4 Optoelectronic Semiconductors

## 4.1 Physics of Optical Radiation

### 4.1.1 Fundamentals and Definition

We obtain impressions of color through our eyes from lightwaves or illuminated bodies. The impressions of color differ quantitatively (brightness) and qualitatively (hue and color saturation). In the special case of LEDs (light-emitting diodes), the color saturation is approximately 100%. The hue is defined as the dominant wavelength and the brightness is defined as the luminance.

In optoelectronics, we designate light as the visible and the adjoining region of the spectrum of electromagnetic radiation (360 to 830 nm).

The optical characteristics of detectors and emitters are described well by the reception and emission characteristic in the far field. Two diagrams are important for an LED in this respect. The angle diagram (Fig. 4.1) specifies how much signal energy a detector which lies in the optical axis receives when the LED is turned through $\varphi$ degrees out of

the optical axis. The irradiance diagram shows how much signal energy a detector which lies in the optical axis receives when the LED is moved in a plane perpendicular to the optical axis.

The color temperature of a light source is defined as the temperature which a blackbody radiator would have to have in order to produce the same impression of color as the light source.

*Radiators*

Thermal radiators (e.g. incandescent bulbs) are characterized by the fact that the supplied energy is initially converted to heat and then emitted as radiation. Thermal radiators are continuum forces (radiators), i.e. the radiant energy is distributed continuously over a broad waveband.

Light-emitting radiators (e.g. LEDs) store the supplied energy as potential energy (electrons are raised from the valence band to the conduction band) and emit it as radiation. They permit high radiant emission levels at low temperatures. Light-emitting radiators are generally line sources with a narrow emission spectrum.

The Planckian radiator is an ideal continuum force (thermal radiator). It is defined as a heated cavity with a small aperture emitting the radiation. Its overall radiation is defined by the Stefan-Boltzmann radiation law, and its spectral emission maximum is defined by Wien's displacement law.

Standard light A, defined in IEC 306 – Part 1 and DIN 5033, is generated with tungsten filament lamps, specially designed for this

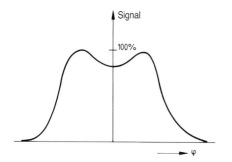

Fig. 4.1    Angle diagram

purpose, at a filament temperature of 2856 K. It approximates the light of the blackbody radiator in the visible region (Fig. 4.2).

*Spectral eye sensitivity*
Within the range of visible radiation from 100 to approx. 105 nm wavelength, the visible region extends from approx. 380 to 780 nm. The spectral sensitivity of the light-adapted human eye is highest in the mid-green region and drops quickly towards blue and red (Fig. 4.3). It is tabulated for a normal viewer in DIN 5031. The photometric units lumen (lm) and candela (cd) are used to rate the luminous intensity and luminous flux in the visible range. These units are based upon the radiation evaluation by the human eye. Radiation-physics units (e.g. Watt/sterad etc.) are used for the rest of the waveband.

For the dark-adapted eye (typically: $<3 \times 10^{-3}$ cd/m$^2$) the sensitivity curve shifts up to 50 nm towards violet.

*Radiant flux*
Radiant flux is the total power emitted in the form of radiation (symbol $\phi_e$, unit Watt). The luminous flux (symbol $\phi_v$, unit lumen lm) is the radiant power weighted with the eye sensitivity $V_{lambda}$.

Typical values are as follows:

1 m$^2$ sun surface:
$\phi_e = 60$ Megawatt
40 W fluorescent tubes:
$\phi_v = 750$ to 3200 lm
100 W incandescent bulb:
$\phi_v = 1600$ lm
Green LED:
$\phi_v = 20$ mlm at 10 mA

At the maximum of eye sensitivity at 555 nm, 1 W of radiant flux corresponds to a luminous flux of 683 lm.

*Radiant intensity*
The radiant intensity $I_e$ (unit W/sr) is the radiant flux per solid angle. The related quantity, weighted with the eye sensitivity $V_{lambda}$, is termed luminous intensity ($I_v$, unit candela = cd, 1 cd = 1 lm/sr).

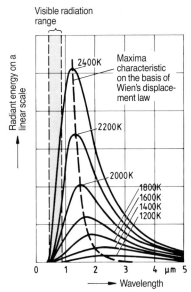

Fig. 4.2
Spectral energy distribution for a blackbody for various temperatures

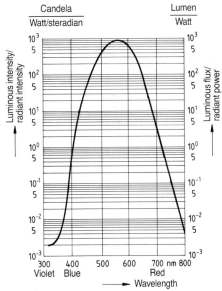

Fig. 4.3
Absolute spectral distribution of the eye sensitivity for photopic vision

Typical values are as follows:

100 W incandescent bulb:
$I_v$ = 110 cd
100 W spotlight:
$I_v$ = up to $10^6$ cd in the beam direction

Semiconductor laser 880 nm, 2 mW (without additional optical system):
$I_e$ = 2 to 5 mW/sr
LED for signalling purposes (10 mA):
$I_v$ = 1 to 300 mcd
IRED for remote control (100 mA):
$I_e$ = 10 to 100 mW/sr

*Solid angle*
The solid angle $\Omega$ (unit sr) describes a part of space delimited by the rays emitted in the form of a cone from a point P (e.g. radiation source) and which end on a closed curve in space. If this curve lies on the sphere with radius 1 (radius 1 m) with P as the centre point and encloses an area of 1 m², the related solid angle $\Omega$ = 1 steradian (1 sr). $\Omega$ = $F/R$ (Fig. 4.4).

*Radiance*
The radiance $L_e$, unit = W/m²sr is the radiant flux per area and solid angle. The related photometric quantity is termed luminance $L_v$ = cd/m². The human eye perceives luminance differences as brightness differences.

The luminance is expressed in units nit (nt), lambert (L) and foot-lambert (fL).

Typical values are as follows:

Surface of the sun
1.5 x $10^9$ cd/m²
Glowing filament of an incadescent bulb
5 to 35 x $10^6$ cd/m²
Modern fluorescent lamp
0.3 to 1.5 x $10^4$ cd/cm²
The night sky
approximately $10^{-11}$ cd/m²

*Irradiance*
The irradiance $E_e$ (unit W/m²) is the radiant flux incident per detector area. The related photometric quantity is termed illuminance $E_v$ (the unit lux: 1 lx = 1 lm/m²) or foot-candle fc (1 fc = 10.76 lx).

Typical values are as follows:

Midday sunshine in the open air
max. 100 mW/cm²
100 000 lx
office workplace
500 lx
Clear night sky with full moon
0.2 lx

An illuminance of 1000 lx corresponds to an irradiance of 4.76 mW/cm² for standard light A.

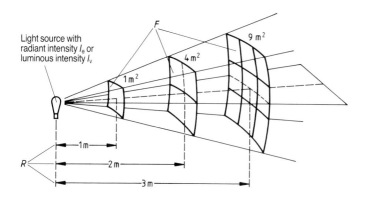

Light source with radiant intensity $I_e$ or luminous intensity $I_v$

F

9 m²
4 m²
1 m²

1 m
2 m
3 m
R

Fig. 4.4
Definition
of the solid
angle $\Omega$ = 1 sr

### 4.1.2 Photodiodes

If light quanta (photons) with adequate energy penetrate a photodiode, electron-hole pairs are produced inside the semiconductor (internal photoelectric effect). The electric field in the space charge region causes a separation of the charge carrier pairs. This causes a current to flow in the outer circuit (Fig. 4.5).

From the point of view of electrical mode of operation, we distinguish between photodiode operation (with bias $V_R$, quadrant B) and photovoltaic operation (quadrant A). The photovoltaic cell acts as a current source which converts radiant energy to electrical energy (Fig. 4.6).

The no-load voltage $V_L$ increases logarithmically with the illuminance regardless of the diode area, and reaches a value of approx. 0.5 V for silicon diodes at 1000 lx. The short-circuit current $I_K$ is proportional to the illuminance and area. The permitted reverse voltage is low (approx. 1 V) so that operation as a photodiode in the reverse direction is possible only restrictedly.

In order to obtain optimum power consumption from a photovoltaic cell, the load resistance must lie in the order of magnitude of $V_L/I_K$.

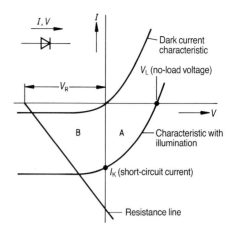

Fig. 4.6   Characteristic of a photodiode

### 4.1.3 Silicon Photodiodes

Silicon photodiodes have very low dark currents ($<10^{-11}$ A/mm$^2$) if they are appropriately rated. This means that they are suitable for detecting very low illuminance values. But they are slow because the charge carriers first have to penetrate the space charge region which is narrow owing to doping, by diffusion. Their photoelectric current is proportional to the illuminance over many powers of ten.

Si-PIN photodiodes are used where speed is important. Most of the light is converted in the relatively broad space charge region so that the charge carriers drift at saturation speed (approx. 50 to 100 km/s) with appropriate biasing. The junction capacitance of PIN photodiodes is low (a few pF) owing to the broad space charge region and thus permits very short time constants, together with a low external load resistance.

The sensitivity $S$ of detectors is the ratio of photoelectric current to the incident radiant power or to the luminous flux, and is greatly dependent upon wavelength, dependent upon the semiconductor material. Fig. 4.7 shows the characteristic of this spectral sen-

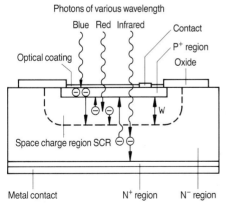

Fig. 4.5
Schematic diagram of a planar silicon photodiode

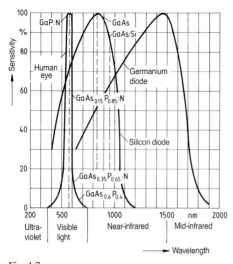

Fig. 4.7
Relative sensitivity of silicon
and germanium photodiodes

sitivity $S$ (unit A/W) for germanium and silicon photodetectors.

One conspicuous factor is that silicon is well adapted to the emission of GaAs with a sensitivity maximum of approx. 850 nm whilst germanium, with its broad maximum around 1.5 μm, even opens up the mid-infrared region up to approx. 2 m. Beyond this, semiconductor compounds even exist, permitting the construction of optimized detectors through to far into the mid IR region:

(e.g. CdS, PbS, InSb, GaInAsP, HgCdTe etc.) in some cases as photodiodes and in some cases as photoresistors.

### 4.1.4 Phototransistors

In the phototransistor, the collector-based junction is designed as a photodiode. Its photoelectric current occurs as the collector current, multiplied by the current gain of the transistor (approx. 100 to 1000). Phototransistors thus supply strong signals and require less post-amplification than photodiodes. But they operate with less of a linear characteristic (owing to the non-linearity of the current gain) and are slower owing to the Miller effect, in conjunction with the relatively large-area collector-base diode (Fig. 4.8).

The mean number of charge carrier pairs triggered by a photon is termed the quantum yield ($\eta$). The maximum achievable sensitivity $S_{max}$ of a non-amplifying photodetector would be produced at $\eta = 1$, i.e. each arriving photon generates one charge carrier pair. All charge carriers are collected and thus contributed towards the photoelectric current. With the energy of one photon

$$E = \frac{hc}{\lambda}$$

($e_0$ = electronic charge, $\lambda$ = wavelength, c = velocity of light, h = Planck constant) we can

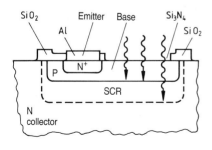

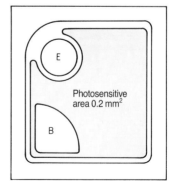

Fig. 4.8    Bipolar phototransistor

conclude the following,

$$S_{\lambda max} = \frac{e_0}{E} = \frac{\lambda}{1.24} \text{ (A/W)} \quad (\lambda \text{ im } \mu m)$$

thus, a maximum sensitivity limit which increases in linear fashion with the wavelength. Practical silicon photodetectors achieve up to 90% of this value at $\lambda = 850$ nm.

In the case of detectors for daylight or artificial light, it is the photosensitivity in nA/lx which is of interest. It refers to a specific illuminance, generally with standard light A. The photosensitivity of detectors for infrared application is, by contrast, generally specified in A. It is related to a specific illuminance (e.g. 0.5 mW/cm²) at a specific wavelength (e.g. 950 nm).

In the case of detectors for very low radiation signals, it is the noise equivalent power (NEP) expressed in W/√Hz, which is of interest. This is the radiant power which is generated at the output of the detector by a signal which has the same magnitude as the noise. The measuring condition (waveband of the light, modulation frequency or bandwidth) is important. This definition results from the fact that, on the one hand, a proportional signal current corresponds to an optical power whilst, on the other hand, the noise mechanisms involved cause an effective noise current which is proportional on the basis of $\sqrt{\Delta f}$.

The reciprocal of NEP, referred to the radiation-sensitive area A, is designated the detectivity $D^*$ (also termed the detection limit).

$$D^* = \frac{\sqrt{A}}{NEP} \left[ \frac{\text{cm/Hz}}{\text{W}} \right].$$

The dark current is defined as the current which flows without irradiation. It is the blocking-state current of the diode in the case of photodetectors, and it is the amplified leakage current of the collector-base junction which serves as the photodiode in the case of phototransistors and photodarlington transistors. The dark current increases with temperature (approximately

doubles per 10 K in the case of silicon) and may be a disturbing factor in the case of phototransistors and, in particular, in the case of photodarlingtons.

### 4.1.5 Light-Emitting Diodes

Light-emitting diodes are semiconductor diodes which emit radiation when current flows in the forward direction. During this process, excess charge carriers are injected into the neutral N- and P-region where some of them recombine and emit a photon (injection luminescence).

By contrast with the incadescent bulb, its emission spectrum is restricted to a narrow waveband which is essentially determined by the energy gap $E_g$ of the semiconductor. III-V compound semiconductors are used as the materials since they have suitable energy gaps and since their band structure permits effectively radiating recombination unlike the indirect semiconductors silicon and germanium.

Diodes emitting infrared radiation (IREDs, Fig. 4.9) are generally manufactured from GaAs ($E_g = 1.43$ eV) or GaAlAs and emit in the near-infrared region between 800 and 950 nm near to the maximum of the spectral sensitivity of silicon photodetectors. They are used in light barriers, remote control systems, optocouplers and for measurement purposes. Their advantages are as follows: Compact size and stability. Low operating temperature, easy modulation capability through to the 100 MHz band, in addition to TTL-compatibility and high efficiency of several percent.

Part of the radiation leaves the diode directly "upwards" or to the side, but even radiation emitted in the direction of the substrate is usable if the substrate itself is transparent and is (partially) mirrored on the underside. On the Burrus diode, the radiation is, as it were, coupled out downwards through a (subsequently etched) "hole" in the substrate,

87

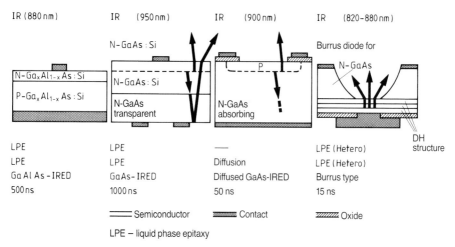

Fig. 4.9   Schematic structure of an IRED chip

whereby the crystal is mounted with the PN junction pointing downwards. This provides particularly favorable launching conditions in optical fibres.

Burrus diodes are very fast owing to their internal structure and are used for fiber-optic information transmission.

Besides diverse metal/glass packages, plastic designs are mainly used. In this case, the plastic body reduces the critical angle of total internal reflection on the chip surface and, thus, the radiant power emerging from the crystal on the one hand, and, on the other hand, the curved surface acts as a lens and focuses the radiation in the axial direction (Fig. 4.10).

Even in the case of the diodes emitting (visible) light (LEDs), the radiation is generated by recombination of charge carrier pairs in the semiconductor with appropriate energy gap $E_g$.

GaAs (for absorbing visible light) and GaP (transparent) are used as substrate. The active zones each consist of GaAsP of differing composition, Ga or GaAlAs, dependent upon wavelength. The frequent combinations are summarized in Table 4.1.

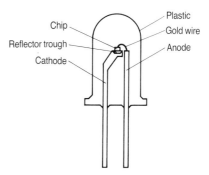

Fig. 4.10
Light-emitting diode of plastic design

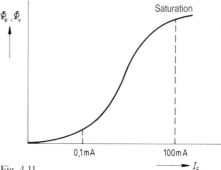

Fig. 4.11
Typical light-current characteristic of a light-emitting diode

Table 4.1   Conventional composition of LEDs

| Colour | Wavelength [nm] | Substrate | $E_g$ [eV] | Active layer |
|---|---|---|---|---|
| Infrared | 950 | GaAs | 1,4 | GaAs:Si |
| Infrared | 800 – 900 | GaAs | 1,4 | GaAlAs |
| Red | 700 | GaP | 2,3 | GaP:Zn,0 |
| Standard red | 660 | GaAs | 1,4 | $GaAs_{0,6}P_{0,4}$ |
| Super red | 635 | GaP | 2,3 | $GaAs_{0,35}P_{0,65}$:N TSN |
| Yellow | 590 | GaP | 2,3 | $GaAs_{0,15}P_{0,65}$:N TSN |
| Green | 565 | GaP | 2,3 | GaP:N |
| Blue | 480 | SiC | 2,8 | SiC |

TSN stands for transparent substrate nitrogen (doped)

The light-current characteristics of IREDs and LEDs show a section of the characteristic in which the non-radiating recombination predominates, an approximately linear part and a part in which saturation of the emission occurs (heating, saturation of the radiating junctions). Increase in temperature of the crystal increases the emission wavelength and worsens the efficiency.

Degradation, i.e. a decrease in output power over service life, is common to all semiconductors which emit radiation. The phenomenon has not yet been fully explained. But, in all probability, degradation is related to the migration or spread of imperfections in the crystal. The service life of IREDs and LEDs is thus limited and lies at around 100,000 hours under normal operating conditions.

The relative spectral emission expresses the radiation distribution of an LED as a function of the wavelength. For the user, this characteristic is generally not very helpful since it can only be measured with difficulty and using time-consuming methods. Consequently, LED spectra are thus defined by the following user-friendly terms:

$\lambda_{peak}$ = Wavelength at which the spectral emission maximum occurs.

$\Delta\lambda$ = Width of the emission spectra measured at the 50% points.

$\lambda_{sp_{eff}}$ = Effective wavelength: Defines the emphasis of the emission and is an important term for applications in spectroscopy.

$\lambda_{dom}$ = Dominant wavelength: Defines the hue of an LED, as perceived by the human eye.

## 4.2  Laser Arrays

Laser array diodes for high powers are suitable for continuous-wave (CW) operation and thus open up new fields of application. This includes pumping neodymium YAG lasers. To date, such lasers have been pumped with high-energy flash lamps. However, since the emitting spectrum of a flashlamp has a véry broad-band characteristic but since the absorption spectrum of the neodymium YAG crystal has a very narrow-band characteristic, the pumping efficiency of the system is low. The wavelength of the GaAlAs laser can, however, be adapted exactly to the absorption maximum of the neodymium YAG laser by selecting a suitable configuration structure of the active laser layer. This affords several advantages:

▷ A high system efficiency is achieved owing to the efficiency of the semiconductor laser which is high anyway (>20 %) and

89

owing to the favorable pumping efficiency resulting from the ideal wavelength matching.

▷ The low thermal loading of the neodymium YAG crystal permits a better radiation quality, a reduced line width and far smaller and lighter cooling facilities.

▷ Semiconductor lasers can be operated with a simple power supply whilst flashlamps require a high-voltage mains power supply unit. The high efficiency permits a long service life of the overall system with GaAlAs high-power lasers as the pumping source.

▷ Owing to the high efficiency, the system as a whole will have a long service life if GaAlAs high-power lasers are used as the pump source.

Other applications of semiconductor lasers include:

▷ The high-power lasers described in this section are also suitable for optical telecommunication in free space owing to the coherence and the high possible modulation frequency (direct modulation is possible).

▷ GaAlAs semiconductor lasers are also suitable for isolated power transmission owing to the high optical power which can be launched into fat fibres. High reconversion efficiencies can be achieved with modern photodiodes.

▷ Likewise, photosensitive high-voltage thyristors can be fired with optically precise simultaneity via a fiber-optic network.

▷ The frequency can be doubled in non-linear crystals owing to the high output power. Coherent blue radiation can be produced by generation of the second harmonic.

▷ GaAlAs high-power lasers are well-suited for use in laser printers owing to the advantages of a semiconductor component over valve or solid-state lasers (geometry, service life, modulation capability and costs).

The name array comes from the 12-strip array (GRINGSCH-SQW structure) in the crystal.

Fig. 4.12   GaAlAs high-power laser

Fig. 4.12 shows a photograph of a GaAlAs laser chip. The laser chip (in the circle) is housed, together with the monitor diode, NTC thermistor and Peltier heat sink in a TO-3 package. The monitor diode detects the radiant power of the mirror on the rear (approx. 10 % of the effective radiation) and can thus be used to control and monitor the radiant power. The array is mounted on a Peltier heat sink which, together with an NTC thermistor as a temperature sensor, permits operation at constant temperature via an external control circuit. This is particularly important if the application requires a very constant wavelength (e.g. when pumping neodymium YAG lasers). The wavelength can be adjusted precisely and maintained constant via the temperature. Section 4.2.2 describes a control circuit for this.

### 4.2.1 Fundamentals of the Semiconductor Laser

The fundamental physical mechanism in the process of generating radiation with semiconductors is the interaction of photons with

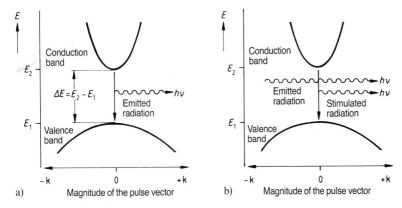

Fig. 4.13
Energy band diagram for illustrating the recombination processes
and radiation generation on gallium arsenide,
a) Spontaneous emission, b) Stimulated emission

charge carriers in the valence and conduction band of the crystal. The semiconductor must have a band structure corresponding to that in Fig. 4.13 in order for radiant recombination to occur. The electron can then jump from the conduction band into the valence band directly, emitting a photon. The energy of this emitted photon corresponds to the energy gap of the semiconductor and is related to the wavelength of the emitted radiation.

In the case of a semiconductor such as germanium or silicon, radiant recombination is not possible since the photon's own pulse is not adequate for complying with the pulse conservation theorem. Pulse compensation during recombination can occur only via a third partner such as phonons (the lattice vibrations occurring in the crystal) or imperfections. This process is termed spontaneous emission and is utilized on light-emitting diodes (LEDs and IREDs).

The laser is based upon the effect of stimulated emission. This occurs when a photon with a wavelength corresponding to $\Delta E$ interacts with a conduction band electron of energy $E_2$. This photon then stimulates the

electron transition (Fig. 4.13b). One particularly noteworthy factor in this case is that the generated photon corresponds to the stimulating photon in respect of wavelength, phase, polarization and propagation direction. The stimulated emission corresponds to an amplification of the incident photon. This is where the name laser comes from: light amplification by stimulated emission of radiation.

At thermal equilibrium, the number of electrons in the valence band of energy $E_1$ is far higher than the number of electrons in the conduction band $E_2$. Consequently, the probability of absorption of an incident photon in this state is far higher than the required stimulated emission. In order to render the process of stimulated emission more probable, inversion of the charge carriers as regards valence and conduction band must be achieved, i.e. the number of electrons in the conduction band of energy $E_2$ must be greatly increased. On the semiconductor laser, this inversion of the charge carriers (population inversion) is achieved by injecting charge carriers into an active crystal volume designed as a PN junction. A specific

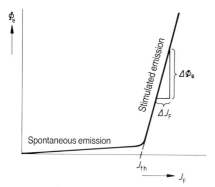

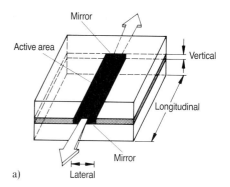

Fig. 4.14  Laser characteristic

minimum injection current is required in order to achieve an adequately high density in the conduction band. This current is designated the threshold current. Fig. 4.14 shows the laser characteristic. The initial spontaneous radiant emission $\phi_e$ changes to stimulated emission when the threshold current $I_{th}$ is exceeded. $I_F$ is the forward current through the laser diode.

Below this threshold current, the laser diode behaves in the same way as a light-emitting diode. Only spontaneous emission occurs. When the threshold current is exceeded, stimulated emission commences and the emitted radiant power increases in linear fashion. Fig. 4.14 shows one further important characteristic parameter of the semiconductor laser, namely the so-called differential efficiency $\phi_e/\Delta I_F$. This is defined as the slope of the laser characteristic.

### 4.2.2 Structure of an Oxide Strip Laser

The following conditions are particularly important in order to guarantee reliable and continuous laser operation even at high temperatures:

▷ Vertical delimitation of charge carrier injection is advantageous in order to produce an adequately high charge carrier density for achieving inversion.

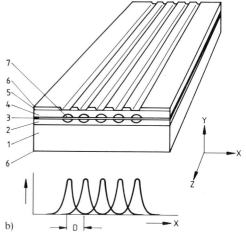

1  Substrate
2  N-GaAlAs hetero-layer
3  Active zone
4  P-GaAlAs hetero-layer
5  Oxide insulation
6  Plating
7  Active mirror area of a stripe

Fig. 4.15
Structure of the GaAlAs/GaAs oxide strip laser

▷ The active layer must be designed as a dielectric waveguide so as to permit a high photon density to occur.

▷ The active crystal volume must be designed as an optical resonator in which the wave which is propagated is partially reflected and thus amplified again.

▷ The mirrors must be optimally coated in order to permit the high power density (MW/cm) on the laser mirrors with high reliability and long service life.

▷ A high crystal perfection is required for effective radiation generation and for low aging rates.

This vertical delimitation is achieved by the so-called double heterostructure: The active layer which is only 0.1 to 0.2 μm thick is located, as shown in Fig. 4.15, between two cladding layers, each with a higher energy gap. This forms potential barriers which limit the injected electrons and holes to the active

zone. Owing to the higher energy gap, the index of refraction is reduced, so that a dielectric layer waveguide (with a width which is as yet, not limited laterally) is produced, similar to an optical fibre. Many solutions are possible to the problem of lateral limiting. On the oxide stripe laser as shown in Fig. 4.15, the current path is limited by applying an insulating oxide layer to a stripe of approx. 3 μm width.

The charge carrier concentration over a narrow zone produces a lateral profile of the imaginary index refraction which stably guides the lateral fundamental mode (wave propagation in an anisotropic medium). The waves can be propagated and amplified only in this zone. Each wave which does not run

Table 4.2  Characteristics of the 12-strip laser array

|  |  | Type | SFH 4801 | SFH 48E1 | SFH 48R1 |
|---|---|---|---|---|---|
| Order number | Q 62702- |  | -P 153 | -P 156 | -P 158 |
| Limit values | $\Phi_{eCW}$ | mW | 200 | 200 | 1000 |
|  | $\Phi_{epuls}$ | mW | 300 | 300 | 1200 |
|  | $V_R$ | V | 3 | 3 | 3 |
|  | $T_{sub}$ | °C | 10…65 | −10…+65 | 10…65 |
| Characteristic data at $T_{sub} = 25\,°C$ | $\lambda_{peak}$ | nm | 805 | 805 | 805 |
|  | $\Delta\lambda$ | nm | 2 | 2 | 4 |
|  | $\eta$ | W/A | 0,35 | 0,35 | 0,35 |
|  | $I_{th}$ | mA | 400 | 400 | 2000 |
|  | $\Phi_{eCW}$ | mW | 150 | 150 | 800 |
|  | $\Phi_{epuls}$ $t_p \leq 10\,\mu s$ $D \leq 0,01$ | mW | 250 | 250 | 1000 |
| Features |  |  | 12-strip | 12-strip | 5×12-strip laser |

parallel to the limit is absorbed and cannot be propagated. This form of wave guidance is termed gain guidance. Such laser diodes are thus also termed gain-guided lasers.

*Control circuit for the laser array*
*SFH 48 E1*

A monitor diode for controlling and regulating the power, a Peltier element for cooling and an NTC thermistor as the temperature sensor are integrated, together with the laser diode in the high-power laser array SFH 48 E1. Together with an external control circuit, these components permit the laser array to be operated under optimum conditions. The power operational amplifier TCA 2465 (2 operational amplifiers in one package) supplies up to 2.5 A output current. Consequently, it is well-suited to this application. The circuit described below maintains the laser array in a stable operating state, and protects the laser against reverse polarity, overcurrent and overvoltage.

The wavelength of the emitted light is dependent upon the operating temperature. This means that it can be adapted to the application within specific limits and kept constant. The emitted light output can be controlled via the current flowing through the laser diode.

The laser array is accommodated in a TO-3 package, together with the monitor diode, a precision NTC thermistor and the Peltier heat sink. The array is mounted on the Peltier heat sink. The Peltier element transports heat from one side to the other, dependent upon the magnitude and direction of the current flowing through. Together with the integrated NTC thermistor, it permits load operation at constant temperature via the external control circuit.

Two independently operating current control circuits are required for operating the laser: The circuit for controlling and stabilizing the temperature and that for the laser's radiant power. The limit values for current and voltage may never be exceeded on the module, not even briefly.

As shown in Fig. 4.16, the two operational amplifiers directly drive the laser diode and

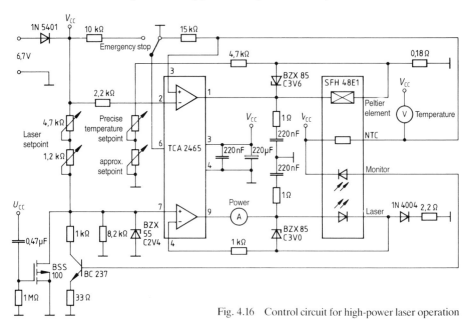

Fig. 4.16   Control circuit for high-power laser operation

Peltier element. The output currents are fed back via shunts as a voltage to the relevant, negative inputs. Consequently, the circuit operates as a proportional (P) controller. Potentiometers permit the setpoints for temperature and light output to be set.

The NTC thermistor (NTC resistor) integrated in the laser package measures the temperature which can be indicated via a voltmeter. The incorporated delay element does not enable the current for the laser until approx. 1 s after switching on. This ensures prompt cooling.

The current supply to the laser and Peltier element is interrupted via the inhibit switch of the operational amplifier for emergency-stop. The circuit is designed for continuous operation of the laser. If a higher current is required for pulsed operation, the operational amplifier TCA 1365B can be used for this purpose (4 A output).

The QW 12-strip laser array provides a continuous output power of 250 mW at a typical threshold current of only 280 mA in CW mode. The differential efficiency is approx. 0.7 W/A in CW mode. This, and the low series resistance (approx. 0.5 $\Omega$), result in an efficiency of over 20%. If the output power is increased up to the point at which the laser characteristic bends off at approx. 600 to 800 mW, it is possible to achieve an overall efficiency of up to 40%.

Laser diodes are also available as modules in hermetically sealed metal packages. The connection leads have DIL spacing.

Table 4.2 shows the most important characteristics of the laser arrays.

## 4.3 Optocouplers

The optocoupler contains a light-emitting semiconductor component (LED) and a light-sensitive semiconductor component

(phototransistor, photo-IC). It can transmit DC voltage signals and AC voltage signals up to a few MHz with complete electrical decoupling. Dielectric strengths of up to a few kV are conventional. DIL plastic packages with 4 to 16 leads are gaining popularity as the type of package.

The coupling factor of an optocoupler defines the ratio of output current to input current. The value specified in the data sheets generally applies at a value of $I_F = 10$ mA (LED) and $U_{OF} = 5$ V (phototransistor).

If high voltage is applied between the input and output side of an optocoupler, field strengths of $10^4$ V/cm may occur inside. Owing to these field strengths, ions may be deposited on the phototransistor chip, and these may lead to a change in the transistor characteristic owing to field effects. In individual cases, this may lead to total unserviceability of the optocoupler. It has been possible to completely eliminate this effect on Siemens optocouplers by applying a weakly conductive *TR*ansparent *IO*n *S*creen (TRIOS®) to the surfaces at risk. In order to improve the surface properties, a silicon nitride layer is also applied beneath the TRIOS layer which is an integral part of the phototransistor. It acts as an impurity atoms passivator and as an optical surface coating (Fig. 4.17).

Transient overvoltages in de kV range may occur in 220 V power systems. Since optocouplers are frequently used for electrical isolation in such systems, they must be insulated appropriately well. The insulation test voltage specified in the data sheet ensures this.

The insulation test is conducted on all modules at the production stage.

*Important optocoupler characteristics*
The main field of application of optocouplers is signal transmission with electrical isolation. The following characteristics determine the possible applications of optocouplers in this respect:

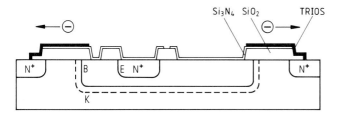

Fig. 4.17
Phototransistor with TRIOS

▷ High switching speed
▷ Transmission of DC and AC voltage signals
▷ Broad temperature range
▷ High resistance to cyclic temperature stress
▷ Compactness
▷ High reliability
▷ High voltage strength
▷ Low aging of the light-emitting diode
▷ Stability of the transistor characteristics.

*Aging of the light-emitting diode*
The quality feature for aging of the light-emitting diodes used is the time in which the radiation at constant current has dropped to half of the initial value. Fig. 4.18 shows the characteristic typical of a large number of components tested. Consequently, the half-life is over 200,000 hours of operation. The diagram shows the relative reduction in the current transfer ratio with flux loading of the coupler diode with $I_F = 60$ mA (measured at $T_A = -25°C$, $I_F = 10$ mA and $U_{OF} = 5$ V).

The half-life of the current transfer ratio is also designated the service life of the component.

*Stability of the transistor*
There may be a high potential difference during operation between a gallium arsenide light-emitting diode and a silicon phototransistor. If there is also a high operating temperature (e.g. 90°C), a field effect may be noticeable in the phototransistor.

100 percent burn-in can be carried out optionally for optocouplers required to meet stringent requirements. This means that they are not delivered until the electrical and optical parameters have stabilized.

## 4.4 LED Displays

Displays are devices for displaying symbols, letters or digits. The most conventional form of LED display is currently still the 7-segment display. Dot matrix displays permit a more flexible representation. They are being used to an increasing extent. Frequently, these display modules contain memory circuits, control circuits and decoding circuits (intelligent displays).

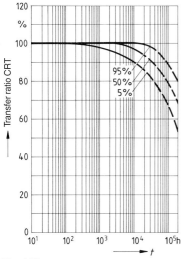

Fig. 4.18
Reduction in the current transfer ratio

LED displays are optoelectronic semiconductor displays. The emission colors are red, yellow, green or orange.

In the simplest case, a display consists of one or two 2.8 to 20 mm high 7-segment displays. However, there are alos more complex display modules which consist either of several segments (e.g. 16) or single dot matrices (5 x 7; 8 x 8 etc.)

Intelligent Displays® are alphanumeric displays with incorporated CMOS decoder, multiplexer, memory and driver. One mod-

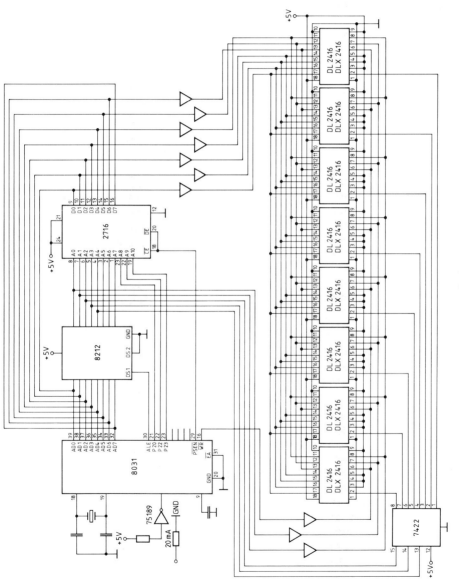

Fig. 4.19 Connection of an intelligent display to the 8-bit controller bus

ule contains 1, 4 or 8 display elements. They must be connected to the microprocessor and microcontroller via an 8-bit bus and cascaded. Fig. 4.19 shows one example application.

By way of example, we shall discuss the Siemens LED Domino displays in further detail. The display modules DLX1414, 2416 and 3416 offer a character height of up to 6.9 mm thanks to the 5 x 7 dot display without lens magnification, and, thus, offer good, distortion-free read-off. They are available in red, green and orange. The modules have 128 characters in ASCII code and can thus display the most important European characters. Fig. 4.20 shows the character set of the Domino family.

## 4.5 Optical Waveguides

New fields of application are constantly being found for optical communications using optical waveguides (OWGs) with glass or plastic fibers. Besides the classical applications in long-range communications, this technology is also used in LANs (local area networks), e.g. for data transmission from mainframes to their peripheries in on-board systems (aircraft, ships, motor vehicles), in measurement and control systems and for cable TV and master antenna television systems.

The advantages of this transmission technology are as follows:

Fig. 4.20    Character set of the Domino family

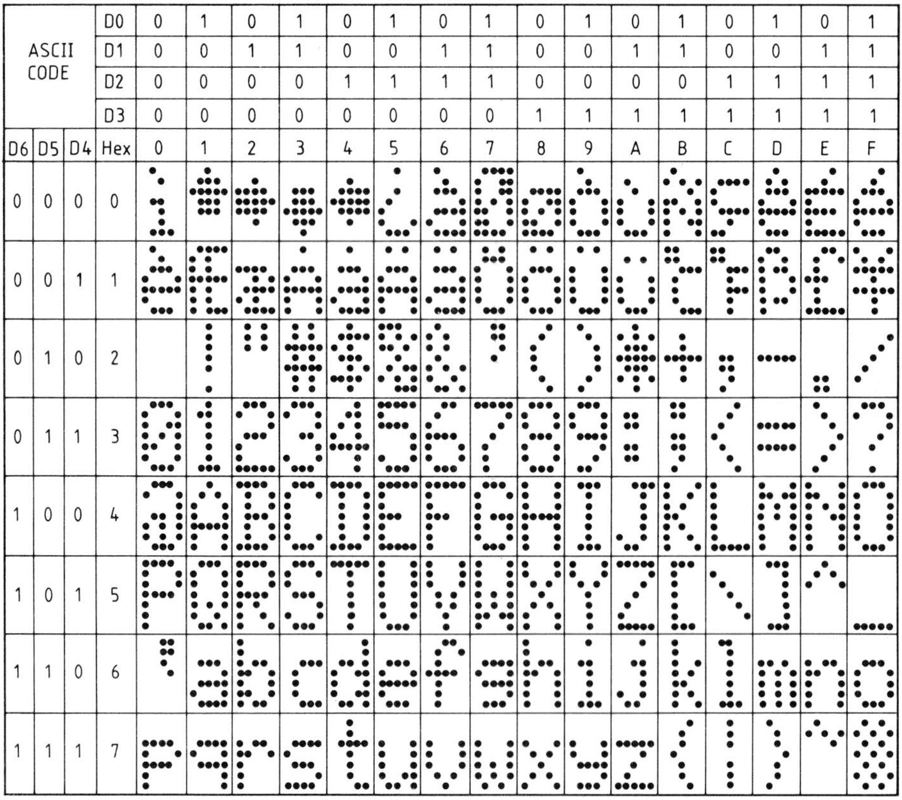

▷ Broad bandwidth
(high transmission capacity)
▷ Electrical isolation between transmitter and receiver
▷ Insensitivity to electromagnetic interference
▷ Extremely difficult to "tap"
▷ No signal radiation and, thus, no crosstalk
▷ No earth loops
▷ No possibility of sparking
▷ Low weight and low space requirement
▷ Unrestricted material availability

The media used for optical transmission are glass or plastic. There are specific applications, semiconductors and coupling elements for both methods of transmission. It is mainly glass fibers that are used for communication at high transmission rates and over long distances or in local applications. Plastic fibers are suitable for low transmission rates in local applications and for a wide variety of applications in control engineering.

Owing to the larger fiber diameter of the plastic fibers (1 mm), the coupling elements are not as critical as is the case on the glass fibers, and, thus are far cheaper. The last section of this chapter describes certain applications of optical transmission using plastic fibers.

### 4.5.1 Optical Fibers as a Transmission Medium

Glass fibers as dielectric waveguides are manufactured either from pure silica glass or from optical multicomponent glass. If a ray of light strikes the end face within a specific critical angle $\Theta_{max}$, it is forwarded within the system as the result of total internal reflection at the boundary between the core and cladding. See Fig. 4.21.

We distinguish between three types of glass fiber:

▷ Multimode stepped-index fiber

This guides one mode spectrum, causing pulse spreading from 20 to 50 ns/km. It is used for lengths up to a few km. The attenuation is a few dB/km. One advantageous factor is easy launching, made possible by the large core diameter (cheap). Disadvantages include the limitation to low bit rates owing to pulse spreading (<34 Mbit/s) and the short repeater spacings under certain circumstances (1−5 km).

▷ Multimode graded-index fiber

The parabolic characteristic of the index of refraction prevents modal dispersion. It is used for lengths up to 20 km. The attenuation is up to 2 dB/km. One advantageous factor is, once again, easy launching owing to the large core diameter. The phase relationship is

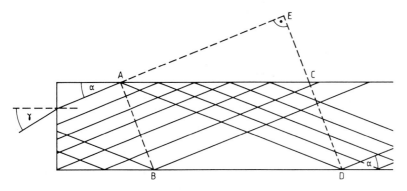

Fig. 4.21   Light paths in the optical fiber

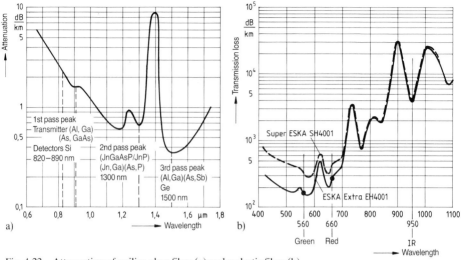

Fig. 4.22  Attenuation of a silica glass fiber (a) and a plastic fiber (b)

largely retained, thus permitting transmission frequencies up to 140 Mbit/s. One disadvantageous factor is the higher price as compared with the other two systems.

▷ (Stepped-index) Single-mode fiber

Only one mode is transmitted in the thin core. The attenuation is 0.1 to 0.2 dB/km,

thus permitting lengths of over 100 km. The critical frequency is approx. 2.4 Gbit/s. The fiber is cheap. One disadvantageous factor is the precise alignment required. High precision connectors are required owing to the thin core diameter.

Owing to the spectral attenuation characteristic of today's glass fibers (Fig. 4.22),

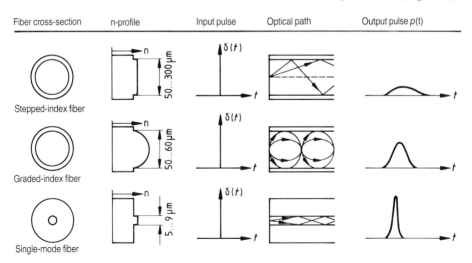

Fig. 4.23  Conventional fiber types and their characteristics

transmitters and receivers for wavelengths around 850 nm are manufactured on the basis of Si, GaAs or GaAlAs, and, for wavelengths around 1300 and 1550 nm on the basis of Si, GaAs or GaAlAs, and, for wavelengths around 1300 and 1550 nm on the basis of Ge and quaternary compounds such as InGaAsP/InP.

The optomechanical connection makes stringent demands in respect of alignment between the semiconductor components and the optical waveguide (only 0.1 m in the case of single-mode fibers). Consequently, complete, frequently customized modules are offered, on which the transmitter and receiver are integrated in an optical waveguide.

Fig. 4.23 shows the conventional fiber types and their characteristics.

### 4.5.2 OWG Plug Connectors for Glass Fibers

The splice connection (inseparable) and the plug connection are available for connecting glass fibers. Splicing involves fusing together the fibers of two OWG cables under an arc. Since high mechanical precision is required for this process (alignment of the fiber cores in the m region), fully automatic splicers are available which perform the alignment process and splicing under the control of a microprocessor. This permits spliced connections with an attenuation of less than 0.2 dB.

Plug connections in optical transmission systems serve to intercouple two fiber-optic components (transmitter, receiver and coupler etc.) simply and reproducibly with low attenuation and with easy separation. Various requirements are made of the mechanical tolerances of the connector components dependent upon the core diameter of the fiber used and the required insertion loss of the plug connection. Thus, for example, the tolerances may not exceed a value of approx. 1 μm in the case of the critical connector dimensions of a plug connection for

graded-index fibers with 50 μm core diameter. The resultant insertion loss is, however, also greatly dependent upon the fiber tolerances.

The plug connectors available on the market are generally designed for specific applications and match the corresponding systems of electro-optical transmitters and receivers. The working committees of the standardization institutes DIN and IEC are working towards extensive standardization of OWG plug connectors.

To date, German Industrial Standard DIN 47256, Parts 1 to 4 (draft) OWG plug connectors FSA with screw connection and German Industrial Standard DIN 47257, Parts 1 to 3 (draft) OWG plug connectors FSB for plug-in module systems have been published.

*Design principles*
The plug connectors offered here are based upon precision guidance of a connector pin in a socket. Essentially, the manufacturing and assembly accuracy determines the insertion loss of a plug connector. The plug connector used on an OWG link must be selected dependent upon the required ambient conditions. There are thus plug connectors made of carbide metal, German silver and plastic available. We distinguish between DIN plug connectors and SMD plug connectors dependent upon dimensions.

### 4.5.3 Transmitter and Receiver Modules for Plastic Fibers

An optical transmission system for local area networks consists at least of the transmitter, optical waveguide and receiver (detector) (Fig. 4.24). The transfer rates are $0-1$, 5 to 60 and 10 to 200 MBd, dependent upon version and intended application. Table 4.3 shows the characteristics of the most important transmission systems for use in local area networks.

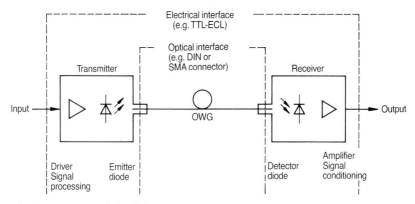

Fig. 4.24　OWG transmission link

Table 4.3　Characteristics of the most important transmission systems

| Transmission system | | 1 MBd | 10 MBd | 50 MBd | 130 MBd | 200 MBd |
|---|---|---|---|---|---|---|
| Symbol rate | (MBd) | 0…1 | 0…10 | 5…50 | 10…130 | 100…200 |
| Operating voltage | (V) | 5 | 5 | 5 | 5 | 5 |
| Signal level | | TTL | TTL | ECL | ECL | ECL |
| Wavelength | (nm) | 850 | 850 1300 | 850 | 1300 | 1300 |
| Typical optical output power of the transmitte | (dBm) | −14.0 | −14.4 −21.5 | −23.0 | −18.9 | −21.0 |
| Fiber type | | G 50/125 [1] | G 50/125 | G 50/125 | G 62,5/125 [2] | G 50/125 |
| Typical optical sensitivity of the receiver at BER $\leqq 10^{-9}$ | (dBm) | −30.0 | −33.0 −33.8 | −34.0 | −34.0 [3] | −33.0 [1] |
| Typical maximum range (with 3 dB reserve) | (km) | 5 | 4 10 | 2 | 4 | 3 |

[1]　2.5 dB/km at 850 nm　　[2]　3.75 dB/km at 850 nm　　[3]　at BER $\leqq 10^{-12}$
　　0.7 dB/km at 1300 nm　　　　1.75 dB/km at 1300 nm

### 4.5.4 Interface Modules for Glass Fibers

Interface modules contain transmitter and receiver modules and the electrical interface in one package. Fig. 4.25 shows a full-duplex transmission system with two interface modules. Simultaneous transmission is possible in both directions on a full-duplex transmission system.

### 4.5.5 Multiplex Systems

Siemens developed OWG multiplex systems for full-duplex operation with 8 chan-

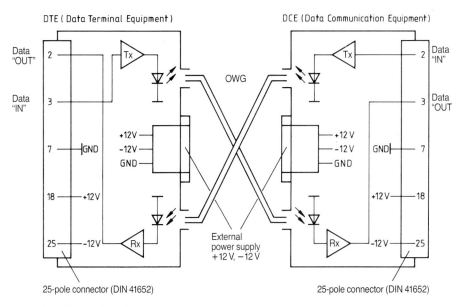

Fig. 4.25   OWG full-duplex transmission system

nels for transmission ranges up to 5 km. With additional multiplex modules, the system can be expanded to 64 channels with one twin optical cable.

Example applications of this are the connection of up to 64 terminals and a data processing system (transfer rate up to 50 kBd per terminal) or central control of a rolling mill, a chemical production plant or the machines on a production line.

### 4.5.6  Coupling Elements for Plastic Fibers

These have a guide which is matched to the cross-section of the optical fiber. The fiber merely needs to be inserted into the guide and fixed, e.g. using a drop of adhesive. The large diameter of a plastic fiber's light-guiding core (1 mm) permits far less critical requirements as regards the mechanical characteristics of the optical coupling elements. The emitter and detector diodes of the SFH series are cheap, and the screw

connection permits separable OWG couplings. In order to connect it, the fiber only needs to be inserted fully into the opening, and the nut screwed tight. In both cases, the protective cladding of the plastic fiber does not need to be removed.

Fig. 4.26 shows the diode designs of the SFH series, Fig. 4.27 shows the designs of the components with screwed connection.

### 4.5.7  Example Applications of Plastic Fibers

Plastic optical waveguides are being used to an increasing extent in industrial control systems, owing to their advantages.

Here are a few examples: Under extreme high-voltage conditions, electrical isolation with the optocoupler integrated in one package is no longer possible. A plastic OWG link solves this problem. Fig. 4.28 shows the circuit of a transmission link. It permits a band rate of 1 MBd over 20 m.

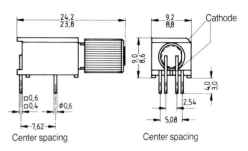

Fig. 4.27
Fiber-optic component with screwed connection

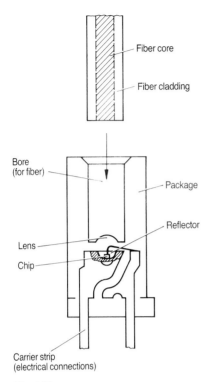

Fig. 4.26
Emitter and detector diodes for plastic OWGs

Apart from being used as optical display elements, plastic OWGs can also be used as sensors. The temperature and bending of the OWG material lead to changes in form of the transmitted light. This can be utilized for measurements. Various fiber-optic light barriers (fork-type, reflex-type) can be configured by separating the fibers. This permits the direction of movement of objects to be detected at the sensor location for instance, with simultaneous electrical potential isolation between the measurement location and evaluation location.

The open fiber ends may be spaced up to 5 mm apart. Several light barriers are normally required in a printer. The electronic circuitry can be accommodated at one location using plastic fibers. No electrical connections are needed to all light barriers. This provides reliable operation, is relatively cheap and is less susceptible to faults;

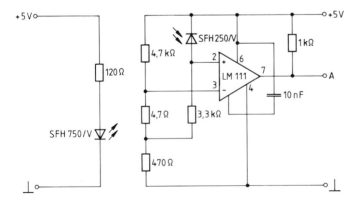

Fig. 4.28    1 MBd optical transmission up to 20 m

the radiated noise characteristics are better and the mechanical configuration is more flexible.

Fig. 4.29 shows a reflex-type light barrier, by way of example.

Typical attenuation values of a commercially available plastic fiber at various ranges and emission levels are as follows:

660 nm ±15 nm: at 1 m −0.3 dB/m;
   at 20 m −0.25 dB/m;
   at 50 m −0.20 dB/m.

950 nm 15 nm: at 1 m −4 dB/m.

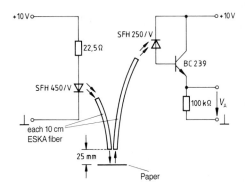

Fig. 4.29   Optical reflex-type light barrier

# 5 Integrated Standard Semiconductors

The term "standard" cannot be defined and applied very precisely. We refer to semiconductor modules as standard if the following conditions apply either individually or jointly.

▷ If a product is used by the majority of users in a specific application category;

▷ If a product which can be used largely universally is offered by several manufacturers and can be used in diverse applications in specific application sectors.

Examples of integrated semiconductors include operational amplifiers, analog-to-digital converters, microprocessors, microcontrollers and memories. Customized modules which have been developed only for one customer for a specific purpose are not standard products. These include integrated circuits for radio telephones or TV sets for instance (custom, semicustom ICs).

## 5.1 Operational Amplifiers

Integrated operational amplifiers are DC amplifiers with a very broad range of application in industrial electronics and low-frequency systems. By way of example, we shall now select the power operational amplifiers from the large number of standardized and specialized operational amplifiers and shall briefly discuss this subject.

*Symbols and designations*
The module symbol of the operational amplifier shows only the output signals and input signals. In specific cases, there are also connections for control or compensation circuits. Fig. 5.1 shows the symbol, whereby terminal 1 identifies the inverting input, terminal 2 identifies the non-inverting input and terminal 3 identifies the output. This results in a positive signal at 1 and a negative signal at 3.

The definitions of the most important designations are given below. All information refers to symmetrical supply voltages.

a) The input zero voltage (input offset voltage) $V_{10}$ is the voltage difference which must be applied to the inputs in order for 0 V to be applied to the output (Fig. 5.2).

$$V_{10} = V_{11} - V_{12}$$

at $V_O$ and generator resistance 50 Ω

Fig. 5.1   Symbol of the operational amplifier

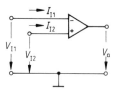

Fig. 5.2
Voltages and currents applied
to the operational amplifier

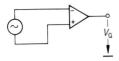

Fig. 5.3  Illustration of the no-load voltage

Fig. 5.4  Illustration of common-mode gain

b) $I_1$ is the mean static input current required for functioning of operational amplifier (Fig. 5.2).

$$I_1 = \frac{I_H + I_{12}}{2}$$

c) The input zero current (input offset current) $I_{IOS}$ is the difference between the input currents in the operating range. It may have a disturbing effect with a high generator resistance (Fig. 5.2).

d) The no-load (voltage) gain $V_{UD}$ is the gain without degenerative feedback (Fig. 5.3).

$$V_{UD} = \frac{V_Q}{V_I}$$

e) The common-mode gain V defines the gain of a signal injected in-phase at both inputs (Fig. 5.4).

### 5.1.1 Power Operational Amplifiers

Power operational amplifiers are a combination of operational amplifier and power driver. This simplifies the user circuits.

Table 5.1 shows the power operational amplifier family with the most important data. One noteworthy feature is the short-circuit strength of all types (with the exception of the TCA 365) in the entire supply voltage range and the free-wheeling diode in the TCA 1365B. No appreciable substrate current flows up to 3 A rated current of the power free-wheeling diode.

*Specifications and characteristics*
Even if only one of the maximum ratings is exceeded, this may destroy the component.

Table 5.1  Data of power operational amplifiers

| Type | Voltage | Current | Minimum gain | Short-circuit-proof to $\pm V_s$ | Internal free-wheeling diodes to $+V_s$ | to $-V_s$ | Package | Thermal resistance $R_{thSO}$ | Inhibit |
|------|---------|---------|--------------|-------------------|-------|-------|---------|-----------|---------|
| | V | A | dB | | | | | K/W | |
| TCA 365 | 36 | 3 | 20 | restricted | | | P-66-5H | 5 | |
| TCA 2365A | 36 | 2.5 | 10 | yes | | | P-DIP-18-L9 | 12 | yes |
| TCA 2365 | 36 | 2.5 | 10 | yes | | | P-SIP-9 | 8 | yes |
| TCA 365B | 42 | 4 | 20 | yes | yes | yes | P-T66-5-H | 3 | |
| TCA 1365B | 42 | 4 | 0 | yes | yes | yes | P-T66-7-H | 3 | yes |
| TCA 2465A | 42 | 2.5 | 0 | yes | yes | yes | P-DIP 16-L10 | 15 | yes |
| TCA 2465 | 42 | 2.5 | 20 | yes | yes | yes | P-SIP-9 | 8 | yes |

An appropriate safety margin with respect to the maximum ratings must always be allowed for when developing a system. The operating range specifies in what temperature, current and voltage range the module may be operated. All specified data apply mutually independently. Characteristic data define specific characteristics at a specific operating point or in an interval. Minimum and maximum values specify the variation, and the typical value specifies the mean value of the Gaussian distribution.

*Output short-circuit strength*
The short-circuit strength of the outputs is ensured by testing at three different operating voltages with respect to $+V_s$ and $-V_s$. An integrated protection circuit guarantees that the power transistors remain within their save operating area (SOA) at all times. The current and voltage are scanned and evaluated for this purpose. The protection circuit reacts in less than 5 μs.

*Common-mode input range*
For many applications, the common-mode range to $-V_s$ is of interest ($-V_s$ is ground potential in the case of asymmetrical power supply). Consequently, an approx. 2 mV higher offset variation has been accepted on the power operational amplifiers and the common-mode range has been extended to $-V_s$.

*Integrated free-wheeling diodes*
If the power operational amplifier drives inductive loads, the voltages induced during the switching operations must be clamped at $+V_s$ and $-V_s$. If the protection circuit intervenes, e.g. owing to overload, the inductive load drives the output voltage above or below the supply voltages when the relevant power element is switched off. This means: If the power element was active with respect to $-V_s$, the diode conducts with respect to $-V_s$ and vice versa. In the TCA 1365 these integrated power diodes are designed for currents up to 3 A.

The reverse recovery time of 100 to 150 ns is adequate. The forward voltage is only 1.3 V at 3 A.

**Notes on application**

*Supply voltage*
The supply voltage must always have low impedance for high frequencies. Consequently, the inductance between the supply voltage terminals of the IC should be as low as possible. In addition, the supply voltages must be blocked off with large, switching-resistant electrolytic capacitors (100 μF) and ceramic capacitors (220 nF) connected in parallel. If the circuit configuration is inadequate, voltage peaks which are added to the supply voltage and which may thus exceed the maximum ratings of the IC may occur in switching mode or with active SOA protection circuit with its high-frequency scans. We shall explain this by way of example of Fig. 5.5:

The operational amplifier is symbolized by a current sink of 5 A which is switched off with the switch at instant $t_0$. The energy stored in 1 m of supply cable with $L = 1$ μH inductance is then transferred in the capacitor $C = 100$ nF in accordance with the equation

$$W_L = LI^2 = W_c = CV^2.$$

The voltage at the capacitor thus increases by $\Delta V = I(L/C)$ to approx. 15 V above the

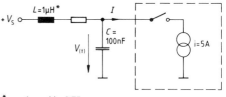

\* e.g. 1 m cable; 0.75 mm

Fig. 5.5
Illustration of how voltage peaks occur on the supply voltage

operating voltage $V_s$ applied to the IC before switch-off. With a capacitor $C = 10\ \mu F$ in parallel with 220 nF, the voltage overshoot remains <1 V if both storage capacitors are positioned close to the module.

*Layout*
The supply and load cables should be designed with as low an impedance as possible since each resistance causes degenerative current feedback or positive current feedback. These parasitic influences are particularly evident in the case of low distortion factor applications since the $-V_s$ and the $+V_s$ lines each conduct only one half-wave of the wanted current. In addition, the cable (line) cross-sections should be designed for the maximum short-circuit current in order to prevent destruction of the board. Owing to the risk of voltage overshoot, the supply lines ($\pm V_s$) and ground should be designed with as low an inductance as possible (twisted) or should be blocked off with adequately large storage capacitors. The feedback network must be connected directly to the output since a section of cable between output and tap may substantially change the transient response.

*Mounting and cooling*
The easy-to-mount P-T66-5 and P-T66-7 packages permit screw-type or clamp-type connections on a flat cooling surface which is arranged vertically on the pc-board. The low thermal resistance of the system package (from the chip to the base plate of the package) of only 3 °C per watt permits high pulse powers. The heat sink must have an adequate thermal capacity. The possible power loss in the operating range as a function of the package temperature is calculated as follows

$$P_v = (T_{jmax} - T_G)/R_{thSG}$$

where

$T_{jmax}$ = Maximum junction temperature (150 °C)

$T_G$ = Package temperature
$R_{thSG}$ = Thermal resistance system-package

For example, a power loss of 20 W may be converted at a package temperature of 85°C. Since powers of up to 50 W are permitted in the case of short-circuit, the cut-out temperature is quickly reached. The IC then reverts to scan mode.

*Reactive loads*
When driving reactive loads, the load line of a resistive load degenerates into an ellipse. This means that higher power losses are converted in the power operational amplifier. Since switch-on of capacitive loads and switch-off of inductive loads are particularly critical in this respect, we shall discuss these cases in detail.

*Capacitive load*
The input admittance of an emitter follower may become negative with capacitive loads, i.e. the emitter follower oscillates. Optimum design of the output stage TCA 1365B (complementary emitter followers) means that this IC withstands load capacitances into the mF range. Fig. 5.6 shows switch-on and switch-off of a capacitive load with the power operational amplifier.

When switching on, the capacitor, for example 10 μF, would have to be charged with a current $I = S \times C = 20$ A if the voltage at this capacitor is to rise with the typical slew rate of the IC of 2 $V/\mu s$. The protection circuit in the IC limits the current to the relevant permitted value. The voltage at the capacitor increases until the transistor reaches saturation. In the case of charge reversal of the capacitor to $-V_s$, the lower power transistor would be loaded. Without an integrated protection circuit, the IC would be destroyed in both cases.

*Inductive load*
Inductive loads can be switched with no problems since the current rises in linear fashion. Switch-off is more critical since the energy stored in the inductor must be dissi-

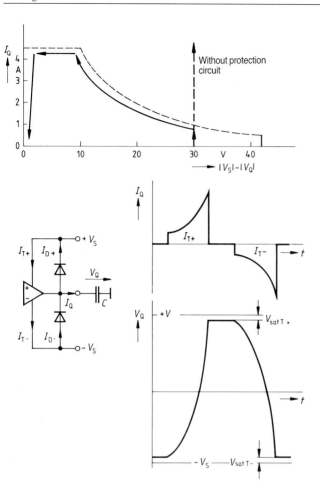

Fig. 5.6
Switching with
capacitive load

pated or restored. The free-wheeling diodes at the output of the operational amplifier are used for this purpose.

Fig. 5.7 shows the conditions applying when switching inductive loads. The slope $dV/dt$ is dependent only upon parasitic loads. With $I_L = 2$ A peak and $C_{par} \sim 100$ pF, we obtain $dV/dt \sim I/C = 20$ kV/µs.

*Motors as the load*
DC motors act in the same way as inductors at the starting instant. If the armature is

permanently magnetized and the motor operates at rated speed, the motor approximately represents an active-power (resistive) load which is connected in series with a DC generator (counter-e.m.f.). Permanent-field motors generate an e.m.f. which is, at maximum, equal to the applied voltage. Series-wound motors or shunt-wound motors, by contrast, may generate a far higher e.m.f. Consequently, only motors whose maximum starting current is equal to the permitted diode current can be oper-

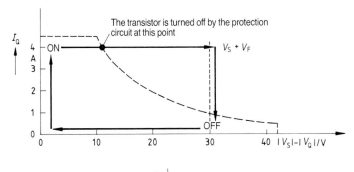

Fig. 5.7
Switching with
inductive load

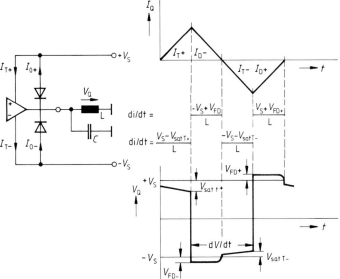

ated with the TCA 1365. Otherwise, additional diodes would have to be connected. Consequently, we shall assume that only permanent-field motors are used below. Fig. 5.8 shows the various cases of operation.

Starting motors is a special case because the starting current lies up to one order of magnitude above the rated current. This means the protection circuit of the IC is activated, and the motor starts with the "quasi-constant current" which the protection circuit permits as a function of the voltage across the relevant integrated power element. This voltage drops with increasing counter-e.m.f. of the motor. Thus, the motor initially starts with a low torque which increases with increasing speed. When decelerating, the motor e.m.f. forces one output below $-V_s$ in each case when the outputs are both switched with respect to $-V_s$ (decelerating to "LOW"). Analogously, when decelerating to

1) Clockwise rotation

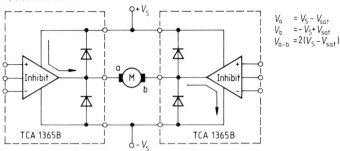

$V_a = V_S - V_{sat}$
$V_b = -V_S + V_{sat}$
$V_{a-b} = 2(V_S - V_{sat})$

2) Braking (CW/low)

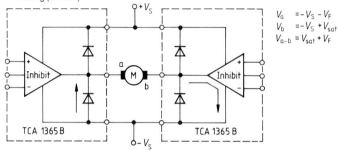

$V_a = -V_S - V_F$
$V_b = -V_S + V_{sat}$
$V_{a-b} = V_{sat} + V_F$

3) Braking (CW/high)

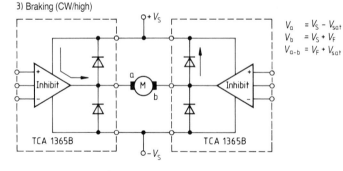

$V_a = V_S - V_{sat}$
$V_b = V_S + V_F$
$V_{a-b} = V_F + V_{sat}$

4) Counterclockwise rotation

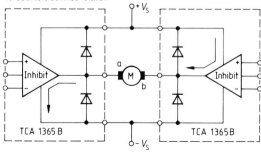

$V_a = -V_S + V_{sat}$
$V_b = V_S - V_{sat}$
$V_{a-b} = -2(V_S - V_{sat})$

Fig. 5.8
DC motor as the load

"HIGH" the corresponding outputs are raised above $+V_s$. If the braking current exceeds the current permitted by the protection circuit, the relevant power element is operated as when starting in constant current mode. This means that the permitted braking current is controlled as a function of the motor e.m.f. minus a diode forward voltage as when starting, the braking torque is also varied as a function of the speed. The only difference is that the torque now increases with dropping speed.

If the motor is to be decelerated more abruptly, its short-circuit current must be lower than the limiting current of the power operational amplifier. If the e.m.f. has dropped below voltage $V_{sat} + V_F = 2$ V when decelerating, the motor coasts unbraked to a stop. The free-wheeling diodes also perform an important function in the case of any voltage peaks which may occur in servo loops with an abrupt change in the setpoint. The overvoltages are effectively limited by feedback. The system then behaves in the same way as an operational amplifier with inductive load in switching mode.

*Malfunctions*

The possibility of the following malfunctions must generally be eliminated when using integrated power ICs.

▷ Discontinuities of the supply voltage lines and/or discontinuities of the lines to the blocking capacitors.

▷ Short-circuits of the operating voltages.

Short-circuits of the output with respect to the operating voltages are not critical and thus do not need to be considered as malfunctions.

**Typical circuits**

Fig. 5.9 shows the power operational amplifier as an inverting and non-inverting amplifier. As is always the case with opera-

tional amplifiers, the rules of offset correction also apply in this case. It must be noted that the input current flows out of the IC terminals owing to the PNP input stages. In the case of high-impedance degenerative feedback networks, this current causes an appreciable voltage drop which effects the operating points in switching mode. The degenerative feedback network should not have too high an impedance since, otherwise, the parasitic capacitance (e.g. of the inverting input with respect to ground) may influence the response characteristic. For the same reason, the degenerative feedback network must also be connected directly at the input. Output compensation is performed by a 1 Ω resistor and a 220 nF ceramic capacitor in series (Boucherot element).

The *RC* network must be connected directly between the output terminal and ground of the module. The supply voltages must be blocked off with switching-resistant electrolytic capacitors and parallel-connected ceramic capacitors. If the inhibit input is not used, it must be connected to $-V_s$ in order to avoid capacitive pick-up.

The amplifier is in standby state when the voltage at pin 3 is 2 V more positive than $-V_s$. It is active when the voltage at pin 3 is no more than 0.5 V more positive than $V_s$.

113

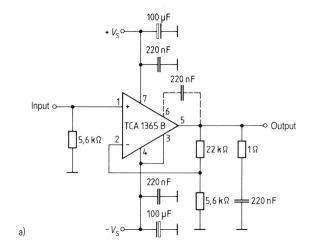

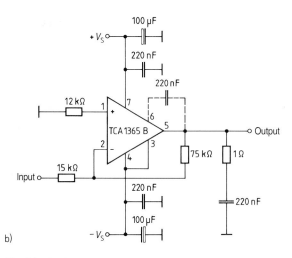

Fig. 5.9  Basic circuits of power operational amplifiers   a) inverting   b) non-inverting

## 5.2 Analog-to-Digital Converters

Test and measurement systems generally involve conversion of analog measurement data to digital values so that these values can then be further-processed digitally. Important aspects are:

▷ Measurement data acquisition and monitoring
▷ Data analysis
▷ Process control

First, we have analog-to-digital converters. Table 5.2 shows an overview of the Siemens types. By way of example here, we present two entirely different A/D converter types: A microprocessor compatible 10-bit A/D converter for conventional tasks in industrial electronics and two very fast 8-bit A/D converters.

### 5.2.1 10-bit A/D Converter SDA 1810

The SDA 1810 module is a monolithic 10-bit A/D converter with microprocessor-compatible interface. The same family also includes 8-bit and 12-bit converters. The SDA 1810 has 8 multiplexed inputs and requires a supply voltage of 5 V. The interface has a width of 8 bits. It is pin-compatible with the industrial standards DAC808 and 809. The 10-bit wide data stream is output in 2-byte format. It can be operated with maximum 2 MHz clock frequency.

The conversion process operates on the basis of the principle of successive approximation with an internal capacitor network. The converter contains a temperature-stabilized comparitor, a multiplexer for 8 inputs and a sample and hold circuit. No external offset or amplification circuits are required. Connection to an 8-bit microprocessor is simplified by the 3-bit address latch and 10-bit data latch. The 8-bit bus can be switched to tri-state.

*Characteristics*
▷ 10 bit resolution
▷ Total error (not corrected) $\pm 1/2$ LSB
▷ Monotonic, no missing codes
▷ 0 to 5 V input voltage range
▷ Conversion time 15 µs
▷ 8 input channels
▷ Microprocessor interface
▷ No offset or gain setting required
▷ Can be operated even without microprocessor
▷ TTL compatible output voltage
▷ Tri-state outputs
▷ Plastic DIP and PLCC 28 packages
▷ Temperature range $-40$ to $+125\,°C$

Fig. 5.10 shows the block diagram and Fig. 5.11 the typical error curve of the converter.

*Connection*
Fig. 5.12 shows the operating pulse timing diagram of the SDA 1810, and Fig. 5.13 shows connection to a microprocessor. Con-

Table 5.2  Overview of analog-to-digital converters

| | | |
|---|---|---|
| SDA 0808A; B; N | 8-bit CMOS | A/D converter |
| SDA 0810A; B; N | 10-bit CMOS | A/D converter |
| SDA 1810N | 10-bit CMOS | A/D converter |
| SDA 6020 | 6 bit Flash | A/D converter,   50 MHz |
| SDA 5200AN; AS | 6 bit Flash | A/D converter,   75 MHz |
| SDA 5200N; S | 6 bit Flash | A/D converter, 100 MHz |
| SDA 8200 | 6 bit Flash | A/D converter, 300 MHz |
| SDA 8010 | 6 bit Flash | A/D converter, 100 MHz |
| SDA 8005 | 8 bit | D/A converter,   7 ns |
| SDA 8020 | hift register for fast data acquisition | |

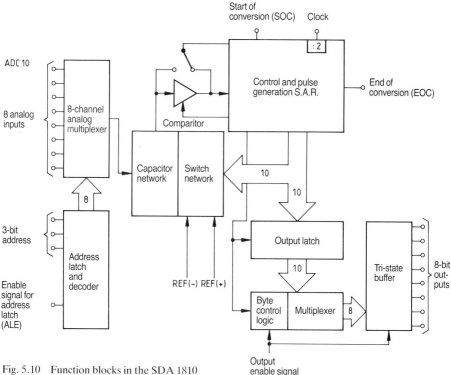

Fig. 5.10    Function blocks in the SDA 1810

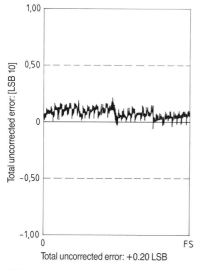

Bild 5.11

version is started by a write command with address ADC-CS Signal EOC (end of conversion) of the converter can signal the end of conversion by an interrupt in the processor.

The first read command with address ADC-CSreads the high-order byte, and the second read command reads the low-order byte. The input signals ADD 0,1 and 2 each select one of the 8 input channels.

*Decoupling of the power supply*
The power supply terminals of the converter should be blocked off with a 10 µF tantalum or electrolytic capacitor, with a 0.01 µF ceramic capacitor connected in parallel with it. The connection leads from the capacitors to the converter should be as short as possible.

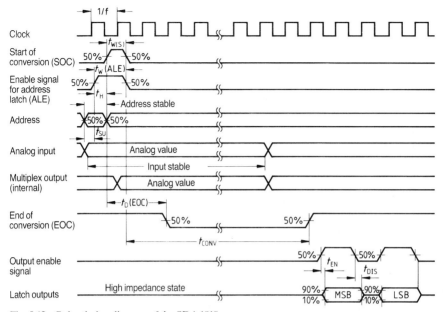

Fig. 5.12   Pulse timing diagram of the SDA 1810

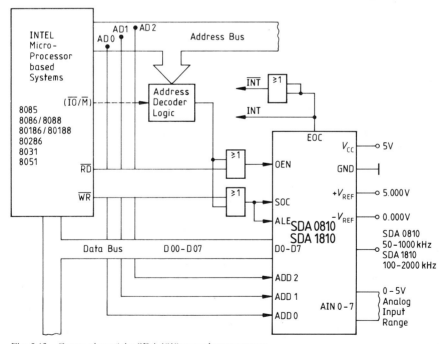

Fig. 5.13   Connection of the SDA 1810 to a microprocessor

117

*Reference voltages*

The same capacitor combination as with the supply voltages is required between the terminal Ref(+) and Ref(−) in order to avoid dynamic errors. In addition, a 0.1 μF ceramic capacitor must be connected between Ref(−) and ground (GND).

*Analog inputs*

The high impedance of the analog inputs permits simple connection to various signal sources. However, they must be able to supply the current for charging the sample and hold capacitor (approx. 50 pF) within 8 clock cycles.

### 5.2.2  High-Speed 8-bit A/D Converter SDA 8010

The increasing demand for digitizing and processing high frequencies opens up broader and broader fields of application for the high-speed A/D converters. Frequently, there is an inadequate knowledge of the function, conversion characteristics and parameters and the external circuitry, despite this

trend. The next section provides the reader with assistance, by way of example of the 100-MHz flash converter SDA 8010.

The SDA 8010 operates on the basis of the parallel principle. Its most important performance features are as follows:

▷  100 MHz conversion frequency
▷  8-bit resolution
▷  Static non-linearity 0.5 LSB
▷  Signal-to-noise ratio 40 db at 30 MHz analog frequency.

The analog input voltage can be injected 0 V-symmetrically or asymmetrically, dependent upon the selected reference voltages. The converter is controlled via two strobe inputs. The converter quality can be optimized within certain limits by variable timing.

The 8-bit output data (volatile) are valid for longer than 4 ns in the case of 100 MHz conversion frequency and the data have attained steady state after maximum 20.5 ns, referred to strobe 2. Owing to this short transient recovery time, the converter can also be used

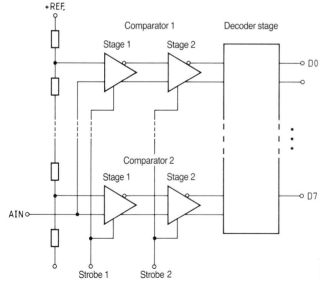

Fig. 5.14
Block diagram of the SDA 8010

for subranging applications. 14-bit resolution can be achieved at approx. 10 to 20 MHz conversion frequency.

*Strobe timing*
The internal circuit of the converter essentially consists of 255 comparators and decoding logic. Fig. 5.14 shows the basic structure of the module. The input comparators have a 2-stage structure. This guarantees that each overall comparator recovers to the signal level required by the decoding logic, even in the 100 MHz range. The two series-connected operational amplifiers are controlled by the relevant strobe signal. Strobe 1 controls the sample and hold time of the first stages and, analogously to this, strobe 2 controls the second stages.

The two-stage structure in conjunction with strobe timing guarantees good conversion quality.

Fig. 5.15 shows the strobe timing. When strobe 1 is LOW, the first comparator stages are in sample or transparent mode. The positive strobe 1 edge determines the actual con-version instant by switching the first comparator stage to hold mode. The result of comparison is then sampled by the second comparator stage (Strobe 2 = LOW) and held for the decoder stage (Strobe 2 = HIGH). The period of validity of the output data is directly proportional to the HIGH time of strobe 2. Thus, the following essential applies to strobe timing S1 ≈ S2. Owing to the finite transient recovery time of the comparator stages, S1 may be somewhat delayed (hold time $t_{H1}$ and negative $t_{SetupStr.2}$). Asymmetrical clock ratios favour the transient response ($t_{Str.1} > 50\%$ and $t_{Str.2} > 50\%$). Strobe timing will now be represented as a 3-dimensional vector: Notation $/t_{Str.1}/t_{Str.2}/t_{SetupStr.2})$. With defined strobe frequency, these three information items suffice for clear reconstruction of the timing.

The various parameters are compared to standard timing with the data (5/3.5/−1.5). Fig. 5.16 shows the effective bits as a function of the analog frequency, averaged from several measurements with components from different production lots.

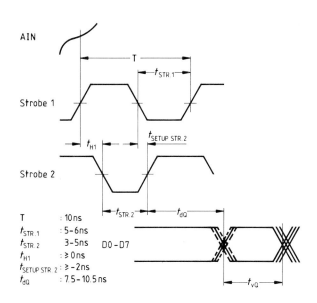

AIN

Strobe 1

Strobe 2

| T | : 10 ns |
| $t_{STR.1}$ | : 5–6 ns |
| $t_{STR.2}$ | 3–5 ns |
| $t_{H1}$ | : ≥ 0 ns |
| $t_{SETUP STR.2}$ | : ≥ −2 ns |
| $t_{dQ}$ | : 7.5–10.5 ns |

D0 – D7

Fig. 5.15
Strobe timing diagram

119

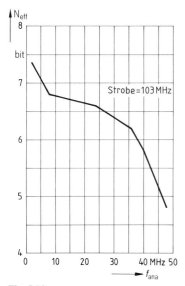

Fig. 5.16
Effective bits as a function of the
analog frequency

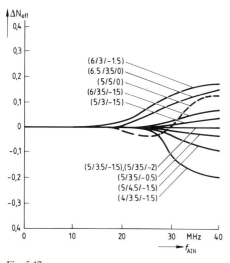

Fig. 5.17
Converter quality as a function of the
strobe parameters

Fig. 5.17 shows the variation in effective bits as a function of the analog frequency with the strobe timing as the parameter and standardized for the timing (5/3.5/−1.5). The timing curves show the relative variation of the effective bits as compared with the standard timing and, thus, also in relation to each other.

There are no appreciable differences in the dynamic response until as of approx. 20 to 30 MHz analog frequency, and these differences ramify at >45 MHz to an interval ≈ ±0.2 bit. Fig. 5.17 shows statistical mean values whose differences should be understood only as a tendency.

At 100 MHz conversion frequency, the LOW time of strobe 1 should lie in the range 5 to 6 ns. The LOW time of strobe 2 should lie between 3 and 5 ns.

In respect of the dynamic characteristics, the setup time for strobe 2 may lie in the interval 0...-2ns. However, an excessively long set-up time (>0 ns) may, in individual cases, have an unfavorable effect on the error rate. Consequently, we recommend a range of −0.5 to 2 ns. This recommendation is not applicable at conversion frequencies <90 MHz.

If we accept a somewhat poorer conversion quality (0.2−0.4 bit) and shorter validity time of the data, the SDA 8010 can be used to implement conversion frequencies up to typically 150 MHz. The shorter time for strobe 1 and, thus, the shorter sample time of the first comparator stages are the reason for the somewhat lower dynamic measured values.

*Cooling of the SDA 8010*
From analog techniques we know that the speed of comparators increases the higher the current available to them. Nevertheless, it has been possible to restrict the power requirement of the SDA 8010 to maximum 1.5 V.

The SDA 8010 may be operated up to approx. 60°C ambient temperature without additional cooling. It may be operated up to approx. 75°C with ventilation (0.5 m/s).

One other possibility of improving the thermal characteristics is to use heat sinks. With a commercially available IC heat sink on the metal cover of the ceramic package for instance, the SDA 8010 can also be used in A/D subsystems specified up to 85°C ambient temperature.

Increasing temperature means an increase in the transient recovery and propagation delay times in the comparators and decoder stages. This prolongs the transient response time of the data and their validity time is reduced. Thus, at high temperatures in particular, we recommend setting the LOW time of strobe 2 to 3 to 4 ns and utilizing the possible set-up time for strobe 2 ($\approx$1 ns) well.

In the other extreme case, at ambient temperatures <0 °C, the digital outputs may tend to oscillate on converters from previous production lots. The reason for this is related to steep current edges in the output transistors which may lead to parasitic positive feedback. This behavior is effectively suppressed if required with a low-rating inductor (approx. 100 nH) between the GND 1 terminal and digital ground.

### Supply voltage

Both the positive TTL-compatible voltage of +5 V and the negative ECL100K-compatible voltage of −4.5 V are required for operating the SDA 8010. However, ECL10K modules whose power supply is specified at −5.2 V (±5%) are implemented in many user systems.

The conversion characteristics are observed by the higher negative supply voltage, but the power loss increases by approx. 150 to 200 mW. This means that the specified maximum power loss limit (1.5 W) and ambient temperature limit (60 °C) are no longer observed, and, thus, additional cooling measures are required.

### The SDA 8010 in application

Conversion of analog to digital quantities is ultimately a measurement process which should be carried out as free of errors as possible in the endeavoured accuracy category. In order to achieve this aim, certain aspects must be taken into consideration when using A/D converters.

### Ground isolation

The interference of digital switching peaks on the mV-sensitive analog input is one source of errors. This can be effectively suppressed by isolating the power supply and ground between the analog and digital section. On the SDA 8010, there are at least two possible methods of distinguishing between the analog and digital sections. As shown in Fig. 5.18, the digital section ($V_{CCD}$, $V_{EED}$ and strobe) is referred to digital ground and the analog section ($V_{CCA}$, $V_{EEA}$, REF and AIN) is referred to analog ground. RF isolation of ground and the power supply is carried out with the inductors $L1$ to $L3$. In the other case (Fig. 5.19) analog ground is only the reference point for the reference voltage and the analog input voltage. All other signals are referred to digital ground. This is legitimate since only the voltage difference between the analog input and the reference voltage applied to the relevant comparator is destined for the conversion result. Isolation of the power supply is still carried out via the inductors $L1$ and $L2$.

Analog and digital ground must be DC-connected ($L3$) in order to avoid common-mode noise at the input comparators. Other important criteria for system design are:

▷ Large grounding areas and practical grounding in order to avoid potential shifts
▷ Designing the signal lines as microstrip lines
▷ Decoupling the DC inputs with low-inductance chip capacitors

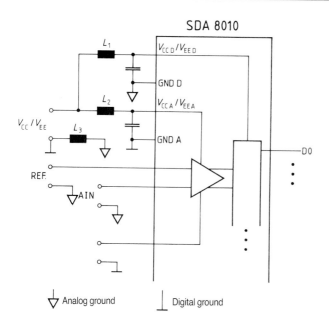

Fig. 5.18
Distinction between
digital and analog ground

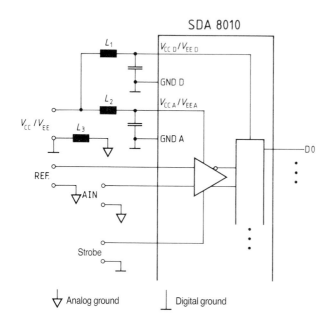

Fig. 5.19
Analog ground as the
reference point for
REF and AIN

*Generating the strobe signals*

In general, A/D conversion is controlled with an existing system clock. Since the SDA 8010 requires two strobe signals for conversion, these signals must be derived from the existing system clock (conversion clock).

In the simplest case, this is carried out by inverting conversion clock with the aid of an ECL-OR element (Fig. 5.20a and b), whereby the circuit shown in Fig. 5.20b must be given preference since the propagation delay of the inverter produces a negative set-up time. If two further OR elements are available, it is possible to shorten the Low time of strobe 2 by one cycle (G2), as shown in Fig. 5.20c. This achieves very good strobe timing.

Fig. 5.21 shows the complete circuit of an A/D subsystem on which the described aspects have been implemented.

*Subranging converters*

Owing to the characteristic that the SDA 8010 has no output latch in which the data can be buffered, the module is suitable for use as an MSB or LSB converter (resolution 14 bit; conversion rate 10 to 20 MHz). The analog input signal is sampled by a sample and hold amplifier and kept at this value for the subsequent conversion process. The first conversion step is carried out with the MSB converter whose conversion result is converted by an 8-bit D/A converter to an inverted, analog voltage value.

The difference 1/2 $(U_{AIN}-U_{DAC})$ is formed at RD and amplified with the wideband amplifier A1 to the level required for the LSB converter. Both conversion results are buffered in a latch and added to a 14-bit binary number in the digital correction register (2-bit error correction).

Owing to the 2-bit error correction, only an accuracy of 1 LSB, referred to 8 bit, is required for the MSB converter, whilst the 8-bit D/A converter and the sample and hold amplifier must comply with an accuracy of 14 bit in steady state.

Stringent requirements are also made in respect of the amplifier for the difference vol-

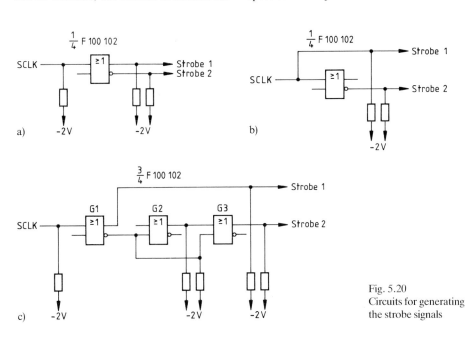

Fig. 5.20
Circuits for generating
the strobe signals

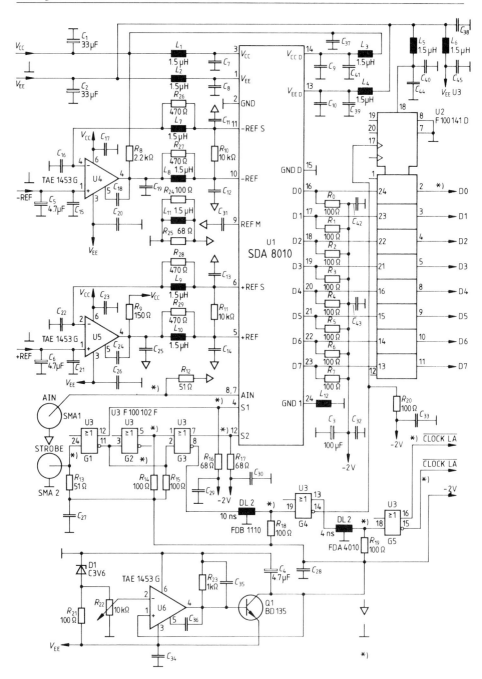

Fig. 5.21   Analog-to-digital conversion system

tage whose gain factor ($A$) must be set very precisely.

$$\frac{\Delta A}{A} = \frac{0.52}{256} = 0.2\%.$$

Digital error correction is carried out by offset addition of the two 8-bit conversion results to form a 14-bit binary number. Since the transfer function of the LSB converter passes through the staircase mid-points of the MSB transfer function, this value must also be corrected by subtraction of 80 H. The subranging converter is controlled via clock I. The high time should be 5 ns constant, and the low time should be variable. All required trigger and strobe signals can be obtained from this input clock via suitable delay lines.

### 5.2.3 High-Speed 8-bit A/D Converter SDA 8200

The converter permits a resolution of 6 bits at 300 MHz sampling frequency. It operates on the basis of the parallel method. It is the first A/D converter which can digitize a 150 MHz input signal with more than 5 bit. The term effective resolution is taken to mean the actually usable resolution at a specific sampling and input frequency. At input frequencies upwards of 70 MHz, the SDA 8200 thus has better dynamic characteristics than all previously available monolithic A/D converters.

Special features are as follows:

▷ Linearity error maximum 1/4 LSB
▷ Data output optionally via integrated 1:2 multiplexers or directly
▷ Overflow bit with programmable output format
▷ Clock generation with symmetrical sinusoidal voltage
▷ Input voltage range ±1 V
▷ Input capacitance 12 pF

Fig. 5.22 shows the effective resolution as a function of the analog input frequency for the A/D converters SDA 8010 (8-bit 100 MHz ADU) and SDA 8200 (6-bit 300 MHz ADU).

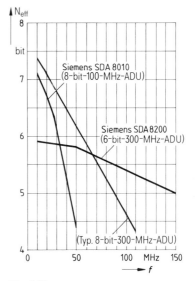

Fig. 5.22
Effective resolution of the high-speed A/D converter

## 5.3 16-bit Microprocessors and Peripheral Chips

Microprocessors are programmable chips modelled on mainframes. Nowadays, the performance of computer systems implemented with them already by far exceeds that of the mainframes constructed 20 years ago. Owing to the great popularity of personal computers, there is a great general awareness of the 8086 family.

Standardization and open architecture were a precondition for the success of the SAB 8086 microprocessor chip family.

Microprocessor chips (MPs) contain the arithmetic and logic unit (ALU), as the section capable of performing calculations, the command decoder and the sequencer. More and more periphery functions are being integrated on one silicon chip.

The microprocessor requires peripheral chips so that it can communicate with the outside world. These peripheral chips are specialized to perform their related task.

The essential peripheral chips and their function are as follows:

▷ Clock generators
▷ Floppy disk controllers
▷ DMA controllers (direct memory access)
▷ Graphic controllers
▷ Input/output ports
▷ Serial interface modules
▷ Mass storage controllers
▷ LAN modules (local area network)
▷ Color palette
▷ Timer and interrupt controller system bus
▷ System bus controller (arbiter)

There are also more and more LSI modules and chips which unite as many different peripheral functions as possible. This permits PCs to be manufactured with less and less integrated circuits and, thus, more cheaply.

Whilst, 10 years ago, interest centered around the 8-bit microprocessor SAB 8080/85, the field is led nowadays by the 16 and 32-bit microprocessors. We will thus restrict ourselves to the most important characteristics of the 8086 family. We shall present a 32-bit RISC processor in the next chapters.

### 5.3.1 The SAB 8086 Family

The SAB 8086 family consists of software-compatible microprocessors with different hardware configurations. Software-compatible means that the 8086 programs can run on all processors.

The important members of the 16-bit SAB 8086 family are as follows:

SAB 8088
    multiplexed 8-bit data/address bus,
    1 Mbyte address space

SAB 8086
    multiplexed 16-bit data/address bus,
    1 Mbyte address space

SAB 80188
    multiplexed 8-bit data/address bus,
    additional periphery characteristics,
    1 Mbyte address space

SAB 80186
    multiplexed 16-bit data/address bus,
    additional periphery characteristics,
    1 Mbyte address space

SAB 80286
    separate 16-bit data/address bus,
    memory protection mechanisms,
    16 Mbyte address space

*SAB 8086*
An address space of 1 Mbyte is available for storing programs and data. This memory area is managed with segments of up to 64 kbyte capacity. Their start addresses are managed in separate registers. Dynamic address generation adds these segment start addresses to form the internal 16-bit addresses for code or data segments. These addressing mechanisms permit programs and data to be shifted in the memory simply and also rapid switchover between various program and data areas.

The address space for the input/output operations is 64 kbyte with variable addressing and 256 byte in each case with fixed addressing. The interrupt system is vector-organized and distinguishes up to 256 interrupt vectors. This includes software-triggered interrupts which occur, for instance, during a program run in the case of division by zero.

The microprocessor SAB 8086 operates at an internal clock frequency of 5.8 or 10 MHz, requires +5 V supply voltages and is supplied in a 40-pin DIL package. Internally, the SAB 8086 is implemented with dual-processor architecture, whereby one processor serves to execute commands and the other controls the interface to the bus. In addition, this processing unit has an upstream queue. Owing to the fact that the processes of command execution, memory access and buffering of commands run asynchronously, the microprocessor SAB 8086 can operate together with relatively slow standard memories (access time 500 ns) despite the high processing speed. The microprocessor SAB 8086 has two operating modes. In the case of simple systems, the processor itself generates the control signals for storage and input/output operations so that less external chips are required. In the case of operating mode for more complex systems, the system control chip, SAB 8288 is also required. This permits multiprocessor structures for instance to be implemented. The 8-bit address bus drivers SAB 8282/8283 (the latter inverting), the bidirectional 8-bit data bus drivers SAB 8286/8287 (the latter inverting), the clock generator SAB 8284 and the interrupt chip SAB 8259A which generates the various interrupt vectors (Fig. 5.23) are available for simplifying the system structure. All standard ROMs, PROMs, EPROMs and RAMs can be connected as the memory. Amongst other things, the corresponding pin-compati-

ble range of chips of the SAB 8080/8085 systems is available as peripheral chips.

The bus arbiter SAB 8289 permits a simple structure of microprocessor systems by coordinating access of several processors to the common system bus. Particular importance has been attached to high flexibility, thus permitting all conceivable system configurations to be implemented in an equally simple way. Thus, the chip supports multibus systems, parallel and daisy-chain priority control and bus lack for implementing semaphores. Semaphore is a control mechanism which controls access operations of several processors to one bus in a similar way to a set of traffic lights.

*SAB 80186/188*
On the SAB 80186/188, system-oriented peripheral functions have been integrated in addition to the 8086 processor. These are as follows: Clock generator and ready logic, bus controller, 2 DMA channels, interrupt

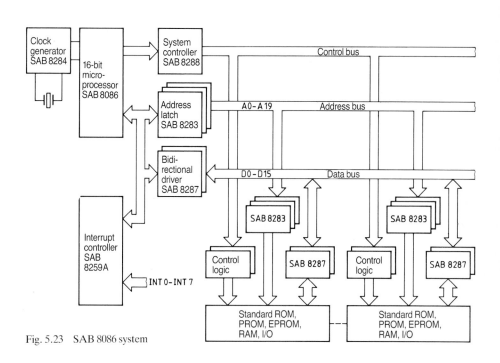

Fig. 5.23  SAB 8086 system

127

controller, 2 16-bit counters/timers, a programmable chip-select logic and a related logic for generating wait cycles (wait states).

All these functions are controlled via a set of registers which is also integrated.

The processor has been substantially improved at certain points, with full compatibility with the SAB 8086. Besides accepting a few new commands, such as Push All and Pop All (saving all registers to the stack and retrieving all registers from the stack), internal sequences have also been speeded up, e.g. by introducing the processor's own address arithmetic unit for computing the effective address from up to four fractions in only two clock cycles.

*SAB 80286*

The SAB 80286 is a further generation of 16-bit processors. Memory management and memory protection and a privilege assignment mechanism, subdivided into four levels, have been introduced. These performance features also characterize the main applications. These are as follows: Personal computers (PC-AT), process automation, workstation systems, switching systems and applications in which several tasks can be processed simultaneously (multitask and multiuser). The incorporated privilege assignment and protection mechanisms prevent the programs accessing forbidden memory areas without authorization and thus destroying data.

The physical address space has been extended to 16 Mbyte, and up to 1 Gbyte (Giga $= 2^{30}$) of virtual address space is available for each program (task) via the memory management unit. Conversion from virtual memory to physical memory is carried out via tables in which all memory areas for a program are defined with descriptors. Access authorization and privilege level are also included. Compliance with these protection measures is monitored by the processor's hardware. In the event of an error, it triggers an internal interrupt. Functions for fast program change (task switch) are also available.

The SAB 80286 operates at an internal clock frequency of 6, 8, 10, 12.5 or 16 MHz. One bus cycle requires two clock cycles. As in the SAB 80286 system already, the processor is supplemented with system chips to form a complete family on the SAB 80286 as well. This includes the SAB 82284 (clock generator), the SAB 82288 (system controller) and SAB 82289 (bus arbiter). Furthermore, address bus drivers SAB 8282A/83A and data bus drivers SAB 8286A/87A, each with a width of 8 bit are available for the system structure. The SAB 8259A is suitable for use as a chip for interrupt control. Fig. 5.24 shows a system concept.

A DMA control chip, the SAB 82258, has been developed, adapted to the performance of the processor. Besides having a transfer rate of 8/10 Mbyte/s (at 8/10 MHz system clock) and the addressing volume of 16 Mbyte, this chip also has other functions. In the case of four independent DMA channels, the module can be programmed for data chaining and command chaining. In addition, one channel can be used as the multiplex channel, whereby this channel can be subdivided into 32 subchannels. One typical application for this is the connection of several visual display units, printers and mass storage units.

The SAB 82258 permits autonomous control and transmission of data. It can also be connected to the SAB 80186 and SAB 8086.

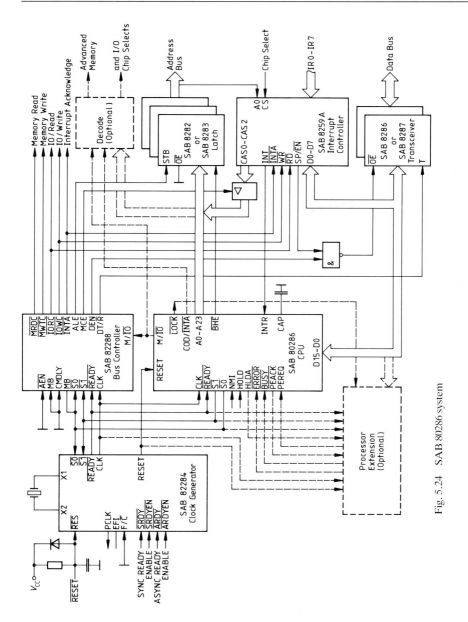

Fig. 5.24　SAB 80286 system

129

### 5.3.2 Peripheral Chips

Below, we shall briefly present a few particularly important types of chip from the large number of peripheral chips.

*Token bus modem SAB 82511*
The essential characteristics of the modem chip are as follows:

▷ The carrier band modem is fully compatible with the IEEE 802.4 and MAP standard (carrier band)
▷ Interface for all standard token bus controllers (e.g. SAB 82511)
▷ Data transfer rate 5 Mbit/s and 10 Mbit/s with phase-coherent FSK modulation
▷ Digital PLL logic and digital demodulation
▷ No external active components are required
▷ Diagnostic loop-back for test purposes
▷ Physical station management possible

▷ Jabber-inhibit timer (watchdog timer)
▷ Differential input/output drivers for serial line
▷ Only one supply voltage (+5 V)

The token bus modem was developed for direct operation together with the SAB 82510 token bus controller for carrier band token bus applications. It operates on the basis of a specific frequency shift keying method at a data transfer rate of 5 Mbit/s and 10 Mbit/s.

The main functions of the modem are generating the receive and transmit clock, modulation and demodulation (frequency shift keying) and producing an electrical interface to the transmitter/receiver cable. The loop-back facility permits the signal to be transmitted to be looped back via the modem to the controller for diagnostic purposes. This combined loop-back between controller and modem permits effective

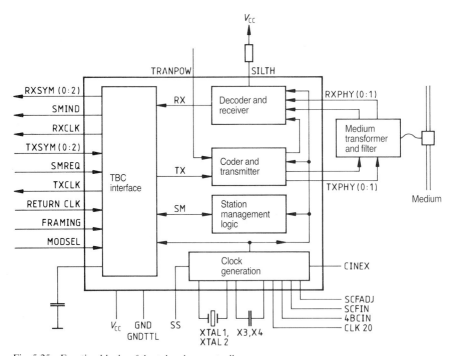

Fig. 5.25   Function blocks of the token bus controller

error detection. A watchdog timer integrated on the chip prevents the station transmitting permanently unintentionally and thus blocking the network. Fig. 5.25 shows the function blocks of the TBC.

*SAB 82258A (ADMA)*
The SAB 82258A – advanced DMA co-processor – is a chip for direct memory access to 8/16 and 32-bit microcomputer systems.

The most important characteristics are as follows:

▷ Four independently programmable and autonomous DMA channels
▷ Multiplexer channel for supporting 32 subchannels (for up to 32 peripheral chips)
▷ Automatic data chaining for combining or distributing data blocks
▷ "Flying" comparison, conversion and verifying functions
▷ Automatic combination/splitting of data (2 byte)
▷ Command chaining for CPU-independent processing with conditional chaining, controllable by peripheral events
▷ Programmable bus loading for a defined bus allocation for CPU and ADMA
▷ Maximum data transfer rate 20 Mbyte/s
▷ Internal 16-bit data bus
▷ Address range and maximum block length 16 Mbyte
▷ SAB 82227 as a favorably priced version (without multiplexer channel, "flying" functions or 32-bit data transfer)

The bus interface permits connection in all Siemens/Intel 8 and 16-bit processors – from the SAB 8088 to the SAB 80286 – without additional interface logic. In independent operating mode (remote mode), the ADMA SAB 82258A can be integrated in various system environments (see example application), for example also in Motorola 680×0 systems.

*Example application*
The example shows the SAB 82258A in independent operating mode with a direct (system-own) input/output bus, interconnected with an 80386 chip (Fig. 5.26).

In this example, the system address range of the ADMA addresses the CPU and requires for this an additional bus allocation by the HOLD/HLDA sequence. The CPU is the bus manager in this case.

The second address range of the ADMA (system-own range) addresses the system-own bus components comprising all the peripheral control chips. These ADMA access operations require no bus allocation and can thus be executed quickly.

Access operations of the central processing unit (CPU) to system-own bus components (peripheral chip, ADMA) are allotted by the ADMA. After a running transfer cycle, the ADMA can quickly release the system-own bus at the request of the CPU (this is indicated by the BREL signal).

*The color palette SAB 82C171*
In modern text-graphic systems, a color palette forms the linking element between digital image display and analog control of the picture tube. The color palette SAB 82C171 implements this function on one chip in CMOS technology. It can be used to display 256 colors or tonal values simultaneously. By contrast with previous systems, these are not permanently preset but freely programmable (even during picture set-up).

The SAB 82C171 is subdivided into four function blocks:

▷ Image memory interface
▷ Color table
▷ Digital-to-analog converter
▷ System bus interface

In a system with the color palette SAB 82C171, the color information for each pixel is read from the image memory as digital code. This maximum 8-bit wide code serves as the address for the color table. This selects one of 256 data words, each with a width of 18 bits.

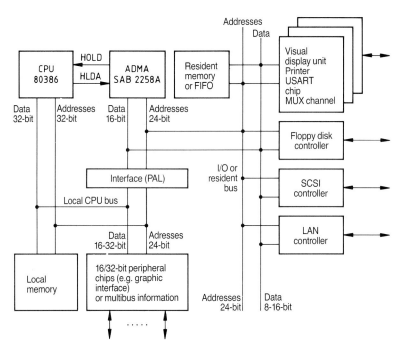

Fig. 5.26   The ADMA in an 80386 system

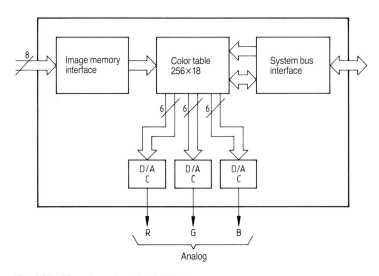

Fig. 5.27   The color palette SAB 82C171

Each set of 6 bits of the address data word are routed to the input of one of three integrated digital-to-analog converters. The analog outputs of the A/D converters directly supply signals R, G, B (red, green, blue) for controlling the picture tube in accordance with standards RS343A and RS170A.

The color table can be loaded with the required color selection via the 8-bit bus of the system bus interface. Each of the 256 color values can be selected as required from 262,144 different values.

This color palette is also used worldwide in PCs with 100% VGA and compatible graphic systems. Fig. 5.27 shows a block diagram of the color palette.

### 5.3.3 The Most Important Microprocessor Types

SAB 8085
  8-bit microprocessor, 3 or 5 MHz
SAB 8088
  8-bit microprocessor, 16 bit, 5, 10, 12 MHz
SAB 80188
  8-bit microprocessor, 16 bit,
  5, 8, 10, 12 MHz
SAB 8086
  16-bit microprocessor, 5, 8, 10, 12 MHz
SAB 80186
  16-bit microprocessor, 8 MHz
SAB 80286
  16-bit microprocessor, 6, 8, 10, 12.5 and
  16 MHz

### 5.3.4 The Most Important Peripheral Chips

SAB 2793
  Floppy disk controller
SAB 8155
  256 byte RAM, input/output channels,
  timers
SAB 8237
  DMA controller
SAB 8256A
  Multifunction chip MUART, 3 or 5 MHz

SAB 8259A
  Interrupt controller, 3 or 8 MHz
SAB 8282A
  8-bit address bus driver
SAB 8283A
  Inverting 8-bit data bus driver
SAB 8284B
  Clock generator for 10 MHz SAB 8086
SAB 8286A
  Bidirectional 8-bit data bus driver
SAB 8287A
  Inverting bidirectional 8-bit data bus
  driver
SAB 8288A
  Bus controller for SAB 8086/8088
SAB 8289
  Bus arbiter for SAB 8086/88
SAB 82258A
  Advanced DMA controller
SAB 82284
  Clock generator for SAB 80286 and
  82258, 8 MHz
SAB 82288
  Bus controller for SAB 80286 and 82258,
  8 MHz
SAB 82510
  Token bus controller
SAB 82511
  Token bus modem
SAB 82556
  Universal interface chip
  (currently in preparation)
SAB 72201A
  Serial multiprotocol communication
  controller
SAB 82CXX
  The peripheral chips 8237/51/53/54/55/59
  in CMOS
SAB 82820
  Serial communication controller (HSCC)
SAB 82C206
  LSI PC chip
SAB 82C171
  Color palette

133

## 5.4 The 32-Bit RISC Processor MIPS

More and more RISC (reduced instruction set computers) are being offered on the market. How do they differ from the conventional CISC (complex instruction set computers)?

*Reduced instruction set*
Surveys conducted during the last few years have shown that the high-level language programs compiled by compilers use only approx. 20 % of the instruction set of the CISC programs surveyed in 80 % of all cases.

If, when selecting the instructions for a processor, one restricts oneself to a few simple and frequently used instructions and also ensures that all important instructions not contained in this instruction selection can be simulated by sequences of the selected instructions which are as short as possible, one obtains a clear and manageable instruction set. If one assumes that most of these instructions require the same number of clock cycles for execution and that the command sequencer can be implemented largely without microcode, it is possible to develop far simpler computer structures. These computer require less chip area, permit higher processing speeds and are simpler and safer to verify.

The chip area saved can be used for implementing particularly time-critical components such as the memory management or cache control unit.

*Instruction format*
A fixed instruction format and only a few addressing modes simplify instruction decoding. It can be "wired" directly and requires no microcode.

*Load/store architecture*
The main memory is accessed only with simple load and store instructions. The other instruction types refer exclusively to a register

set integrated in the CPU (central processing unit). This permits simple addressing of 32/32-bit general purpose registers.

*Architecture-supporting optimizing compilers*
The relatively few and simply structured instructions and pipelining require supporting and optimizing compilers (complex function can be generated from simple instructions. The register assignment must be optimized and the pipeline must be operated as efficiently as possible with instruction sequences). Even though RISC programs require approx. 30 % more instructions than comparable CISC programs, the computing power is higher for many systems implemented since, owing to parallel processing of instructions, a far lower ratio of instructions to number of clock cycles can be achieved than is the case with CISC programs.

*History*
The first RISC architecture was developed by IBM in 1975. In the early 80s, RISC concepts were also developed at Berkeley University and Stanford University. There are two development trends: The pure (puristic) RISC processor architectures of universities and the commercially usable systems of industry. The high costs of hardware and software development lead to endeavors to standardize the systems.

The concept of the SAB R3000 developed by MIPS originated in the MIPS project of Stanford University, initiated by Prof. Hennessy in 1981. Today, it is being followed up by Siemens, NEC and IDT, Performance and LSI Logic.

### 5.4.1 The Instruction Set of the SAB R2000 and SAB R3000

The SAB R2000 is software-compatible with the SAB R3000. However, the R3000 can operate with a higher clock frequency, can operate a larger external cache memory and is supplied in a different package.

Table 5.3    Instruction types of the SAB R3000

| OP | Description |
|----|-------------|
| *Load/store instructions* | |
| LB | Load Byte |
| LBU | Load Byte Unsigned |
| LH | Load Halfword |
| LHU | Load Halfword Unsigned |
| LW | Load Word |
| LWL | Load Word Left |
| LWR | Load Word Right |
| SB | Store Byte |
| SH | Store Halfword |
| SW | Store Word |
| SWL | Store Word Left |
| SWR | Store Word Right |
| | |
| *Arithmetic instructions (ALU immediate)* | |
| ADDI | Add Immediate |
| ADDIU | Add Immediate Unsigned |
| SLTI | Set on Less Than Immediate |
| SLTIU | Set on Less Than Immediate Unsigned |
| ANDI | AND Immediate |
| ORI | OR Immediate |
| XORI | Exclusive OR Immediate |
| LUI | Load Upper Immediate |
| | |
| *Arithmetic instructions (3-operand, register-type)* | |
| ADD | Add |
| ADDU | Add Unsigned |
| SUB | Subtract |
| SUBU | Subtract Unsigned |
| SLT | Set on Less Than |
| SLTU | Set on Less Than Unsigned |
| AND | AND |
| OR | OR |
| XOR | Exclusive OR |
| NOR | NOR |
| | |
| *Shift instructions* | |
| SLL | Shift Left Logical |
| SRL | Shift Right Logical |
| SRA | Shift Right Arithmetic |
| SLLV | Shift Left Logical Variable |
| SRLV | Shift Right Logical Variable |
| SRAV | Shift Right Arithmetic Variable |
| | |
| *Special instructions* | |
| SYSCALL | System Call |
| BREAK | Break |

| OP | Description |
|----|-------------|
| *Multiply/Divide instructions* | |
| MULT | Multiply |
| MULTZ | Multiply Unsigned |
| DIV | Divide |
| DIVU | Divide Unsigned |
| MFHI | Move From HI |
| MTHI | Move To HI |
| MFLO | Move From LO |
| MTLO | Move To LO |
| | |
| *Jump and branch instructions* | |
| J | Jump |
| JAL | Jump And Link |
| JR | Jump to Register |
| JALR | Jump And Link Register |
| BEQ | Branch on Equal |
| BNE | Branch on Not Equal |
| BLEZ | Branch on Less than or Equal to Zero |
| BGTZ | Branch on Greater Than Zero |
| BLTZ | Branch on Less Than Zero |
| BGEZ | Branch on Greater than or Equal to Zero |
| BLTZAL | Branch on Less Than Zero And Link |
| BGEZAL | Branch on Greater than or Equal to Zero And Link |
| | |
| *Coprocessor instructions* | |
| LWCz | Load Word from Coprocessor |
| SWCz | Store Word to Coprocessor |
| MTCz | Move To Coprocessor |
| MFCz | Move From Coprocessor |
| CTCz | Move Control To Coprocessor |
| CFCz | Move Control From Coprocessor |
| COPz | Coprocessor Operation |
| BCzT | Branch on Coprocessor z True |
| BCzF | Branch on Coprocessor z False |
| | |
| *System control processor (CPO) instructions* | |
| MTCO | Move to CPO |
| MFCO | Move from CPO |
| TLBR | Read indexed TLB entry |
| TLBWI | Write Indexed TLB entry |
| TLBWTR | Write Random TLB entry |
| TLBP | Probe TLB for matching entry |
| RFE | Restore From Exception |

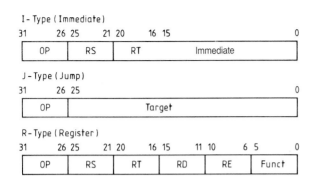

Fig. 5.28
Instruction formats of the
SAB R3000
(Source: G. Kane,
MIPS R2000 RISC architecture)

The most important characteristics of the instruction set are as follows:

▷ Simple register-to-register operations
▷ Simple and uniform instruction format
▷ Uniform data format
▷ Coprocessor auxiliary instructions
▷ Main memory access only via load/store operations

The 74 instructions of the reduced SAB R3000 instruction set can be subdivided into six groups (see Table 5.3):

▷ Load/store instructions
for transferring data between the internal registers and the memory
Instruction type = "immediate"

▷ Arithmetic instructions:
Arithmetic, logical and shift instructions
Instruction type = "immediate register"

▷ Jump and branch instructions for program branching and for calling
subroutines
Instruction type = "register, immediate or jump"

▷ Coprocessor instructions
for supporting operation with coprocessors
Instruction type = "immediate"

▷ Coprocessor O instructions
for controlling the "on-chip" coprocessor
(system control processor) which, amongst

other things, performs the memory management and exception handling function
Instruction type = "register"

▷ Special instructions
for generating software interrupts (traps)
Instruction type = "register"

The instruction set of the SAB R3000 uses three identical 32-bit formats with constant ranges (see Fig. 5.28)

### 5.4.2 CPU Architecture

The RISC CPU architecture directly illustrates the instruction set. The main points of emphasis are instruction execution in one machine cycle, internal registers and instruction pipeline.

The uniformity and similarity of the instruction formats are the precondition for fast instruction execution via the instruction pipeline of the RISC architecture.

Data transfer within the internal register array is exceedingly fast. This applies in particular to the register-register operation. In order to utilize the internal register structure as well as possible, the compiler attempts to minimize the number of memory access operations. It attempts to keep all variables required in one period, wherever possible, in the register simultaneously. Since most registers are also implemented as "general purpose" registers (operand, address, index and

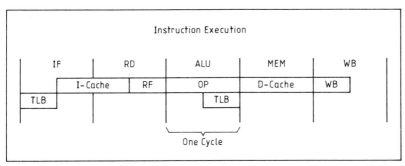

Fig. 5.29   The five pipeline steps (source: as for Fig. 5.28)

stack point registers etc.), this results in complex optimization tasks for the compiler.

The instruction pipeline principle also speeds up the instruction execution time. Pipelining means simultaneously instruction processing. Instruction execution is disected into five time slots on the SAB R3000. Each time slot corresponds to one execution phase. Whilst the first instruction is already in the fifth execution phase, the fourth phase of the second instruction, the third phase of the third instruction, the second phase of the fourth instruction and the first phase of the fifth instruction are being processed at the same time (Fig. 5.29). Conditional branch

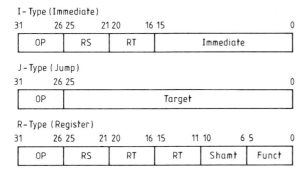

Where:

| OP | Is a 6-bit operation code |
|---|---|
| RS | Is a 5-bit source register specifier |
| RT | Is a 5-bit target (source/destination) register or branch condition |
| Immediate | Is a 16-bit immediate, branch displacement or address displacement |
| Target | Is a 26-bit jump target address |
| RD | Is a 5-bit destination register specifier |
| Shamt | Is a 5-bit shift amount |
| Funct | Is a 6-bit function field |

Fig. 5.30
Instruction processing in the pipeline
(source: as for Fig. 5.28)

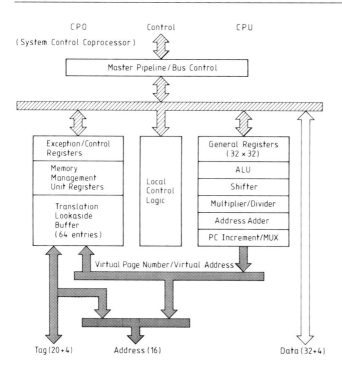

Fig. 5.31
Function blocks of the
SAB R3000

and load/store instructions may delay the pipeline sequence. These delays are also minimized by optimising compilers.

The five instruction steps are as follows:

▷ IF: 'Instruction fetch' (instruction cache, TLB = translation lookaside buffer)
▷ RD: 'Read' (RF = register fetch)
▷ ALU: 'Operation perform'
▷ MEM: 'Access memory' (data cache)
▷ WB: 'Write Back'

Each part of the instruction is approximately one clock cycle long. Thus, one instruction execution is almost completed with each clock cycle. The identical instruction structure permits a uniformly fast instruction throughput (Fig. 5.30). The compiler attempts to optimize instruction flow so that the pipeline steps are always fully utilized.
The SAB R3000 (see Fig. 5.31) which can operate up to four coprocessors simultaneously

contains an "on-chip" system control coprocessor (CPO) with a "memory management" unit and a translation-lookaside buffer (TLB). It can operate up to 64 tasks, whereby a virtual address space of 2 GByte is available to each task.

### 5.4.3 System Architecture

The difference between instruction and data storage and the mode of addressing of I/O chips presents special requirements to the system developer. If the performance of the RISC is fully utilized, high-speed cache memories are required for the frequently used instructions or data respectively. The slower main memory should be accessed as little as possible.

For this reason, the SAB R3000 supports an external instruction and data cache of 4 x 256 kbyte each (Fig. 5.32). Since a cache stores

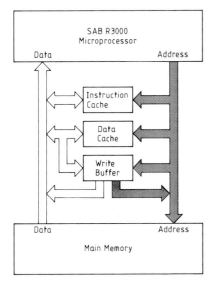

SAB R3000
Microprocessor

Data — Address

Instruction Cache

Data Cache

Write Buffer

Data — Address

Main Memory

Fig. 5.32 Memory structure of the SAB R3000

data only temporarily, all data must also be stored in the main memory. The write buffer accepts the data and addresses output by the CPU and stores them in the far slower main memory.

The coprocessors assume part-tasks of the central CPU, for example floating-point arithmetic operations. The floating-point arithmetic coprocessor SAB R3020 also has a pipeline structure.

### 5.4.4 Compiler

A RISC processor can also be programmed with Assembler. However, the various, complex optimization rules would make this appear advisable only in exceptional cases. Normally, a suitable high-level language (HLL) is used for programming.

MIPS compilers are available for the following languages:

C
PASCAL
FORTRAN
COBOL
ADA
PL/I
LISP

The efficiency and performance of the RISC processor can be used optimally only if a program code optimized for it is available. This can be obtained only with an optimizing compiler tailored to meet the needs of the RISC processor.

### 5.4.5 Characteristics of the MIPS Chip Family

*SAB R2000A, 32-bit RISC processor*
The essential characteristics are as follows:

▷ RISC integer CPU
▷ Load/store architecture
▷ On-chip memory management
▷ On-chip cache control for external instruction and data caches (each 4 x 64 kbyte)
▷ On-chip translation lookaside buffer (fully associative, 64 entries)
▷ Virtual address space 64 x 2 Gbyte
▷ 5 pipeline steps
▷ Supports up to 3 coprocessors
▷ Supports multiprocessor systems
▷ Clock-instruction ratio 1.2
▷ 28,500 dhrystones
▷ Extensive software basis
▷ Average 12 x VAX11/780 (with 16.67 MHz)
▷ Compatible with the data and address conventions of the processors 68 000, IBM 370, NS 32000 and DEC VAX
▷ All operations are 32-bit operations
▷ 32 general-purpose registers (32-bit wide)
▷ Fully compatible with all R2000 MIPS processors of other manufacturers

*SAB R2010A, 32/64-bit floating point coprocessor*
The essential characteristics are as follows:

▷ Fully complies with the specifications of the ANSI/IEEE 754-1985, IEEE Standards for binary floating-point arithmetic

139

▷ All operations are 64-bit operations
▷ Sixteen 64-bit floating-point number registers
▷ 32-bit status and control register
▷ Load/store architecture
▷ Single-cycle load/store instructions
▷ Single and double computing precision
▷ 6 pipeline steps
▷ Smooth integration of the floating-point and fixed-point instruction set
▷ 4.6 linpack single precision MFlops (at 16.67 MHz)
▷ 14 M whetstones (at 16.67 MHz)
▷ Fully compatible with all R2010 MIPS processors of other manufacturers

*SAB R3000, 32-bit RISC processor*
The essential characteristics are as follows:

▷ RISC integer CPU
▷ Load/store architecture
▷ On-chip memory management
▷ On-chip cache control for external instruction and data caches (each 4 x 256 kbyte)
▷ On-chip translation lookaside buffer (fully associative, 64 entries)
▷ Virtual address space 64 x 2 Gbyte – 5 pipeline steps
▷ Supports up to 3 coprocessors
▷ Supports multiprocessor systems
▷ Clock-instruction ratio 1.2
▷ 44,000 dhrystones
▷ Extensive software basis
▷ Average 20 x VAX11/780 Mips (with 25 MHz)
▷ Compatible with the data and address conventions of the processors 68 000, IBM 370, NS 32000 and DEC VAX
▷ All operations are 32-bit operations
▷ 32 general-purpose registers (32-bit wide)
▷ Fully compatible with all R3000 MIPS processors of other manufacturers

*SAB R3010, 32/64-bit floating*
*point coprocessor*
The essential characteristics are as follows:

▷ Fully complies with the specifications of the ANSI/IEEE 754-1985, IEEE Standard for binary floating-point arithmetic
▷ All operations are 64-bit operations
▷ Sixteen 64-bit floating-point number registers
▷ 32-bit status and control register
▷ Load/store architecture
▷ Single-cycle load/store instructions
▷ Single and double computing precision
▷ 6 pipeline steps
▷ Smooth integration of the floating-point and fixed-point instruction set
▷ 7 linpack single precision MFlops (at 25 MHz)
▷ 17 M whetstones (at 25 MHz)
▷ Fully compatible with all R3010 MIPS processors of other manufacturers

## 5.5 8-Bit Microcontrollers

Ideally, microcontrollers are single-chip systems. All components required for the system are integrated on one chip: computer kernel, instruction, data memories and input/output. Microcontroller applications permit economically optimum solutions in the most favorable case.

The most widespread 4-bit microcontroller applications are pocket calculators, wrist watches and cameras. 8-bit microcontrollers are used primarily in industrial, consumer and automotive electronics. 16-bit microcontrollers are also used to an increasing extent in industrial and automotive electronics as well as in data processing and communication applications.

Up until 10 years ago, one spoke of microcomputers. The designation microcontrollers is intended to emphasize the special suitability for control tasks. But since the limits between microcontrollers and processors are becoming more and more fluid, we nowadays also speak of "embedded control".

Microprocessors and microcontrollers are programmable chips modelled on main frames. Computer systems implemented with microprocessors are requiring more and more integrated chips; besides the microprocessor which contains the arithmetic unit, they also require instruction and data memories and peripheral chips. In the minimal case, microcomputers make possible an operable system with only one chip. All absolutely necessary system components are integrated in the microcontroller.

The limits between microprocessors and microcontrollers are becoming more and more indistinct. Even though a single-chip system, if it is economically feasible, should always be endeavoured, many microcontrollers are operated as microprocessors. The integrated functions frequently do not suffice for the tasks to be performed. On the other hand, more and more peripheral functions are being integrated in the microprocessors. One example of this is the SAB 80186 as compared with the SAB 8086.

Five to six years ago, it was still possible to list the number of applications on two pages. By now, the list of applications is so numerous that we must content ourselves with specifying the main fields of application.

▷ Industrial electronics
In particular measurement systems, control systems and automation engineering, motor control systems etc.

▷ Consumer electronics
The main points of emphasis are TV sets and video recorders.

▷ Automotive electronics
Engine management systems, transmission control systems and instrument control systems in addition to air conditioning are the central applications.

▷ Data processing
Microcontrollers are used in virtually all types of peripheral devices. They manage the PC keyboards, data storage devices and communication links and perform minor decentralized tasks in input/output control.

▷ Leisure and household electronics
Chess computers, home weather stations, radio-controlled clocks, typewriters, washing machines and sawing machines, oven ranges and heating control systems are a few obvious applications.

▷ Medical engineering
More and more microcontrollers in medical equipment are automating measurement, monitoring and dosage tasks.

### 5.5.1 The SAB 8051 Family

In 1980/81, Intel marketed the 8051 as the successor to the 8048. As is always the case with successful products, there are a large number of different versions. Since then, over 100 million of these chips and chips based on them have been sold. Fig. 5.33 shows the sales trend of the 8051 MC family. Fig. 5.34 shows the family tree and Fig. 5.35 shows the second sources.

All members of the SAB 8051 Siemens family are based upon the computer kernel of the SAB 8051. They are thus software-com-

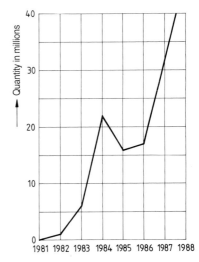

Fig. 5.33
Sales trends of the 8051 family

patible with the SAB 8051. Table 5.4 shows the basic types. There are different package versions and temperature ranges.

Fig. 5.36 shows the logic symbol and Fig. 5.37 shows the block diagram of the SAB 8051.

The essential characteristics of the SAB 8051 are as follows:

▷ 8-bit CPU
▷ 1.2 to 12/16/20 MHz oscillator frequency
▷ 1 µs instruction cycle time at 12 MHz oscillator frequency
▷ 8-bit multiplication and division each in 4 instruction cycles
▷ Bit-processing instructions by Boolean processor
▷ 5 interrupt sources with 2 priority levels

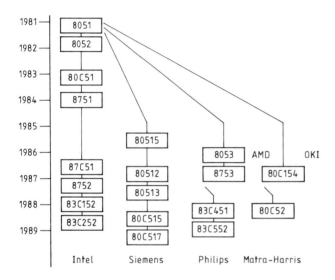

Fig. 5.34
Family tree of
the 8051 family

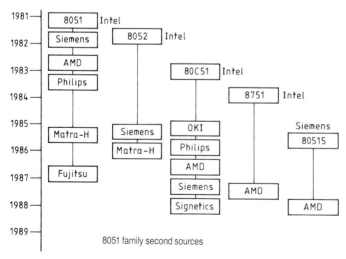

Fig. 5.35
Second sources of
the 8051 family

142

▷ 4 kbyte internal ROM, can be expanded externally up to 64 kbyte
▷ 128 byte internal RAM, can also be expanded externally up to 64 kbyte
▷ Standby mode for internal RAM
▷ 128 directly addressable bits in the RAM

▷ 21 directly addressable special-function registers
▷ 48 directly addressable bits in the special-function registers
▷ Serial, full-duplex interface with 4 operating modes and variable baud rates

Table. 5.4   The Siemens SAB 8051 family

| Type | Version | Oscillator frequency [MHz] | RAM [byte] | ROM [kbyte] |
|------|---------|---------------------------|------------|-------------|
| 8051/C51 | ROM version | 12/16 | 128 | 4 |
| 8031/C31 | Non-ROM version | 12/16 | 128 | – |
| 8052/C52 | ROM version | 12/16 | 256 | 8 |
| 8032/C32 | Non-ROM version | 12/16 | 256 | – |
| 80515/C515 | ROM version | 12 | 256 | 8 |
| 80535/C535 | Non-ROM version | 12 | 256 | – |
| 80C517 | ROM version | 12 | 256 | 8 |
| 80C537 | Non-ROM version | 12 | 256 | – |

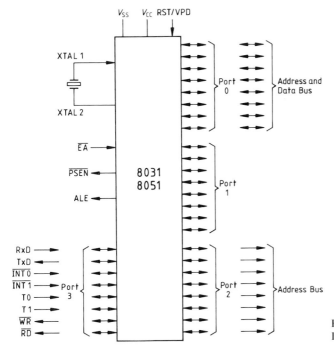

Fig. 5.36
Logic symbol of the SAB 8051

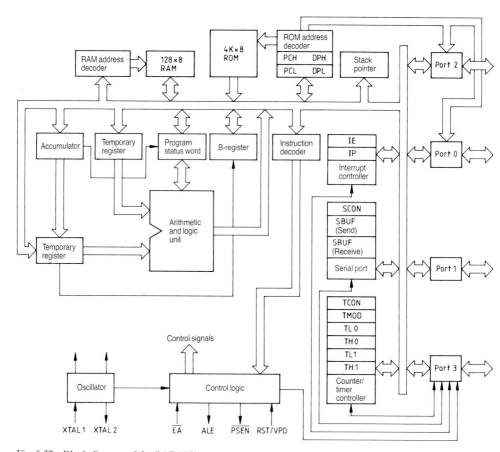

Fig. 5.37  Block diagram of the SAB 8051

▷ 8085 compatible bus interface
▷ Two 16-bit counters/timers
▷ DIL 40 and PLCC 44 packages
▷ Temperature ranges 0 to 70, −40 to 85 and −40 to 110 °C
▷ NMOS/CMOS versions
▷ Idle and power-down modes in the CMOS version

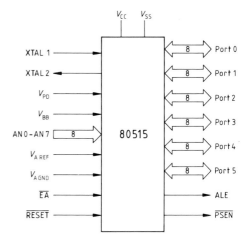

Fig. 5.38    Logic symbol of the SAB 80515

*SAB 8052*

The SAB 8052 corresponds to the 8051. The additional characteristics are as follows:

▷ 5 new special-function registers
▷ ROM area doubled to 8 kbyte and RAM area doubled to 256 byte
▷ 1 additional 16-bit counter/timer with re-load and capture modes
▷ An additional interrupt source (timer 2)
▷ Improved serial interface

*SAB 80515*

Fig. 5.38 shows the logic symbol and Fig. 5.39 shows the block diagram of the SAB 80515.

These are the characteristics which the SAB 80515 includes, in addition to the 8051 characteristics:

▷ System clock output (fosc/12)
▷ 8 kbyte internal ROM, can be expanded externally up to 64 kbyte
▷ 256 byte internal RAM, can be expanded externally up to 64 kbyte
▷ 12 interrupt sources and 4 priority levels
▷ Own baud rate generator for 4800 and 9600 baud at 12 MHz oscillator frequency
▷ A third 16-bit counter/timer – Four 16-bit reload/capture input/compare output functions
▷ 16-bit watchdog timer
▷ Analog-to-digital converter with 8-bit resolution
    8 multiplexed analog inputs Sample and hold time 5 µs (at 12 MHz)
    15 µs conversion time
        (including sample time at 12 MHz) programmable reference voltages for achieving up to 10-bit resolution
▷ 68 pin PLCC package

*SAB 80C517*

The SAB 80C517 includes all functions of the SAB 80C51. Fig. 5.40 shows the logic symbol and Fig. 5.41 shows the block diagram of the SAB 80C517.

Extended and additional characteristics of the SAB 80C517, by comparison with the 80C51:

▷ 80C51 and 80C515 upward-compatible
▷ RAM/ROM and external memory as on the 80515
▷ Extended arithmetic unit
▷ Division 32/16-bit in 6 µs
    Division 16/16-bit in 4 µs
    Multiplication 16 x 16-bit in 4 µs
    (at 12 MHz oscillator frequency in each case)
▷ 8 16-bit data pointers for external memory access
▷ Extended watchdog functions, oscillator watchdog
▷ An additional serial interface
▷ 9 ports with 56 digital inputs/outputs and 12 digital or analog inputs

145

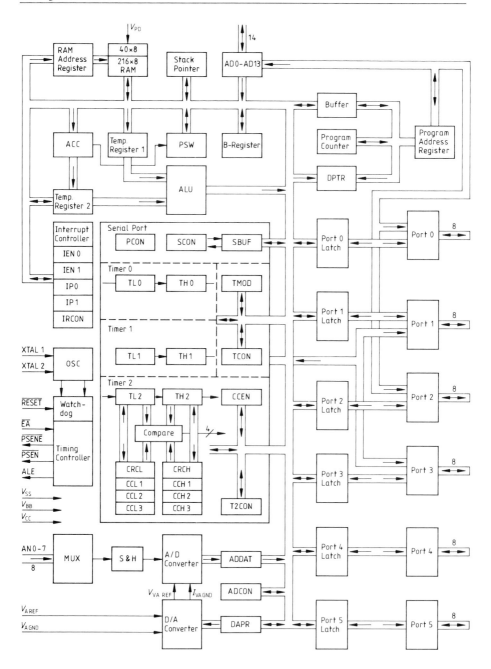

Fig. 5.39   Block diagram of the SAB 80515

▷ 5 16-bit timers (3 counters/timers, watch-dog and compare)
▷ Up to 21 pulse width-modulatable output signals with up to 166 ns resolution
▷ A/D converter with programmable reference voltages, 8-bit resolution and 15 s conversion time as on the 80515
▷ 14 interrupt sources with 4 priority levels
▷ 84-pin PLCC package

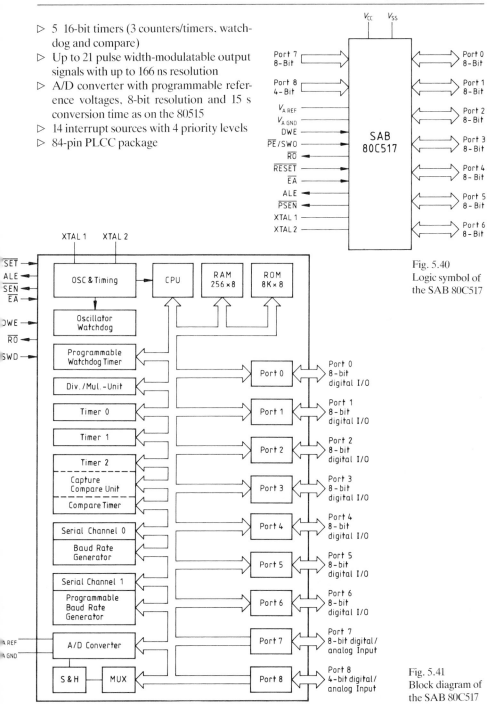

Fig. 5.40
Logic symbol of
the SAB 80C517

Fig. 5.41
Block diagram of
the SAB 80C517

## 5.6 The 16-bit Microcontroller SAB 80C166

Whilst the Siemens 8-bit microcontrollers are based upon the 8051 computer kernel, the SAB 80C166 contains an original Siemens processor architecture (Fig. 5.42). The periphery concept which has been successful on the 8-bit microcontrollers has been adopted and extended for the 80C166.

The essential performance features of the SAB 80C166 are as follows:

▷ High efficiency and performance for real-time applications
▷ Fast CPU data throughput
▷ Extremely fast response to interrupts
▷ Largely autonomous periphery functions
▷ Basis of a flexible family concept for the 1990s (SAB 80C16X)
▷ Expandable RAM/ROM area
▷ Modular periphery design, simple periphery interface

*CPU architecture*

▷ 16-bit CPU
▷ 20 MHz CPU clock (40 MHz crystal)
▷ Instruction cycle time for most commands is 100 ns
▷ Register architecture
▷ Registers and register banks can be freely configured within the entire internal RAM
▷ Flexible and fast interrupt system with maximum interrupt response time of 500 ns (with internal ROM and 40 MHz crystal)
▷ Interrupt system expandable up to 60 interrupt sources and vectors
▷ 16 freely programmable priority levels
▷ Hardware-trap functions
▷ 8-channel peripheral event controller for simple interrupt processing

*Instruction set*

▷ Flexible addressing modes
▷ Bit, byte and word-data types

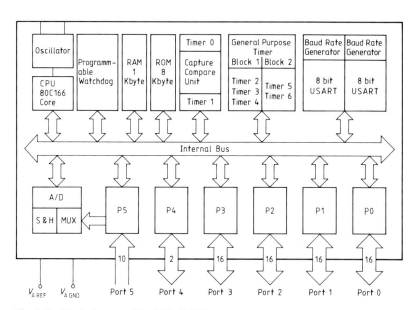

Fig. 5.42   Block diagram of the SAB 80C166

▷ Multiplication (16×16-bit) in 500 ns and division (32/16-bit) in 1 μs

▷ Multiple shifting and rotation in one machine cycle

▷ Optimized Boolean arithmetic and bit processing

▷ Register bank switchover (≙ context switch) in 100 ns

*Characteristics*
Memories:
8 kbyte ROM on-chip
1 kbyte RAM on-chip
256 kbyte address range
8 or 16-bit multiplexed data/address bus
16-bit non-multiplex mode

Watchdog:
Programmable 16-bit timer

A/D converter:
10-bit resolution
10 input channels
10 μs conversion time
Many different channel scanning operating modes

Serial interface:
Two independent sync./async. serial channels, programmable
asynchronously up to 625 kBaud and programmable
synchronously up to 2.5 MBaud.

Timers:
Five 16-bit up/down timers/counters
Diverse operating modes
200/400 ns resolution
Reload/capture functions

CAPCOM unit:
Unit for pulse-width modulation/Event measurement

Sixteen 16-bit compare/capture registers
Two 16-bit reload timers
(400 ns resolution)

Port:
76 bit-addressable I/O ports
High-impedance inputs

Package:
Plastic quad flat pack 100 (PQFP-100)

Temperature range: −40 to +110 °C

Availability:
Customer samples Q1/90

## 5.7 Memories

Three factors essentially determine the outstanding importance of semiconductor memories:

▷ The constantly and rapidly rising storage capacity. Although 1 kbit memory chips were the ultimate 20 years ago, nowadays 1 Mbit memories are standard.

▷ The continually increasing quantities. This year, half a billion 1 Mbit memory chips will probably be produced.

▷ The demand which is continually growing faster and faster and which is growing faster than the supply.

This trend will also continue and will be even more pronounced in the next few years. The capacity of the chips is growing to 4, 16 and 64 Mbit. A decline in demand is not anticipated.

The reasons for this trend today are related to the ever-increasing popularity of PCs, the increasing introduction of 32- bit processors, workstations and larger computer systems and the programs which have more and more capabilities. Programs for artificial intelligence (AI) will increase demand still further.

### 5.7.1 Memory Types

Most memories are RAMs (= random access memories). We distinguish still further between dynamic RAMs (DRAMs) and static RAMs (SRAMs).

In the case of ROMs (= read only memories), the memory contents are written in either mechanically or electrically as early as the production stage. Programmable read-only memories (PROMs = programmable ROMs) are programmed by the user him or herself. There are ROMs which can be erased electrically or with ultraviolet light (EEPROMs and EPROMs).

We shall discuss the static and dynamic memories in greater detail at a later point.

*Static memories*
On static memories, the storage cells are formed by two feedback inverters (bistable circuit), whereby logical information item "0" or "1" is assigned to the two stable states. In the block diagram in Fig. 5.43, the two load resistors have been replaced by two transistors T3 and T4 with fixed bias owing to the less space required. The transistors T5 and T6 serve to select the memory locations. If they are rendered forward-biased via the row-select line, the information can be recognized when reading by the potential difference of the column lines, whilst the bistable circuit is set to the required state via these lines when writing. The stored information is retained for as long as the operating voltage lies within its specified range.

Static, byte-oriented memories are being used to an increasing extent in small computer systems for control tasks. The CMOS-RAMs SAB 81C51 and 80C52 are examples of this. Their most important characteristics are as follows:

▷ CMOS technology
▷ 256 or 512 x 8 bit
▷ Multiplexed address and data bus
▷ Tristate address/data inputs
▷ Power consumption in standby mode 1 A, in operation 500 A, typical value
▷ Supply voltage range from 2.5 to 6 V
▷ Data buffering in standby mode 1 V

These RAMs are particularly well suited for data buffering in microcontroller systems. Fig. 5.44 shows a block diagram of the SAB 81C51 in a microcontroller system.

*Dynamic memories*
On dynamic memory elements, the information is stored as a charge in a capacitor. The basic circuit diagram shown in Fig. 5.45 represents today's conventional single-transistor cell on which the information appears as an abrupt change in potential on the data line, dependent upon the capacitor charge, as

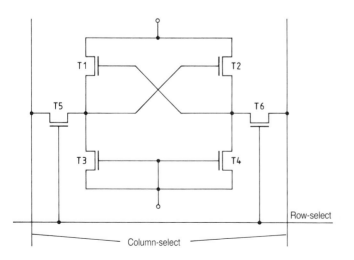

Fig. 5.43
Bistable circuit in the static memory

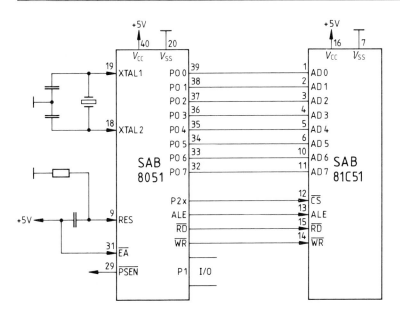

Fig. 5.44   Static RAM with microcontroller

soon as transistor T1 is rendered forward-biased via the row-select line.

Owing to the inevitable leakage currents, the stored information (capacitor charge) must be refreshed periodically. Refreshing is carried out in the chip by read cycles at the refresh addresses, whereby the entire row is refreshed when a memory element is activated. Since discharge of the capacitor charge occurs faster at high temperatures, observance of the minimum refresh time (usual value: 4 ms with 256 kbit and 16 ms with 1 Mbit) must be ensured, particularly at the maximum permitted operating temperature. Very large cell arrays per chip can be implemented owing to the low circuit complexity.

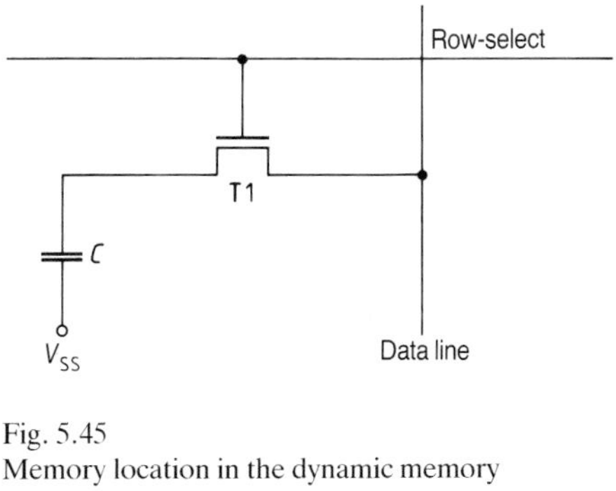

The advantages of static memories over dynamic memories are related to the more simple connection to the processor chips. Their disadvantage is the substantially larger chip area by comparison with dynamic memories. This is reflected in the maximum possible capacity and in the price.

Figs. 5.46 to 5.48 show the pin assignment, block diagram and block diagram in test mode for chip HYB 511000A-70/-80/-10 as an example of a dynamic memory.

Fig. 5.45
Memory location in the dynamic memory

151

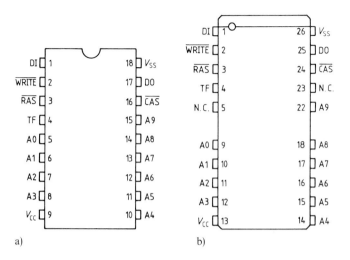

Fig. 5.46
Pin assignment of the
HYB511000A-70/80/-10
a) Package P-DIP-18-T,
b) Package P-SOJ-26/20

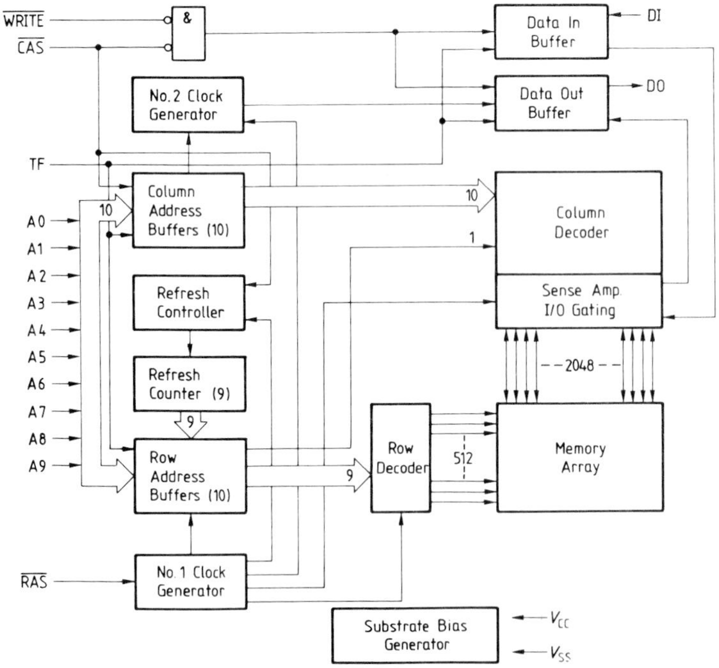

Fig. 5.47
Block diagram of the SAB HYB511000A

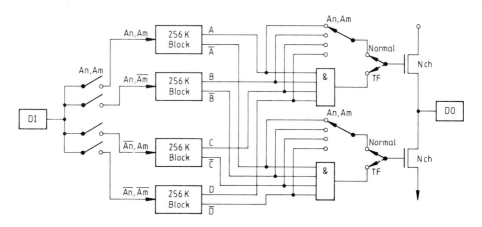

Fig. 5.48   Block diagram of the SAB HYB511000A in test mode

### 5.7.2  Memory Technologies

Semiconductor memories are subdivided into two groups on the basis of their manufacturing methods (see also the introduction to technology in the first chapter):

*Bipolar memories*
Bipolar memory chips consist of transistors incorporating TTL (transistor-transistor logic) or ECL (emitter-coupled logic) technology. ECL chips have particularly high speeds. They are very user-friendly, owing to their compatibility with the relevant circuit technology. By contrast, they have a higher power consumption and a lower scale of integration. They can be used to advantage wherever a high operating speed is required.

*MOS memories*
MOS field-effect transistors incorporating N-channel technology are used on MOS memory chips. Circuits incorporating N-channel technology have a high LSI capacity, achieve a relatively high operating speed owing to the greater mobility of the charge carriers and are compatible with TTL technology. Overall, MOS technology provides all preconditions for favorably priced production of high-capacity memory chips owing to the simplicity of the structures, the small number of manufacturing steps and the electrical characteristics of CMOS transistors. MOS chips can be improved still further with the aid of various technology types.

*CMOS technology*
P- and N-channel transistors are integrated adjacently on the same substrate in complementary-channel technology. Since the transistors in one current path are always biased in opposite directions with CMOS circuits, this results in an extremely low bias current. However, other advantages such as higher switching speed and greater interference immunity are offset by a far more complex and expensive manufacturing technique.

In the case of high capacities, there is no alternative to CMOS technology.

### 5.7.3  Test Techniques

On semiconductor memory chips, operability may be impaired by a large number of technology and circuit-related fault and error mechanisms. This requires a tester with which any write/read cycles can be generated with non-linear addressing (test patterns). In addition, experience has shown that the testing effort increases with the number of bits. This great testing effort requires complex, computer-controlled test systems with programmable test pattern generators and adjustable time and voltage conditions, with which all critical operating states can be simulated.

So-called burn-in (Chapter 10 Quality) is carried out in order to guarantee the high required reliability of semiconductor memory chips. The chips are operated under increased voltage and temperature conditions ("burnt-in") in order to discover any weak points which could lead to premature failures in use.

### 5.7.4 Handling MOS Memory Chips

Even though MOS circuits are largely protected against destruction by electrostatic discharge (ESD) by suitable internal protection structures, they number amongst the electrostatic-sensitive devices (ESDs), as virtually all microelectronic circuits do, incidentally.

The following basic principle in particular must always be observed when handling them: Possible potential differences between the chip pins and all parts with which these pins come into contact must be equalized via high-impedance materials (approx. $10^6 - 10^9$ $\Omega$/cm) and brought to earth potential. Persons, workstations and machines etc. must be earthed in accordance with the applicable regulations.

# 6 Information Technology

Information technology means processing and transmitting or transferring data. We shall now discuss ISDN in greater detail, as an example from the diverse areas of telecommunications engineering.

Modern communication networks offer efficient and convenient services for voice, text and data communication. Suitable components for subscriber terminal equipment, switching and transmission systems are required in order to permit these services to be offered economically. Siemens has developed and manufactures a comprehensive range of integrated components for various applications in telecommunications engineerings. The following chapter describes their applications and technical features.

## 6.1 ISDN – Integrated Services Digital Network

Since the invention of telegraphy, various communication networks have been developed for voice, text and data communication in the field of telecommunications engineering.

In the Federal Republic of Germany to date, we have seen the introduction of the telephone network (for telephony, facsimile transmission, interactive videotex and data transmission), the Datex-L network (data transmission with line switching), the Datex-P network (data transmission with packet switching) and special networks.

But different communication networks mean additional effort and expenditure on maintenance and development of the networks for the network provider. The disadvantages for the subscribers are higher connection costs, different charge structures and different standards for the terminals.

Owing to this situation, endeavors were made worldwide to combine as many communication services as possible in one network.

In 1980, the CCITT, the most important international standardization commission in the field of telecommunications engineering, passed the following general recommendations for the integrated services digital telecommunications network ISDN:

ISDN is defined by:

▷ A transparently transmitted bit rate of 64 kbit/s between user terminals

▷ The basic access with 2 B-channels (speech/data channels) and a D-channel (signalling channel)

▷ Internationally standardized interfaces

▷ Several terminals can be connected to one basic access for the various ISDN services

▷ One call number for all ISDN services is available for each ISDN basic access

▷ Capability of subsequent integration of ISDN broadband services (bit rates higher than 64 kbit/s)

The abbreviation ISDN = integrated services digital network describes the essential features of the network. Integrated services network means that all services for voice, text and data communication are offered in one communication network with one network access. Digital network designates the digital transmission and switching of the information between the terminal equipment.

Concepts for implementing the ISDN were drawn up in various standardization commissions such as the CEPT, on the basis of the general recommendations.

Finally, the CCITT General Assembly of Torremolinos passed 35 recommendations in 1984, describing the network concept, the services in the ISDN, the interfaces and signaling.

One important factor in favor of the feasibility of the ISDN concept is the availability of low-cost, LSI circuits for coding and decoding, transmission, switching and signaling. Siemens has developed and manufactures a complete family of chips for the various ISDN fields of application.

## 6.2 Subscriber Line Connection in the ISDN

A transparent, digital link is established between the terminal equipment in the ISDN. The digital through-switching system between the exchanges, available in the digital telephone network is extended through to the terminal equipment in the ISDN.

The terminal equipment meets the following requirements:

▷ Digital signal transmission via the existing twin copper wires,

▷ Connection of several items of terminal equipment by a standardized user-network interface and

▷ A common call number for all terminals of various services connected to a user-network interface.

The ISDN subscriber line is subdivided into two complexes (Fig. 6.1): the S-interface and the U-interface.

The U-interface represents the subscriber line in the telephone network which starts in the ISDN exchange at the line termination LT and terminates at the subscriber in the network termination NT.

The S-interface is the interface of the subscriber line area. It is located between the network termination NT and the terminal equipment TE.

Two possibilities of network access are defined in the ISDN concept (Fig. 6.2).

The basic access BA serves to connect individual subscribers and small private branch exchanges PBX. Larger PBXs are connected to the ISDN with the primary access PA.

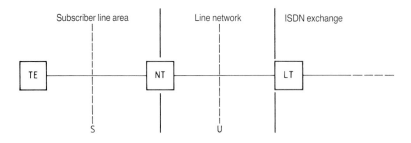

Fig. 6.1   ISDN interfaces

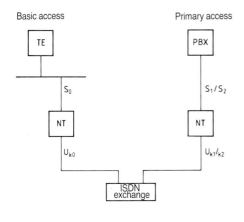

Basic access        Primary access

Fig. 6.2    ISDN network access

## 6.3 The Basic Access BA

The basic access in the subscriber line area has the $S_0$ interface and is connected to the exchange via the $U_{K0}$ interface (Fig. 6.3).

The basic access has two B-channels each with 64 kbit/s for information transmission. The D-channel with a transmission speed of 16 kbit/s is used to transmit signaling data, but also for transferring P-data (packet-oriented data).

*Basic access 2B+1D*
B – 64 kbit/s for voice, text and data
B – 64 kbit/s for voice, text and data
D – 16 kbit/s for signaling, P-data

The basic access consequently has a net data transfer rate of 144 kbit/s.

*$S_0$ interface*
The $S_0$ interface is a passive 4-wire bus, the S-bus. Up to eight terminals (Fig. 6.3) can be connected simultaneously to the S-bus. Terminals without $S_0$ interface standard can be connected to the S-bus via a terminal adapter TA. Since the basic access has two B-channels, two links to the network can be estab-

lished simultaneously. This permits the subscriber to change between the various ISDN services during a connection (mixed combination), or a subscriber can communicate simultaneously with two distant stations (multiple communication).

These two forms of communication make additional requirements of the ISDN exchanges since these exchanges must process and manage several connections from one call number simultaneously.

In addition to the 144 kbit/s net bit rate of the basic access, other data are transmitted on the S-bus for synchronization and monitoring purposes. The overall data transfer rate of the S-bus is 192 kbit/s.

*$U_{K0}$ interface*
The $U_{K0}$ interface is a 2-wire interface, i.e. the digital signals are transmitted bidirectionally and simultaneously on the existing twin copper wires. In addition to the 144 kbit/s net bit rate of the basic access, the $U_{K0}$ interface requires a further 16 kbit/s for synchronization and maintenance purposes.

The existing line network of the Deutsche Bundespost Telekom is designed for transmission of the telephone frequency band from 300 Hz to 3.4 kHz. The line loss increases greatly at frequencies greater than 4 kHz. This means that reflected and received signals on the transmit side have the same order of magnitude at the 4-wire/2-wire transition. Thus, the $U_{K0}$ interface requires a transmission method which can separate the received signals from the reflected signals.

The adaptive echo cancellation method (Fig. 6.4) has proven to be a suitable method. Adaptive echo compensation simulates the echo behavior of the line and determines the echo characteristic of the transmitted signals with transversal filters.

The resultant cancellation signal is subtracted from the received signal at the receive side so that the received signal, not subject to echo, is then available.

157

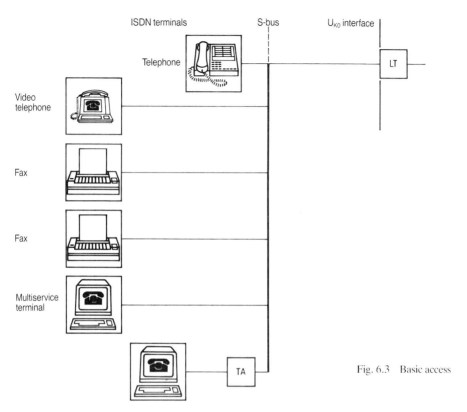

Fig. 6.3   Basic access

Since line repeaters are used for the $U_{K0}$ interface, the binary signal must be recoded to form a ternary signal with no DC component, i.e. a three-level signal. Important criteria for selection of the transmission code are the power density spectrum, the clock content, monitoring capability and the implementation expense and effort. A decision has been taken in favor of the 4B3T code (MMS43) for the area of the Deutsche Bundespost Telekom.

4B3T coding involves each set of 4 bits of the binary signal being combined and converted to a ternary signal. Consequently, the transmission speed of the $U_{K0}$ interface is reduced from 160 kbit/s to 120 kBaud.

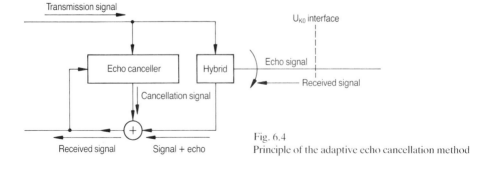

Fig. 6.4
Principle of the adaptive echo cancellation method

## 6.4 Components for the Basic Access

Siemens manufactures a complete family of modules which fully meets the ISDN interface standards for the ISDN basic access. The modular concept of the IOM interface (ISDN-oriented modular) permits the user to draw up the best configuration for his application. Fig. 6.5 shows the frame structure of the IOM interface, and Fig. 6.6 shows the modules for the basic access as they are used.

*S-bus interface circuit (SBC) PEB2080*
The BSC performs bit transmission (physical transmission) on the 4-wire S-bus be-

tween the network termination NT and the terminal equipment TE. The chip performs the transmit and receive functions, collision detection on the S-bus, setting facilities for the various applications and activation/deactivation of the S-bus. The maximum transmission range for point-to-multipoint links (up to 8 terminals can be connected to the S-bus with the SBC) is 150 m. The maximum range is 1 km with a point-to-point link. The SBC can be used both in terminals and in the network termination thanks to the IOM interface (Fig. 6.6). Fig. 6.7 shows a block diagram of the SBC.

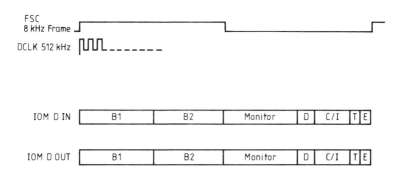

B1, B2 : Circuit Switched Voice / Data
D      : D Channel
C / I   : Command / Indicate

Fig. 6.5   Frame structure of the IOM interface

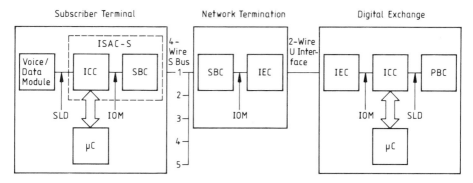

Fig. 6.6   Modules for the basic access

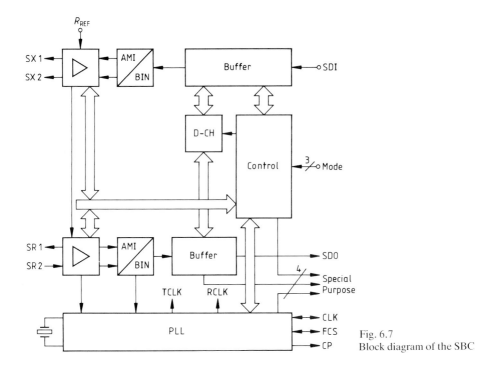

Fig. 6.7
Block diagram of the SBC

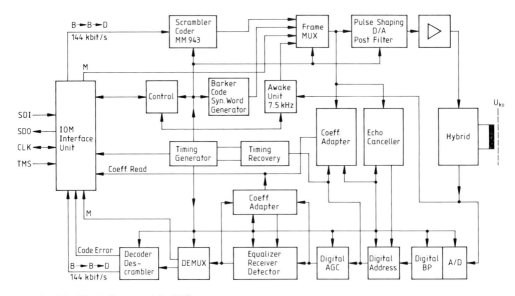

Fig. 6.8   Block diagram of the IEC

*ISDN echo cancellation circuit (IEC) PEB 2090*

The IEC (Fig. 6.8) performs the task of bit transmission (physical transmission) on the $U_{K0}$ interface. It operates on the basis of the adaptive echo cancellation method and achieves a transmission range of up to 9.5 km with one 0.6 mm cable. The main features of the IEC are as follows:

▷ Bidirectional data transmission on the $U_{K0}$ interface
▷ 4B3T coding/decoding
▷ Adaptive echo cancellation
▷ Clock and frame recuperation
▷ Programmable for NT and LT application
▷ IDM interface

*ISDN communication controller (ICC) PEB 2070*

The main task of the ICC (Fig. 6.9) is processing the D-channel protocol in the terminal equipment TE and in the line termination LT of the exchange. The ICC has an LAPD controller (LAPD: Link Access Procedure for D-channel) and a 64-byte FIFO buffer in the transmit and receive directions for this purpose. Dependent upon the programmed operating mode and the type of signaling frame, the ICC either processes the LAPD protocol independently or forwards it to a signaling controller.

One other function of the ICC is switching through the B-channels from the line side to the serial interface A or the SLD interface port.

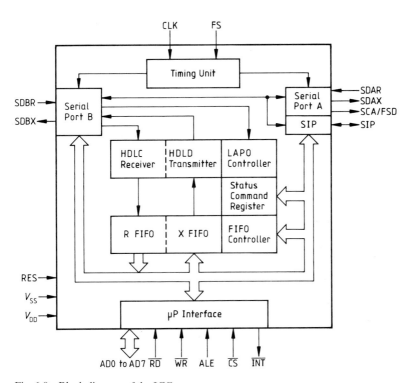

Fig. 6.9   Block diagram of the ICC

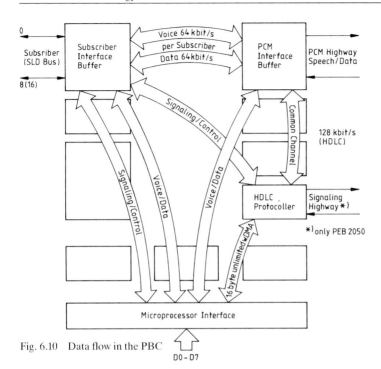

Fig. 6.10   Data flow in the PBC

*Peripheral board controller (PBC)*
*PEP 2050*

The PBC is used both on the SLMA (Subscriber Line Module Analog, see 6.2.8) and on the SLMD (Subscriber Line Module Digital, corresponding to the digital exchange in Fig. 6.6). The main task of the PBC is freely programmable time slot assignment of the up to 16 PCM input channels to the output-side PCM highway (24, 32, 48 or 64 time slots).

In addition, the PBC processes data flow for monitoring and signaling purposes. For this purpose, it can switch over the data stream between the lines of the subscriber line module analog, the PCM highway, the microprocessor interface and the signaling highway. Fig. 6.10 shows the data flow in the PBC. With the HDLC controller (HDLC: High-Level Data Link Control) for the signaling highway, the PBC can process a part of the HDLC protocol independently.

*Serial communications controller (HSCC)*
*SAB 82520*

The HSCC (Fig. 6.11) is a universally programmable chip for serial data transmission with two independently operating HDLC channels in each case. Dependent upon operating mode, the HDLC processes a large part of the X.25, LAPD/LAPB protocol without support from an additional microprocessor. The HSCC has various capabilities of clock generation and clock recuperation via a digital PLL for each channel, a baud rate generator and an oscillator.

The HSCC has a bus collision detection logic. By programming, the HSCC can also be used for data transmission in a PCM system (in a freely programmable time slot).

162

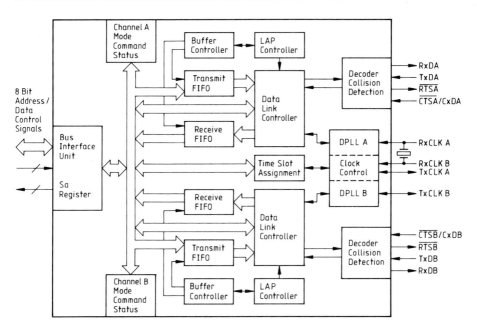

Fig. 6.11   Block diagram of the HSCC

## 6.5  The Primary Access PA

The primary access PA is defined in the ISDN concept as a network access for medium-sized and large private branch exchanges. By contrast with the basic access, only the point-to-point connection is permitted for the primary access (basic access: Point-to-multipoint via S-bus). Two possible methods of implementing this technically are scheduled owing to different developments in the individual countries.

The CEPT concept (in accordance with the European standardization commission Conférence Européene des Administration des Postes et des Télécommunications) shown in Fig. 6.12 and which is based on the PCM 30 system, is used in Europe and many other countries.

On the PCM 30 systems, 32 channels (time slots), each with 8 bits are transmitted in a time frame of 125 µs. The transmission speed of the PCM 30 system is consequently 2.048 Mbit/s. Only 30 of the 32 channels are available for information transmission (B-channels) and 1 channel is available for signaling as the D-channel. The first channel is used for synchronization and servicing purposes.

*CEPT primary access*
B1  − 64 kbit/s for voice, text, data

⋮

B30 − 64 kbit/s for voice, text, data
D   − 64 kbit/s for signaling

The T1 concept which is based on the PCM 24 system is used in the USA and Japan. The transmission speed of a PCM 24 system is 1.544 Mbit/s since it transmits 24 channels, each with 8 bit plus one F-bit in a 125 µs time frame. The F-bit in the PCM 24 system is used for synchronization and servicing purposes.

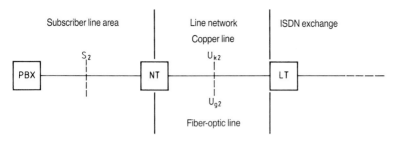

Fig. 6.12   Interfaces on the CEPT concept

*T1 primary access*
B1  −64 kbit/s for voice, text, data
⋮
B23 − 64 kbit/s for voice, text, data
D    − 64 kbit/s for signaling

The primary multiplex technique is, however, not only used as the ISDN network access but is also used to interconnect private branch exchanges, to connect local area networks (LANs) via gateways to private branch exchanges, to connect data terminals and for many other applications requiring a high data transfer rate.

## 6.6  Components for the Primary Access

The tasks of the interface board for S and U interface of the primary access can be subdivided into 4 function blocks (Fig. 6.13).

The Siemens module concept meets the requirements of the CEPT application and the requirements of the T1 application. Fig. 6.14 shows the modules for the primary access.

*ISDN primary access transceiver (IPAT)*
*PEB 2235*
The IPAT is the interface module for the line side. It contains the transmit and receive function for PCM transmission. Its main features are as follows:

▷ Line interface for CEPT and T1 application
▷ PLL for generating the transmission clock of the PCM link
▷ Facility for switching test loops to the line and system side
▷ Conversion of the ternary-coded data on the line side to binary-coded data to the system side and vice versa.
▷ Programmable transmit pulse waveform for the T1 application.

*Advanced CMOS frame aligner (ACFA)*
*PEB 2035*
The ACFA is a universal PCM frame synchronization (alignment) module. Its most important functions are as follows:

▷ Frame and superframe alignment for CEPT and T1 application
▷ Coding and decoding of the transmission code for CEPT and T1 application (HDB3, B8ZS, AMI code)
▷ Detection of transmission errors using the CRC method (cyclic redundancy check)
▷ Detecting PCM errors and PCM alarms
▷ Facility for switching test loops for test and diagnostic purposes
▷ 2.048 Mbit/s system interface
▷ Connection facility for an optical transmission system

*Serial communications controller (HSCX)*
*SAB 82525*
The high-level serial communications controller extended is a universally program-

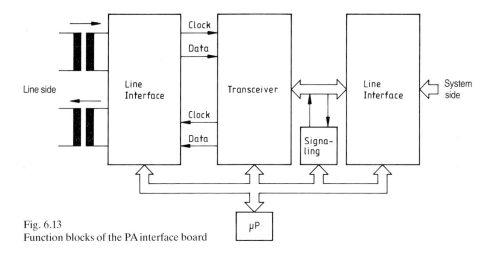

Fig. 6.13
Function blocks of the PA interface board

mable module for serial data transmission. It has two independently operating channels. The HSCX has two functions in the application for the primary access.

▷ Transmission of the signaling data on the D-channel for CEPT and T1 application

▷ Transmission of data at a transmission speed >64 kbit/s via the primary access (DMA access)

The main features of the HSCX are as follows:

▷ Two independent channels for serial data transmission

▷ Protocol support of LAPD, LAPB, HDLC, SDLC

▷ Data rate up to 4 MBit/s

▷ Modem monitoring lines

▷ Time slot allocation with freely programmable word width for transmission in PCM systems

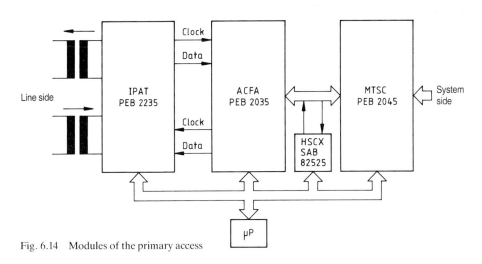

Fig. 6.14   Modules of the primary access

▷ Fast data transfer via DMA interface
▷ Multiplexed and demultiplexed address data bus

*Memory time switch CMOS (MTSC)*
*PEB 2045*
The MTSC can be programmed for two operating modes. In the standard mode, the MTSC operates as the switching module. The second mode is the primary access application (PA mode). The MTSC in PA mode serves as the interface module to the system interface. The data received by the MTSC via the 2.048 Mbit/s synchronous interface from the ACFA are switched through to PCM transmission links with 2.048, 4.096 or 8.192 Mbit/s transmission speed, dependent upon the system interface. Monitoring lines for activating external line drivers are also provided.

## 6.7 Analog-to-Digital Interface

The transition to the ISDN network is made via the digitization of the telephone network. In the digital telephone network, the subscriber terminals are connected to the exchange via analog subscriber lines. In the exchange, the analog signals are converted to digital signals. This task is implemented by the SLMA (Subscriber Line Module Analog). The functions of the SLMA are summarized in the acronym "BORSCHT". The letters of this acronym have the following significance:

B – Battery feed (power feeding)
O – Overvoltage protection
R – Ringing
S – Signaling
C – Coding (PCM coding/decoding)
H – Hybrid
T – Testing

One other task performed by the SLMA is allotting the 64-kbit/s PCM data to time slots of a 2.048 Mbit/s PCM system interface.

## 6.8 Components of the Subscriber Line Module Analog

Fig. 6.15 shows the structure of an SLMA (Subscriber Line Module Analog).

The SLIC performs the task of battery feed, ringing signal injection, signaling, the test function and overvoltage protection.

The PBC performs the same tasks on the SLMA as on the SLMD (Subscriber Line Module Digital).

*Signal processing codec filter (SICOFI)*
*PEB 2060*
The SICOFI is a flexible codec filter module. The main task of the SICOFI is coding of the analog signals to produce PCM data and decoding PCM data to produce analog signals. For digitization of voice signals, the SICOFI has a band-limitation low-pass filter in order to prevent fold-back effects. The SICOFI performs other functions with programmable filters:

▷ Adapting the SLIC input impedance to country-specific requirements
▷ Implementing the electronic hybrid
▷ Linearizing the frequency response in the transmit and receive direction
▷ Gain setting in the transmit and receive direction

Fig. 6.16 shows the signal flow in the SICOFI.

*Memory time switch CMOS (MTSC)*
*PEB 2045*
In the application shown in Fig. 6.15, the MTSC operates in standard mode, i.e. as a switching module. The MTSC offers the possibility of switching each of the 512 PCM channels of 16 PCM lines at the input to each of the 256 PCM channels of 8 PCM lines (Fig. 6.17). The data of the 512 PCM channels at the input are stored in speech memory SM. The data of the speech memory addressed by the connection memory CM are switched to the output of the MTSC.

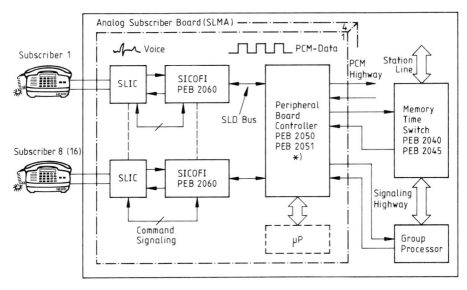

Fig. 6.15   Structure of an SLMA

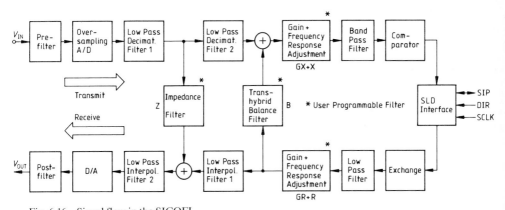

Fig. 6.16   Signal flow in the SICOFI

The MTSC offers the possibility of switching 2.048 Mbit/s, 4.096 Mbit/s and 8.192 Mbit/s PCM systems using the TDM/SDM method.

Parallel connection of two MTSCs permits nonblocking switching of 512 PCM channels at the input to 512 PCM channels at the output (Fig. 6.18).

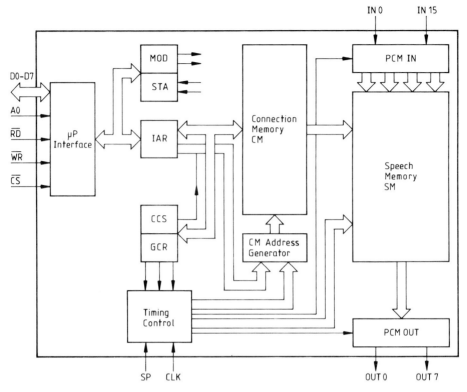

Fig. 6.17  Block diagram of the MTSC

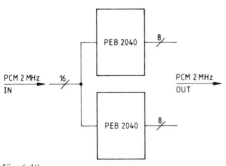

Fig. 6.18
Nonblocking switching of
512 PCM channels

## 6.9  Analog Telephone Sets

The function of a traditional telephone can be subdivided into 3 blocks:

▷ Calling
▷ Ringing
▷ Listening and speaking

These 3 task blocks are implemented by the mechanical bell, the dialswitch, the hybrid transformer and the receiver inset and transmitter inset. These subassemblies do not make possible any additional convenience features for the telephone user.

Siemens developed integrated modules for analog telephone terminals (Fig. 6.19) in order to offer additional convenience features for calling, dialing and speaking, but also in order to be able to manufacture cheaper telephones.

There are different components with differing convenience features for the 3 function blocks. Telephones with such integrated circuits afford the following characteristics amongst others:

Pushbutton dialing
Last number redialing
Speed calling
Open listening
Handsfree talking

*Tone ringer module*
The incoming ringing signals are detected by the tone ringer module and generate signals used to drive piezoelectric transducers. The various modules differ in respect of the pulse duty factor of the signals generated and the input impedance of the modules.

Features of the tone ringer modules are as follows:

| PSB6520 | $f_{1T}/f_{2T} = 1.38$ |
|---|---|
| PSB6521 | $f_{1T}/f_{2T} = 1.25$ |
| PSB6530 | as for PSB6520 but with high input impedance |
| PSB6531 | as for PSB6521 but with high input impedance |

The frequency $f_{1T}$ of the tone ringer modules can be set via an external resistor. The switchover frequency is determined by an external capacitor. The required rectifier and the overvoltage protection facility are integrated in the tone ringer IC. Fig. 6.20 shows the block diagram of the tone ringer IC.

If the incoming ringing signal is only to be indicated and is not to be converted to an audible signal, the ring detector PSB6620 can be used. The module is used in telephone answering sets, fax units and Btx units etc. Fig. 6.21 shows one example application.

*Pushbutton set*
On modern telephones, the dialing unit consists of a pushbutton set. As regards the dialing methods, we distinguish between dial pulsing which is used in the public net-

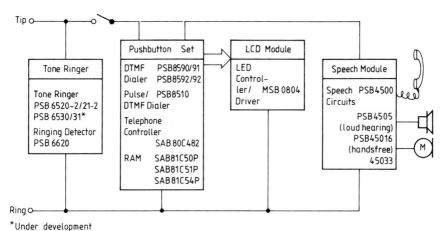

*Under development

Fig. 6.19    Integrated components for analog telephone sets

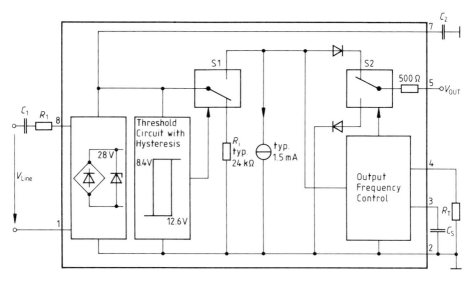

Fig. 6.20    Block diagram of a tone ringer module

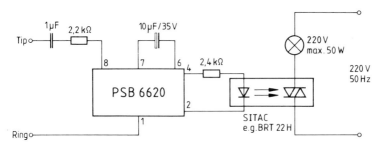

Fig. 6.21  Example application of the ring detector

work and dual-tone multi-frequency dialing DTMF which is used almost exclusively in PBXs. Modules PSB8591 and PSB8593 are designed for DTMF. The PSB-8510-X family (Fig. 6.22) is a pushbutton set module which can be used both for dial pulsing and for DTMF. The relevant dialing method is set by pin programming. The PSB8510-X offers last number redialing and the scratchpad function as further convenience features.

*Speech module*
The essential tasks of the speech module are voice transmission and the hybrid function. These tasks are performed by the IC PSB4500/01. One further feature of the speech modules in the PSB4500/01 is a special circuit for avoiding signal distortion in the transmit direction, the anti-clipping circuit. The speech modules have an amplifier in the receive direction for magnetic, dynamic and piezoelectric receiver insets.

170

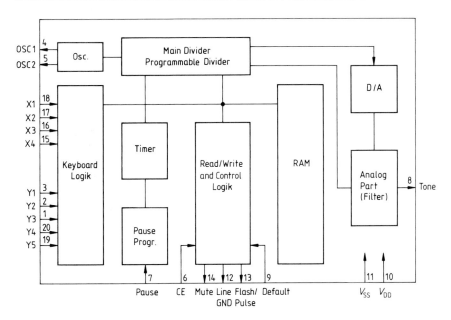

Fig. 6.22  Block diagram of the PSB 8510-X

The convenience speech module PSB4503 makes available 3 supply voltages (also including an adjustable and controlled supply voltage) for external components, besides the conventional speech module functions.

The control module for open listening (PSB45010) and the handsfree control IC PSB45030 are powered and driven preferably by the PSB4505. A 50 Ω loudspeaker can be connected directly.

# 7 Automotive and Industrial Electronics

The fields of application automotive and industrial electronics are very closely related. All the electronics to be found in the car can also be found in industrial applications. The special features of automotive applications lie in the high safety requirements and the extremely electronics-unfriendly environment in which the circuits have to be operated.

## 7.1 Automotive Electronics

Electronic systems are being used to an ever-increasing extent in the car. Such systems are designed to

▷ increase economy,
▷ improve safety,
▷ reduce environmental pollution,

▷ increase comfort and convenience and
▷ keep the driver better informed.

The open-loop and closed-loop control tasks involved can be performed only by using electronics. Automotive electronics essentially consists of a large number of independent individual systems.

Special features involved are the continually increasing number of car models and types, the wish for freely combinable optional equipment and the standardization of the market with its many and varied regulations.

All requirements and conceptions taken together make it more and more urgently necessary to elaborate a concept for "organizing" the electronic systems in the car.

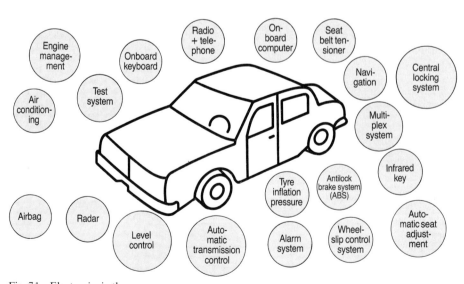

Fig. 7.1    Electronics in the car

Such an overall concept for automotive electronics must be upward-compatible and must permit easy integration of future subsystems.

Consequently, with the aid of integrated circuits, new capabilities have been created and these have led, for instance, to decentralization of the automotive electronic system.

Applications such as those in Fig. 7.1 also ensure that the space for installing electronic systems is becoming more and more compact and the cable harness for instance, can be replaced by a multiplex cabling system.

The reliability aspects are of particular importance. Higher engine performance means an exponential increase in the conditions which the electronic systems must withstand. The electronic components must

▷ have an extremely high thermal loading capacity (−40°C to, in some cases +190°C)
▷ be immune to atmospheric conditions (air, oil and fuel etc.) and
▷ withstand voltage loads of defined overvoltages (80 V) more.

*The automotive electronic system*
Fig. 7.2 shows the basic structure of an automotive electronic system.

The sensors have the task of converting physical quantities such as pressure and temperature etc. to signals which can be evaluated electrically, such as voltage, frequency and pulse width. The Hall sensors listed in Fig. 7.3 are frequently used for this. Other possible sensors include:

▷ Semiconductor sensors
▷ NTCs, PTCs or thermistors
▷ Optical sensors
▷ Magnetoresistors
▷ Ultrasonic sensors
▷ Inductive sensors

See also Chapter 3.3 Sensors.

Amplifiers, signal converters A/D and/or D/A converters are used to forward and condition signals. Here, there are several ICs which will be considered in Chapter 7.2 Industrial Electronics with example applications owing to their importance. The signals conditioned by these components are frequently forwarded to a microcontroller and/or its supporting peripheral ICs.

At the output side, actuators, lamps and motors etc. are operated and indicators/dis-

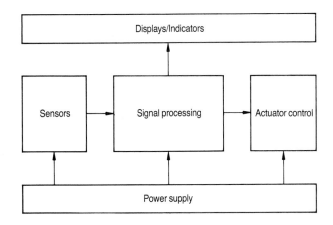

Fig. 7.2
Structure of the automotive electronic system

173

plays are driven. These loads generally require high operating currents for higher voltages which they cannot, however, draw directly from the microcontroller. The actuator control, also termed power interface is available for this, and it is designed as a relay, discrete semiconductor or integrated circuit.

In many applications, relays no longer meet the more stringent requirements in respect of operating frequency, pick-up time and service life, despite their undisputed economic and technical maturity. Furthermore, no diagnosis of the connected load is possible without additional electronics. Consequently, the following facilities are selected for implementation:

▷ Drive ICs
▷ Power bridge ICs
▷ Intelligent power switch ICs
▷ Smart power transistors

As already mentioned at the start, the group of indicating instruments are further output-side loads. Indicating is one of the most important functions of automotive electronic instruments. Without indicators, it would not be possible to indicate drive data or defects, and the driver would not recognize these.

Since indicators such as LEDs, clocks or speedometers are driven in different ways one requires special indicator/display drivers. Finally, we must also consider the

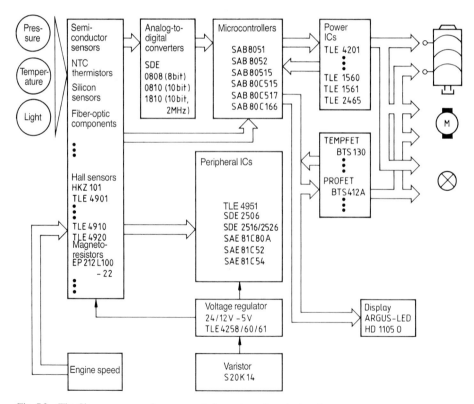

Fig. 7.3   The Siemens range of components for automotive electronics

power supply systems which provide or condition the energy for the entire electronic system. ICs for voltage control with very low power loss and which also include additional protection and control functions for the automotive electronic system are used for this.

*Integrated circuits for automotive applications*

The ICs shown in Fig. 7.3 listed with the relevant function areas, provide a good overview of the product and application diversity of integrated circuits in the car.

You can find all maximum ratings, ratings and diagrams in the Data Book ICs for industrial applications and in the individual data sheets.

*Smart power transistors*

The fundamentals of SIPMOS transistors are explained in Chapter 3.2.1.

The Smart power family is a combination of power transistor and logic. They essentially comprise switching transistors which protect themselves against short-circuit, overvoltage and overtemperature by means of integrated sensors and which thus guarantee higher reliability. The group of "Smart SIPMOS transistors" includes the sub-groups TEMPFET and FET.

The TEMPFET protects itself against overtemperature and overload and, with a suitable additional circuit, also against short-circuit. It switches with respect to battery (N-channel) or with respect to ground (P-channel).

The PROFET protects itself against short-circuit and overtemperature, detects load discontinuities and can switch off in the event of undervoltage. It is TTL/5 V-CMOS compatible and switches loads in the ground circuit. The switch status is signalled.

Other Smart products for open load detection in on-state for faster switch-off of inductive loads and for higher operating voltages are being developed.

## 7.1.1 Applications

### Air conditioning in automobiles

An air conditioning system in automobiles should meet the following requirements:

▷ Comfortable interior temperature
▷ Keeping the windows and windscreen free of condensation and ice
▷ Low energy consumption
▷ Easy-to-operate

Most of the systems fitted as standard meet these requirements only with major restrictions. Consequently, Siemens has equipped several test vehicles with various microcontroller-equipped systems, which have proven their worth.

The microcontroller SAB 80C515 is particularly suitable for this application owing to its powerful computer kernel and, primarily, owing to its versatile on-chip periphery. Refer to Chapter 5.5. Besides the SAB 80C515, the power bridges for motor control (TLE 4201) must also be mentioned as other IC elements of this application.

The temperature inside the vehicle is regulated dependent upon a selectable setpoint. Essential control elements for this are the mixing flap and the compressor of the refrigeration system. The mixing flap determines what portion of the air flowing into the passenger compartment has to pass the heat exchanger of the heating system. Its position can be set precisely by the microcomputer.

If heating is not required, the water supply to the heat exchanger is disconnected by a digitally actuated valve. This additionally reduces the temperature in the summer time. The refrigeration system ensures that, even at high outside temperatures, the inside temperature setpoint is reached, provided the power of the system permits this. The compressor of this system is switched on and off by the microcontroller.

Fig. 7.4 shows the block diagram of the air-conditioning system with the connected func-

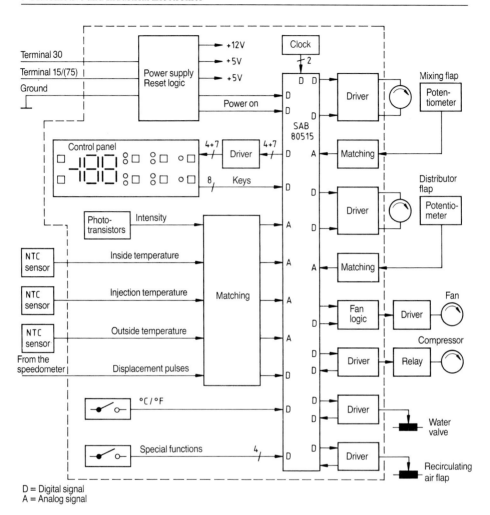

D = Digital signal
A = Analog signal

Fig. 7.4    Block diagram of the air conditioning system

tions. The temperature control sequence is shown in Fig. 7.5.

The diagram in Fig. 7.6 shows the distributor flap setting as a function of the injection and interior temperature. The temperature inside the vehicle is essentially dependent upon the mixing flap setting which is computed by the microcontroller using a so-called cascade control. The deviation of the interior temperature from the setpoint deter-

mines the setpoint for the injection temperature in an external servo loop. The internal, faster servo loop adjusts the mixing flap so that the injection temperature actually reaches the temperature setpoint. As compared with a simple control system for the mixing flap, corresponding to the deviation between setpoint and actual value of interior temperature, this two-stage system affords the advantage of greater stability; moreover disturbances which influence the injection

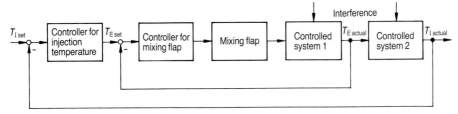

Fig. 7.5    Automobile interior temperature control

temperature can be compensated for quickly (e.g. engine temperature and outside temperature changes, switching the compressor on or off, switching over between fresh air and circulating air). In addition, limits for the minimum and maximum value of the injection temperature can be defined easily. If the parameters are set correctly, the time ratio is no worse than that of a simple control system.

The setpoints for injection temperature and mixing flap setting are computed on the basis of a digital PID algorithm. This means that they depend partially upon the temperature difference itself (proportional component) and upon the integral (integral component) and the variation (differential component) of this difference. The diversity of parameters which can be set with the two control systems

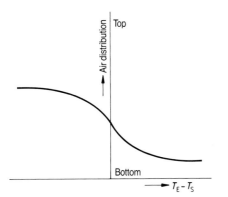

Fig. 7.6
Distributor flap setting as a function
of the injection and interior temperature

permits very good matching to the relevant vehicle. For example, by setting the D-component to zero, one obtains PI action. If "H" or "L" is indicated instead of the temperature setpoint, the control algorithm is deactivated, and the mixing flap is positioned for strongest or weakest heating.

The control does not function in "defrost" condition either. Maximum rating output is selected in this case. When switching over to normal operation, the flap initially resumes the previous setting.

The setting of the distributor flap normally depends upon the difference between injection temperature and interior temperature (Fig. 7.6). Cooling air is blown upwards to a greater extent and heating air is blown downwards to a greater extent. The microcontroller sets the effective setpoint in relation to the actual end positions of the flap (see next example). In the case of the special functions "air distribution top" and "defrost", the air is blown fully upwards, and in the case of "air distribution down", the air is blown fully down. If "air distribution center" is selected, half of the air is blown upwards and half of it is blown downwards.

Fig. 7.7 shows the control circuit for the mixing and distributor flaps. Both flaps are set in the same way, by motors and linkages, which can either move in both directions or stop. Modules of type TLE 4201 for instance are used as motor drivers. The microcontroller controls them via the ports P50 and P51 (mixing flap) and P52 and P53 (distributor flap).

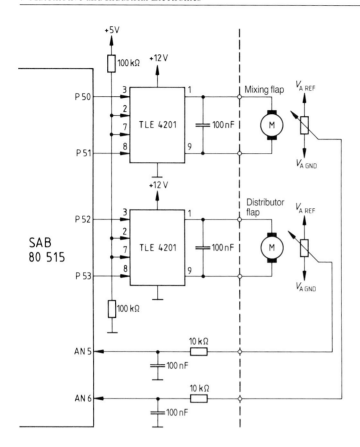

Fig. 7.7
Control of mixing
and distributor flaps

The flap setting is signalled to the A/D converter of the computer by the voltage at a potentiometer. It is permanently connected to the flap and is powered by the analog reference voltages. An RC network filters off interference. When the difference between the setpoint and actual value of a flap exceeds a specific tolerance threshold, the motor is operated in the relevant direction.

The flaps should reliably reach their two end positions (mechanical stops). On the other hand, the motor should not be on continually in these positions, for reasons related to the service life of the mechanical system. It is not easily possible to precisely adjust the potentiometer in order to solve the problem. Consequently, the system detects a stop position by virtue of the fact that the actual value no longer approaches the setpoint, despite the motor being on. The motor is then switched off and the actual value is stored. Later, the system stops as early as when this value is reached.

Redetermining the stop is not possible until after a certain period (approx. 10 min.) or until the ignition is switched on or until the user selects a limit setting at the press of a key. The only precondition for this method of stop detection is that the electrical range of the potentiometer is not fully utilized by the flap angle.

The system presented represents but one implemented example. The function can be changed easily, provided the sensors and control elements remain the same, simply by modifying the program or the stored tables.

## Low-drop voltage regulators

Low-loss voltage regulators in particular are required in the field of automotive electronics. One example of such regulators is the TLE 4260. It also contains a standby and reset function. The module automatically generates a reset signal when it is switched on and can power an external RAM in standby mode. The main regulator of the module switches off via an inhibit input. Fig. 7.8 shows one typical application.

*Electrical operating data of the TLE 4260*

Input voltage
min. 5.7 V, max. 40 V

Standby current consumption
0.6 mA

Output voltage
$5 V \leqq 5 \%$

Output current
max. 500 mA

Low-drop voltage    typically 0.45 V,
max. 0.7 V at 500 mA

Load dump
fixed up to 65 V

*Reset signal*

If the output voltage reaches its full value and if a defined period has elapsed, the TLE 4260 generates a switch-on reset signal. This delay time can be adapted to the relevant re-

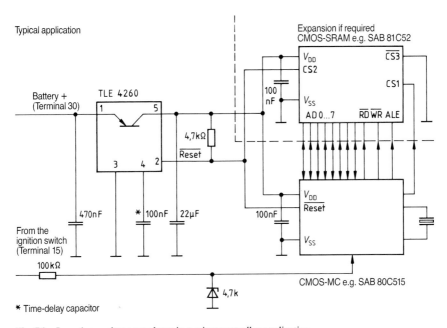

Fig. 7.8   Low-drop voltage regulator in a microcontroller application

quirements by means of a capacitor which can be connected to pin 4. If the capacitor is short-circuited, the reset signal is tripped externally. If the output voltage of the regulator drops below the specified value, the reset signal is also activated. Brief interruptions of the input voltage do not trip a reset signal if the back-up capacitor at the regulator output can buffer them.

*Standby*
If the output current of the regulator drops below 10 mA, it deactivates the reset function. This reduces the regulator's own current consumption to maximum 0.6 mA. The output voltage remains stable in this case. This is the case if the system sets itself to power-down mode. If the output current increases again to over 10 mA, the reset function is reactivated. If the output voltage is less than approx. 4.2 V, a reset signal is also generated. This signal remains active until the output

voltage is once again in the operating voltage range ($\geqq 4.5$ V).

The module is short-circuit-proof. It can be operated within a temperature range of $-40$ to 150 °C and switches off automatically if the temperature exceeds 150 °C. The TLE 4260 is supplied in a P-T66-5 package.

**Current-monitoring ICs**

Monitoring of various lamps is becoming a standard feature more and more frequently on cars of the upper and medium price brackets. Faults in the vehicle's lighting system are indicated and can be repaired immediately. The TLE 4951; G is a central component for this system. Standard comparitors cannot be used for this application in the vehicle since their inputs cannot be loaded with voltages $> V_g$.

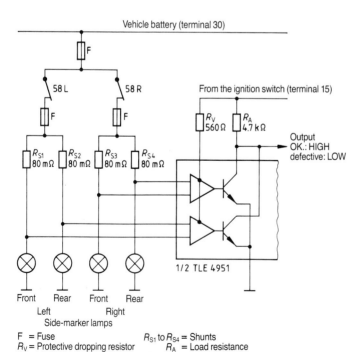

F = Fuse                              $R_{S1}$ to $R_{S4}$ = Shunts
$R_V$ = Protective dropping resistor       $R_A$ = Load resistance

Fig. 7.9
Lamp monitoring with the TLE 4951;G

Moreover, the quad comparator TLE 4951;G can be used in a wide variety of applications for circuit monitoring of relays, valves, electric motors and glow plugs etc.

*Special features of the TLE 4951;G:*
Operating voltage range from 4.5 V to 32 V
Temperature range from –40 to 125 °C
Input currents 25 µA
Switching thresholds can be set to <10 mV
$V_g$-independent input voltage range up to 32 V
Inputs protected against reverse polarity up to ±45 V
Load dump fixed up to 80 V, with series-connected resistors up to 80 V
Open-collector outputs permit additional circuit variations
Operating temperature from −40 to 125 °C

Fig. 7.9 shows a balance circuit for monitoring 4 lamps with two comparators (1/2 TLE4951).

## 7.2 Industrial Electronics

The field of industrial electronics can be subdivided into

▷ Power engineering and
▷ Measuring and control engineering.

Power engineering is the branch of electronics which deals with conversion of electrical energy. Typical fields of application include

▷ Battery chargers
▷ Electrolysis
▷ Drives for rail vehicles and
▷ AC and three-phase AC power controllers

Measuring and control engineering is used wherever

▷ Processes are controlled either with closed-loop or open-loop control systems
▷ Measured values are acquired
▷ Sensors indicate specific states or statuses and
▷ Motors are operated.

Typical applications include

▷ Electrical and electronic measuring instruments
▷ Numerical control systems and industrial robots
▷ Process computers (automation)
▷ Electromedical equipment

The following sections discuss industrial control systems, test and measurement applications, power control systems and other ICs and their fields of application.

### 7.2.1 Industrial Control Systems

The application-specific ICs in the field of industrial control systems essentially comprise:

▷ Operational amplifiers
▷ Comparators
▷ Proximity switch ICs

Please refer to Chapter 5.1 for the fundamentals of operational amplifiers. We shall discuss the following applications in further detail:

▷ Follow-up control system
▷ Proximity switches
▷ Switched-mode power supply units

*Follow-up control system*
Actuating facilities driven by electric motors are frequently operated with a potentiometer. The setpoint which is thus set is a measure of the motor adjustment. In turn, the motor adjusts the follow-up potentiometer which is mounted on the motor spindle and which represents the actual value. The overload-proof and short-circuit-proof double power operational amplifiers TCA 2465 are suitable for setpoint-actual value comparison and for direct motor drive.

Fig. 7.10 shows the circuit.

*Proximity switches*
The special features of the proximity switch IC TCA 305 are a narrow variation range of the electrical data and low current consumption. This permits inductive proximity

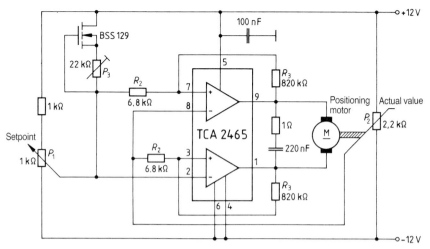

Fig. 7.10   Follow-up control system with power operational amplifier

switches to be implemented with a low tolerance of the technical data. We shall describe one application, taking the form of a circuit for inductive proximity switches with two connections for 117 V and 220 V, configured with a high-blocking capability SIPMOS transistor. It operates as a power circuit breaker and simultaneously provides the power supply for the proximity switch. The circuit (Fig. 7.11) is designed for an operating voltage range of 48 V to 250 V. Its minimum operating voltage is limited only by the permitted residual voltage at the output terminals. In the above specification of the operating range, it has been assumed that the residual voltage should be 20 % of the system voltage. The SIPMOS transistor BUZ 50B in the TO 220 package is used as the switching transistor. Its turn-on resistance is 8 , thus leading to a negligibly low voltage drop. Noise voltage peaks from the mains and from inductive loads are limited to 700 V (at 10 mA) with the varistor at the input of the proximity switch.

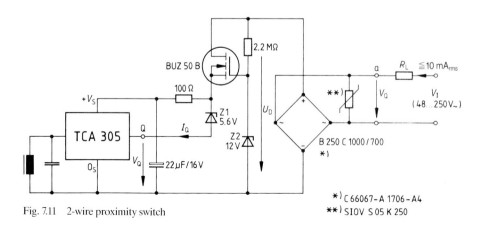

Fig. 7.11   2-wire proximity switch

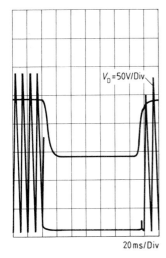

V_D =50V/Div

20 ms/Div

Fig. 7.12
Output voltage and IC delay voltage of the
proximity switch

In OFF state, the output stage of the TCA 305 (open collector of an NPN transistor) is reverse-biased. The AC input voltage is rectified with a bridge-connected rectifier so that a peak voltage of 350 V is produced at the drain of the SIPMOS transistor. The Zener diode Z2 is energized via the 2.2 MΩ dropping resistor and, thus, the gate voltage is limited to 12 V. A voltage of approx. 9 V ($V_{Z2}-V_{GS}=12$ V $-3$ V) is produced at the source. This voltage powers the IC via the 100 Ω resistor. The electrolytic capacitor bridges the voltage gaps.

The current consumption of the circuit comprises the IC supply current of max. 1 mA and the current through the 2.2 MΩ dropping resistor approx. 0.1 mA, so that the total current consumption in OFF state is max. 1.1 mA.

In ON state, the output transistor of the TCA 305 is forward-biased and the source is switched to ground via the 5.6 V Zener diode Z1. The following voltage is produced at the drain:

$$V_{Dmin} = V_{QL} + V_{Z1} + V_{GS}$$
$$= 0.15\,V + 5.6\,V + 3\,V \approx 8.8\,V$$

where $V_{QL}$ = minimum output voltage of the TCA 305. $V_{GS}$ = gate-source threshold voltage of the BUZ 50B.

The voltage at the output terminals of the proximity switch increases to $V_{Rest} = 10$ V owing to the rectifier. The maximum output current is limited by the IC to approx. (rms) 10 mA. Fig. 7.12 shows the characteristic of the output voltage $V_S$ and the IC delay voltage $V_D$.

### 7.2.2 Test and Measurement Applications

Testing and measurement systems generally deal with conversion of analog measurement data to digital values so that these values can then be further processed. Important aspects include

▷ measurement data acquisition and monitoring
▷ data analysis and
▷ process control.

Analog-to-digital converters are of prime importance (see Chapter 5.2).

The increasing need to digitize and process high frequencies opens up broader and broader fields of application for the fast A/D converters. This trend is frequently opposed by inadequate knowledge of the function, conversion characteristics and parameter and the external wiring.

### 7.2.3 Power Control Systems and Drives

Electrical and electronic equipment and systems are powered with power supply units and batteries. Conventional power supply units consist of mains transformer, rectifier and charging capacitor (Fig. 7.13a). A stabilized current or voltage supply is achieved by a stabilizer. Stabilizer circuits generally have substantial losses and require a correspondingly large mains transformer.

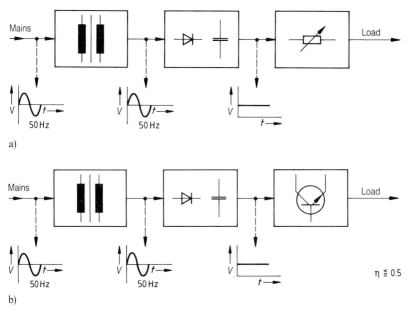

Fig. 7.13   Conventional power supply unit with secondary-circuit rectification

This increases the overall losses, the heating of the unit increases and generally needs to be limited by means of a fan. Overall, this produces an unsatisfactory efficiency since, in the event of mains overvoltage, the series transistor has to absorb the entire differential power (Fig. 7.13b).

During the next few years, switched-mode power supply units will, to an increasing extent, supersede conventional power supply units. The reasons for this are as follows:

▷ the trend towards miniaturization
▷ the reduction in power loss of an item of equipment and
▷ the increasing current requirement of large digital systems.

This development is promoted by new, even more efficient passive and active components such as the SIPMOS transistor and special-purpose, LSI open-loop and closed-loop control circuits. We shall now initially state the fundamentals of switched-mode power supply systems, and in the following section, discuss the SNT-IC series TDA 4918/19 specifically.

*Switched-mode power supply units*
Switched-mode power supply units are clocked power supply units which chop the rectified, filtered mains voltage. Using the semiconductors only as switches means only switching and forward power losses. This results in the characteristically high efficiency of a switched-mode power supply unit by comparison with analog methods. Control is performed either by varying the pulse duty factor at constant frequency or by varying the frequency with fixed or variable pulse duty factor. The voltage which is chopped in this way can be transformed and rectified to form any other voltage (Fig. 7.14).

The frequency of this AC voltage which has a square-wave, trapezoidal or, occasionally, even sinusoidal waveform lies in the range of a few kHz to a few 100 kHz. Small transformers with ferrite cores can be used owing to this high operating frequency. The ferrite core transformer serves not only to transform the voltage and electrically isolate the circuit from the mains but also to store the magnetic energy, dependent upon the operating principle. Owing to operation in switching mode, switched-mode power supply units produce harmonics which may cause disturbance to radio and TV reception and to telecommunications systems. The law requires that all electrical equipment, appliances and systems which generate radio-frequency energy have circuits for limiting the interference level. It is thus necessary to observe legal regulations.

If a switched-mode power supply unit is connected to a DC source (e.g. a battery) and not to the mains, we speak of a DC transformer, also termed DC/DC converter or switched-mode regulator. If the voltage at the output is not rectified, we call the unit a DC/AC converter or power inverter.

If the switched-mode power supply unit is powered from the mains and if we dispense with output-circuit rectification, we then have an AC/AC converter, i.e. an AC power converter. In English, the term switched-mode power supply is abbreviated to SMPS. Advantages of switched-mode power supply units over conventional power supply units include, for instance:

▷ very high efficiency (≈90%),
▷ weight and space saving (≈60%),
▷ low filtering effort required ($C$, $L$),
▷ no audible oscillation if $f$ is selected at >20 kHz.

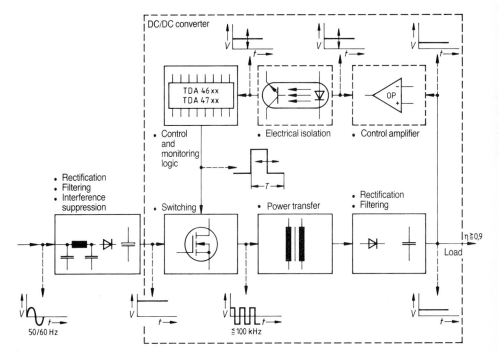

Fig. 7.14  Function schematic of the switched-mode power supply unit

Switched-mode power supply units can be used in

▷ TV sets, AF power amplifiers, video equipment and measuring instruments,
▷ voltage and current regulators for industrial purposes and the laboratory,
▷ power supply systems for fluorescent lamps and low-volt halogen lamps,
▷ RF and AF generators,
▷ motor control systems, final control elements and accumulator chargers,
▷ power supply systems for the railways and Post Office and
▷ personal computers

*Basic circuits for SMPSes*
For the developer, designing an SMPS starts with having to find the best possible solution from a wide variety of circuit variance for the problem in hand. The operating principle of an SMPS essentially determines its characteristics and production effort and expense. In the following section, we shall present the basic circuits of the most frequently used DC/DC converters. In order to give the reader a better understanding, we shall initially outline the classification of switched-mode power supplies (Fig. 7.15).

*Converter circuit principles*
We basically distinguish between two different converter principles: The forward converter and the flyback converter. The designation forward converter can be explained by the response characteristic of the arrangement in which a flow of energy occurs between the primary circuit and secondary circuit during the off-state phase of the semiconductor switch. In the primary circuit, the magnetizing current is superimposed upon the load current. Consequently, preconditions must be created in order to ensure that the transformer can demagnetize. On single-ended forward converters, this is carried out during the ON phase of a semiconductor switch. In the case of push-pull and bridge circuits, the ON phase of the second semiconductor switch occurs after the ON phase of one semiconductor switch and after a brief OFF phase of both semiconductor switches.

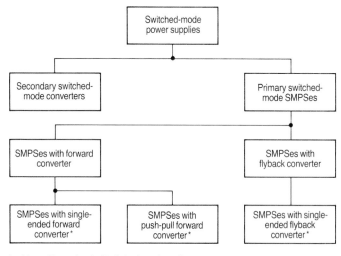

* with or without electrical isolation from the mains

Fig. 7.15
Overview of switched-mode power supplies

The term flyback converter can be explained by the fact that energy is supplied into the transformer and stored during the ON phase of the semiconductor switch, and this energy is emitted to the secondary circuit in the OFF phase.

*The forward converter*

We shall discuss the mode of operation of the forward converter by way of example of the graphic symbol showing the single-ended forward converter (Fig. 7.16a). This converter has a smoothing capacitor $C_{IN}$ in the input circuit. It has the function of smoothing the rectified mains voltage, supplying the pulsed currents required by the converter, with low inductance, and absorbing the magnetizing current fed back from the transformer. The transformer of the forward converter has a ferrite core with no air gap in order to attain high magnetic coupling of the windings.

The primary winding is connected to the input voltage by means of a SIPMOS transistor. When the transistor is forward-biased, a square-wave voltage which is induced dependent upon the transformation ratio is produced in the secondary winding, thus producing a current flow in the secondary winding via the rectifier diode D1 and the output-circuit smoothing choke $L_{OUT}$ (Fig. 7.16b and c, period $T_{ON}$). The current in the secondary winding induces a current in the primary winding, dependent upon the transformation ratio. In addition to this load current, the so-called magnetizing current is superimposed in the primary winding.

The magnetizing current must be reduced again during the OFF phase of the transistor. The demagnetizing winding, as the third transformer winding, serves this purpose. It has the same number of turns as the primary winding, but has a smaller conductor cross-section since only the magnetizing current flows through this winding in the transistor's OFF phase. The demagnetizing winding has the opposite polarity to the primary and secondary winding this being indicated in the

graphic symbol by dots at the starts of the windings. The demagnetizing winding is connected directly to the input voltage via a diode D3. During the ON phase of the transistor, the same voltage as in the primary winding is induced in the demagnetizing winding, and, consequently, twice the input voltage is applied to the diode D3 in the reverse direction.

During the OFF phase of the transistor, the energy stored in the transformer core owing

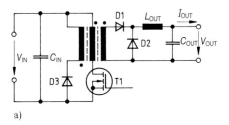

a)

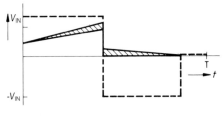

b)    ‒ ‒ ‒ Voltage at the primary winding
       ——— Current in the primary winding
       \\\\\\\ Magnetizing current

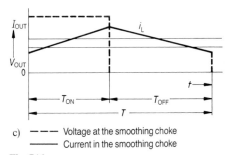

c)    ‒ ‒ ‒ Voltage at the smoothing choke
       ——— Current in the smoothing choke

Fig. 7.16
Single-ended forward converter
a) Graphic symbol,
b) and c) Response characteristic
in steady-state operation

187

to the magnetizing current must be dissipated again so that the magnetizing current does not increase at will and so that the ferrite core does not reach magnetic saturation. Consequently, a free-wheeling diode D2 is provided in the secondary circuit. The current through the smoothing choke $L_{OUT}$ continues to flow via this diode when the voltage at the secondary winding drops to zero or becomes negative. The diode D1 decouples the secondary circuit from the transformer during this operating phase. This permits the polarity to reverse at the windings.

The magnetizing current now flows via diode D3 and the demagnetizing winding back into the input-circuit smoothing capacitor. This means that twice the input voltage is now applied to the transistor as the reverse voltage. Demagnetization of the transformer is ensured if the voltage-time area, i.e. the area which the voltage at the primary winding encloses above the time access, is at least equal to that during the ON period during demagnetization. For this reason, for instance, the maximum ON period on the single-ended forward converter must not be more than 50 % of the period.

The smoothing choke $L_{OUT}$ serves to generate a constant energy flow from the current or voltage signal which occurs during the ON time $T_{ON}$ at the secondary winding of the transformer, and to limit the current rise in the transformer. The smoothing capacitor $C_{OUT}$ at the output smoothes the current ripple of the choke and serves as an energy accumulator in the event of load variations. The response characteristic of the forward converter is defined by the following formula.

$$V_{OUT} = V_{IN} \cdot \frac{n_2}{n_1} \cdot \frac{T_{ON}}{T}.$$

$n_1$: Number of turns of the primary winding.
$n_2$: Number of turns of the secondary winding.

*The flyback converter*

This converter also has a smoothing capacitor $C_{IN}$ in its input circuit which has the function of smoothing the rectified mains voltage and supplying the pulsed currents required by the converter with low inductance. Unlike the single-ended forward converter, in this case the magnetizing current is not fed back to the input capacitor but is supplied to the output-circuit smoothing capacitor $C_{OUT}$ (Fig. 7.17a).

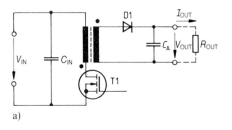

a)

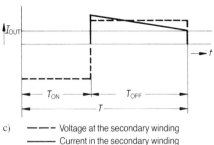

b) — — — Voltage at the primary winding
—— Current in the primary winding

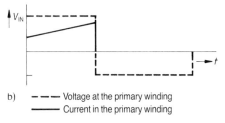

c) — — — Voltage at the secondary winding
—— Current in the secondary winding

Fig. 7.17
Flyback converter a) Graphic symbol,
b) and c) Response characteristic in steady-state operation with trapezoidal current characteristic in the transformer windings

The basic version of the flyback converter has two windings which have the reverse polarity (cf. dots for identifying the starts of the windings). When the SIPMOS transistor T1 is forward-biased, the anode-cathode voltage of the rectifier diode D1 is negative, i.e. no current flows in the secondary winding of the transformer. The magnetizing current flows in the primary winding. Since the flyback converter uses a ferrite core with air gap, a far higher inductive current flows, and this builds up a magnetic field in the air gap. In addition, when the transistor is forward-biased, magnetic energy is stored in the flyback converter transformer (primarily in the air gap).

When the transistor is rendered reverse-biased, the voltage at the windings reverses. The voltage at the secondary winding increases until the rectifier diode D1 is rendered forward-biased, i.e. to the value of the output voltage $V_{OUT}$. Since the magnetic flux in the transformer has a constant characteristic, the current of the primary winding, transformed on the basis of the transformation ratio, flows in the secondary winding at the instant at which the transistor is rendered reverse-biased. Consequently, the rectifier diode D1 must power a capacitor $C_{OUT}$ directly, capable of absorbing the high current.

The input voltage, plus the output voltage which is transformed on the basis of the transformation ratio, occurs at the transistor during the OFF time as the reverse voltage. With standard rating, this corresponds to somewhat more than twice the input voltage. We distinguish between flyback converters with trapezoidal current characteristic in the transformer and flyback converters with delta current characteristic. In the case of a trapezoidal current characteristic (Fig. 7.21b, c) the transistor is rendered forward-biased again before the current on the secondary winding has dropped to zero. The essential feature of this mode of operation is that the peak current values occurring, referred to

the output current, are far lower than is the case with operation with delta current characteristic.

The response characteristic in the case of trapezoidal current characteristic is defined by the formula:

$$V_{OUT} = V_{IN} \cdot \frac{n_2}{n_1} \cdot \frac{T_{ON}}{T} \cdot \frac{1}{\dfrac{T_{ON}}{T}}.$$

From this, we can see that the output voltage $V_{OUT}$ changes when the pulse duty factor $T_{ON}/T$ is changed. However, the relationship between the output voltage and pulse duty factor is not a linear relationship but, rather, a hyperbolic relationship. This means that the output voltage becomes infinitely high when the pulse duty factor almost reaches 1. Consequently, flyback converters may not be operated without a load resistor or without a closed control loop since the output voltage and, thus, also the reverse voltage of the transistor may assume high values.

*Secondary switched-mode converter or switched-mode regulator by way of example of a single-ended forward converter*
On switched-mode power supply units with several output voltages, it is necessary to select one of these voltages for obtaining the controlled variable, which means that this voltage is then the best regulated voltage (Fig. 7.18, voltage $V_{OUT1}$). Regulation of the other voltages is less exact. Consequently, they may need to be stabilized using suitable in-phase regulators (voltage $V_{OUT3}$) or switched-mode readjustment circuits (voltage $V_{OUT4}$). This latter switched-mode regulator represents a secondary switched-mode converter.

*Selection criteria for switched-mode power supply units*
Table 7.1 compares forward converters and flyback converters. Table 7.2 shows the power

189

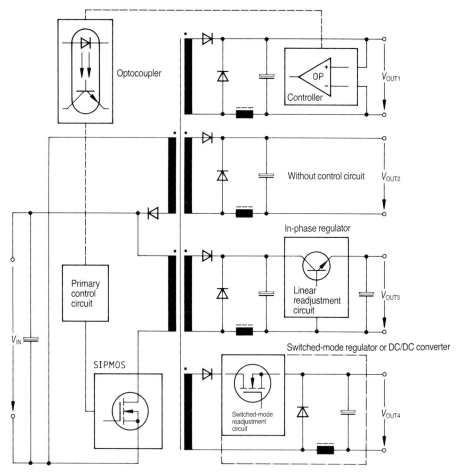

Fig. 7.18    Single-ended forward converter with several differently controlled output voltages

ratings which can be achieved for the various types of converter. Table 7.3 and 7.4 show the graphic symbols, voltage and current characteristics and the advantages and disadvantages of various versions of flyback converter and forward converter.

**Components for switched-mode power supply units**

Siemens offers a broad range of semiconductors and passive components for this applica-

tion. In addition, a wealth of experience, gained over many years, is made available to the developer in the form of application, rating and RFI suppression assistance.

The components in switched-mode power supply units can be subdivided functionally as follows:

*Semiconductor components*
▷ Diodes at the input and output for rectification

▷ SIPMOS and bipolar transistors for switching or chopping
▷ Integrated circuits for fixed-frequency and freely oscillating circuits, for open-loop control, closed-loop control and monitoring functions.

▷ Optocouplers for electrical isolation in the control loop and for control signal transmission

▷ Operational amplifiers for amplifying the controlled variable

Table 7.1   Comparison of forward and flyback converters

|  | Forward converter | Flyback converter |
|---|---|---|
| Number of components required | higher | lower |
| Smoothing choke and free-wheeling diode | necessary | not applicable |
| Transformer core | no air gap | with air gap |
| Magnetic coupling when switching | better | worse |
| Voltage overshoot when switching | less | greater |
| Interference from magnetic fields | less | greater |
| Current amplitudes in relation to the load current | far lower | far higher |
| Pulse current loading of the components | less | greater |
| Interference suppression and smoothing of the input and output variables dependent upon the current ripple | simpler | more complex |
| Control of the energy flux when the pulse duty factor is changed by | varying the voltage-time area | storing variable energy portions |
| Generation of several simultaneously rigidly circulated DC secondary voltages by adding further secondary circuits conditionally possible | conditionally possible (choke current may not be intermittent) | easily possible |
| Dynamic control response of the output variables | slower (owing to smoothing chokes) | fast |

Table 7.2   Power ranges of the various types of converter

| Power [W] | ≤ 100 | 100 ... 300 | 300 ... 1000 | 1000 ... 3000 | > 3000 |
|---|---|---|---|---|---|
| Single-ended flyback converter | × | × |  |  |  |
| Single-ended forward converter | × | × |  |  |  |
| Half-bridge converter |  | × | × |  |  |
| Full-bridge converter |  | × | × | × |  |
| Push-pull converter |  | × | × | × | × |

Table 7.3   Versions of flyback converter

| No. | Graphic symbol | Designation | Advantages |
|---|---|---|---|
| 1 | 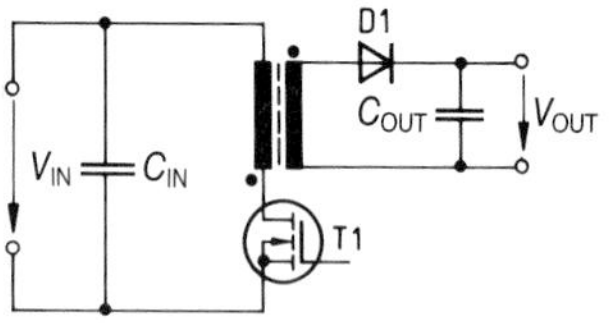 | Flyback converter | • Several output voltages can be regulated simultaneously<br>• Broad control range in the case of operating voltage variations ("stepless transformation ratio") |
| 2 | 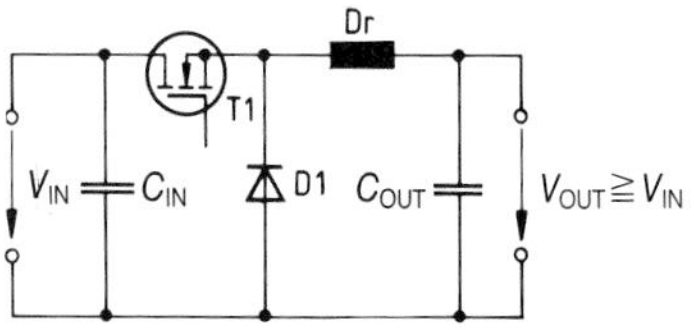 | Buck converter | • SIPMOS reverse voltage $V_{DS} \approx V_{IN}$<br>• Simple choke<br>• No problem with magnetic coupling<br>• Low stress on the output capacitor<br>• Pulse duty factor $T_{ON}/T = 1$ possible |
| 3 | 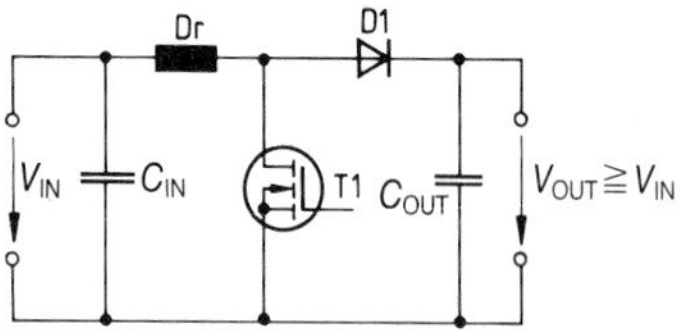 | Boost converter | • Simple choke<br>• No problems with magnetic coupling |
| 4 | 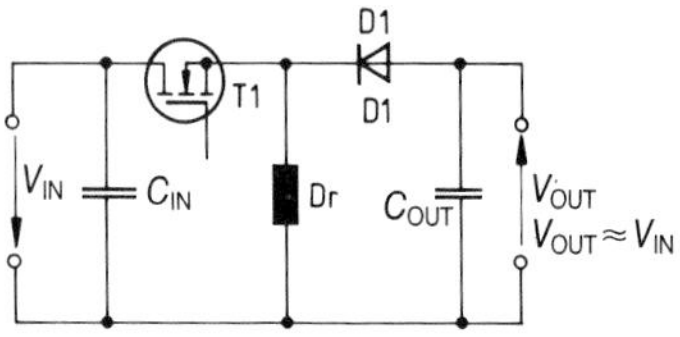 | Buck-boost converter | • Simple choke<br>• No problems with magnetic coupling |
| 5 | 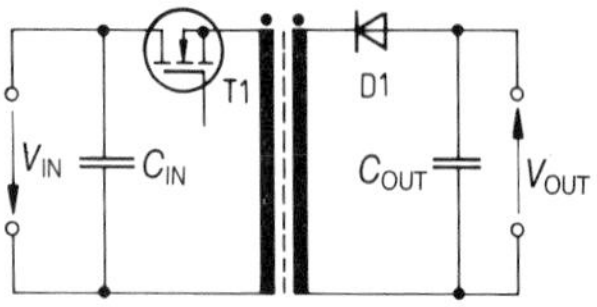 | Flyback | Buck-boost converter with electrical isolation between input and output voltage is identical to flyback converter in the illustration above. |

| Disadvantages | Pulse duty factor | a: Voltage characteristic at the transistor<br>b: Secondary winding or choke current | c: Current characteristic in the input capacitor<br>d: Current characteristic in the output capacitor |
|---|---|---|---|
| • Power transistor reverse voltage $V_{DS} > 2 V_{IN}$ conventionally<br>• Heavy stressing of the capacitor and the diode at the output<br>• Good magnetic coupling necessary<br>• Large core cross-section with air gap required<br>• Problems resulting from magnetic radiation and eddy currents | $\dfrac{T_{ON}}{T} = 0.5$ | <br>With trapeziodal current characteristic in the transistor or in the primary winding | |
| • No electrical isolation between input and output voltage<br>• Drive circuit must "float" | $\dfrac{T_{ON}}{T} = 0.5$ | | |
| • Power transistor reverse voltage $V_{DS} \simeq V_{IN} + V_{OUT}$<br>• No electrical isolation between input and output voltage<br>• Moderate stressing of the output capacitor | $\dfrac{T_{ON}}{T} = 0.5$ | | |
| • Power transistor reverse voltage $V_{DS} \simeq V_{IN} + V_{OUT}$<br>• No electrical isolation between input and output voltage<br>• Heavy stressing of the output capacitor<br>• Drive circuit must "float"<br>• Output voltage negative with respect to input voltage | $\dfrac{T_{ON}}{T} = 0.67$ | | |
| | $\dfrac{T_{ON}}{T} = 0.5$ | <br>With delta current characteristic in the transistor or in the primary winding | |

193

Table 7.4   Versions of forward converter

| No. | Graphic symbol | | Designation | |
|---|---|---|---|---|
| 1 | | | Single transistor forward converter | • The core can be demagnetized easily<br>• Uncomplicated |
| 2 | | | Push-pull converter | • The drive circuits of the two transistors have the same potenital |
| 3 | | | Two transistors forward converter | • SIPMOS reverse voltage $V_{DS} \approx V_{IN}$<br>• The core can be demagnetized easily<br>• The transformer may have a high leakage inductance |
| 4 | | | Single-ended push-pull converter | • SIPMOS reverse voltage<br>• The transformer may have a high leakage inductance |
| 5 | | | Full-bridge push-pull converter | • SIPMOS reverse voltage<br>• The transformer may have a high leakage inductance |

| Disadvantages | Pulse duty factor | a: Voltage characteristic at the transistor<br>b: Secondary winding or choke current | c: Current characteristic in the input capacitor<br>d: Current characteristic in the output capacitor |
|---|---|---|---|
| Power transistor reverse voltage $V_{DS} > 2\,V_{IN}$<br>Demagnetizing winding required<br>Good magnetic coupling between primary winding and demagnetizing winding required | $\dfrac{T_{ON}}{T} = 0.5$ | | |
| Power transistor reverse voltage $V_{DS} > 2\,V_{IN}$<br>• Balancing problems<br>Good magnetic coupling between the two primary windings required<br>• Risk of both transistors being rendered forward-biased simultaneously | $\dfrac{T_{ON}}{T} = 0.42\,(2\times)$ | | |
| • Electrically isolated drive circuit required | $\dfrac{T_{ON}}{T} = 0.5$ | | |
| • Balancing problems<br>• Risk of both transistors being rendered forward-biased<br>• Electrically isolated drive circuit required | $\dfrac{T_{ON}}{T} = 0.67$ | | |
| • Balancing problems<br>• Risk of both transistors of one half bridge being rendered forward-biased simultaneously<br>• Electrically isolated drive circuit required | $\dfrac{T_{ON}}{T} = 0.42\,(2\times)$ | | |

*Passive components*

▷ Al electrolytic capacitors at the input and output for filtering, smoothing and stabilizing
▷ SIFERRIT cores for transformers and storage chokes for power transmission and storing energy
▷ Radio interference suppressors in the primary circuit

*Integrated circuits for switched-mode power supply units*

Open-loop control, closed-loop control and monitoring circuitry takes up a large part of SMPS development. It determines the characteristics and reliability of the SMPS and must guarantee perfect and reliable functioning in all operating ranges.

Integrated circuits with their ingenious circuit technology, high complexity and compact design are far superior to discrete control circuits, particularly as regards reliability, quality, characteristics and price. This permits extensive standardization of SMPSes and simplification of their circuit technology. The development costs are cut so that even smaller quantities are economical.

*TDA 46xx family*

The integrated circuit family TDS 46xx was originally designed only for extremely economical, mains-isolated flyback converters. Thus, this series of modules was the right solution for the entertainment industry. Other applications, such as the following were added over the course of time

▷ extended mains voltage range
▷ optocoupler control
▷ single-ended forward converters

Even though the first module of this series, the TDA 4600, was suitable only for low-cost bipolar transistors, today's generation (e.g. TDA 4605) is also intended for driving MOS transistors. Many millions of modules from this family are already in use today, and they are being used for more and more new fields of application.

*TDA 49xx family*

There is a trend towards higher switching frequencies on switched-mode power supply units owing to the availability of new ferrite components and electrolytic capacitors. In the case of mains-powered switched-mode power supply units, the frequencies may be up to 200 kHz, and in the case of DC transformers up to 300 kHz. All conventional switched-mode power supply unit principles can be implemented with little external effort using the integrated open-loop and closed-loop control modules for switched-mode power supply units TDA 4918 and 4919.

The essential characteristics of these modules are as follows:

▷ TDA 4918 for push-pull applications, maximum 150 kHz operating frequency
▷ TDA 4919 for single-ended applications, maximum 300 kHz operating frequency
▷ Voltage and current mode possible
▷ Integrated output drivers with +0.5 A and −0.7 A
▷ Direct driving of SIPMOS power FETs
▷ 3.5 mA closed-circuit current
▷ 1 % reference voltage tolerance
▷ Two comparators with programmable hysteresis
▷ Current-limiting comparator
▷ 9.6 to 30 V reference voltage range IC undervoltage cut-off with hysteresis
▷ Freely wireable control amplifier
▷ Biasing with volt-second limiting
▷ Soft start
▷ DIL 20 and SO 20 packages

### 7.2.4 Product Overview

*Switched-mode power supply units, voltage regulators*

TDA 4700;A    Integrated control circuit for single-ended and push-pull switched-mode power supply units

| | |
|---|---|
| TDA 4718;A | Integrated control circuit for single-ended and push-pull switched-mode power supply units |
| TDA 4714A;B | Switched-mode power supply IC |
| TDA 4716A;B | Switched-mode power supply IC |
| TDS 4814A | IC for sinusoidal mains current consumption |
| TDA 4918A;G | Switched-mode power supply IC with SIPMOS driver output |
| TDA 4919A;G | Switched-mode power supply IC with SIPMOS driver output |

*Thyristor and triac drive circuits*

| | |
|---|---|
| TCA 785 | Phase control |
| TLE 3101 | Phase control |
| TLE 3102 | Phase control |
| TLE 3103 | Phase control |
| TLE 3104 | Phase control |

*Motor controllers*

| | |
|---|---|
| TCA 1560 B | IC for motor control |
| TCA 1561 B | IC for motor control |
| SLE 4520 | Pulse-width modulator IC |
| TCA 955K | Rotational speed controller |

*Timer circuits*

| | |
|---|---|
| SAB 0529;G | Programmable digital timer |
| SAB 0530 | Programmable digital timer, 50 Hz |
| SAB 0531 | Programmable digital timer, 60 Hz |
| SAB 0532;G | Programmable digital timer, 50/60 Hz |

*AF generator circuit*

| | |
|---|---|
| SAB 0600 | Three-tone door chime |
| SAB 0601 | Single-tone door chime |
| SAB 0602 | Two-tone door chime |
| SAB 0700 | Signal tone generator |

*ICs for professional radio equipment*

| | |
|---|---|
| TBB 042 G | Mixer |
| TBB 200;G | PLL frequency synthesizer |

| | |
|---|---|
| TBB 202;G | Dual-modulus divider |
| TBB 212;G | Dual-modulus divider |
| S 89 | Variable divider for 500 MHz |
| TBB 302 | Programmable Schottky diode matrix $8 \times 6$ |
| TBB 303 | Programmable Schottky diode matrix $7 \times 6$ |
| TBB 304 | Programmable Schottky diode matrix $4 \times 8$ |
| S 1531 | AF amplifier for 1 V |

*Other ICs*

| | |
|---|---|
| SLB 0586 | Electronic dimmer switch |
| TBB 278;G | Video pulse generator |
| SLE 43215P/SH 100 | Heating programmer |

*Industrial control systems*

Simple operational amplifiers:

| | |
|---|---|
| TAA 762;A;G | Operational amplifiers with Darlington input |
| TAA 765 A;G | |
| TCA 332;A;G | |
| TCS 335 A;G | |
| TAE 1453 A;G | PNP operational amplifiers |
| TAF 1453 A;G | |
| TBA 221 B | Operational amplifiers |
| TBA 222;BSI | |
| TBB 741 G | |
| TBB 742 G | |

Two-stage operational amplifiers:

| | |
|---|---|
| TAA 2762;A | Twin operational Tw amplifiers |
| TAA 2765 A | |
| TCA 2332;B | Twin operational amplifiers with Darlington input |
| TCS 2335 B | |
| TAE 2453 A;G | Twin PNP operational amplifiers with Darlington input |
| TAF 2453 A;G | |
| TBB 1485 B;G | Twin operational amplifiers |

Quad operational amplifiers:

| | |
|---|---|
| TAA 4762A | Quad operational amplifiers |
| TAA 4765A | |

197

TBC 4332A ⎫ Quad operational
TBE 4335A ⎬ amplifier with
⎭ Darlington input

TAE 4453A;G ⎫ Quad operational
TAF 4453A;G ⎬ amplifiers

Power operational amplifiers:

TCA 365;B ⎫ Power operational
TCA 1365;B ⎬ amplifiers

TCA 2465;A  Twin power
operational amplifier

Comparators, triggers:

TCA 105;B;G  Triggers

TCA 312;A;G ⎫ Comparator with
TCA 315 A;G ⎬ Darlington input,
⎭ TTL-compatible

TCA 322;A;G ⎫ Comparator,
TCA 325 A;G ⎬ TTL-compatible

TCA 345 A  Trigger

TCA 965  Window
discriminator

ICs for sensor applications, optical sensors, Hall circuits, proximity switches:

TFA 1001 W  Photodiode with
amplifier

TCA 205A;K ⎫
TCA 305A;G;K ⎬ Proximity
TCA 355B;G ⎭ switch

Driver and interface circuits, level converters and transistor arrays:

FZL 4141;E ⎫ Quad drivers with
FZL 4145;E ⎬ short-circuit
⎭ signaling

FZH 2115 ⎫ Driver and level
FZH 215 S ⎬ converter with
⎭ automatic threshold switchover

TCA 671;G ⎫
TCA 871;G ⎬ Transistor arrays
TCA 971;G ⎬ with 5 NPN
TCA 991;G ⎭ transistors

# 8 Consumer Electronics

The demands made of consumer electronics equipment are becoming ever more stringent. These demands relate to improved and additional features and cheaper systems owing to greater integration.

## 8.1 Car Radio

The catchphrases relating to new demands made of the car radio are multipath suppression, background receivers for frequency diversity systems and RDS (radio data system).

Perfect in-car VHF reception is becoming more and more difficult owing to the increasing density of transmitters. Obstacles between the transmitter and receiver block the wanted signal (causing fading), and scattering surfaces reflect it and thus produce multipath interference. Cross modulation or intermodulation occurs when traveling past powerful transmitters, and powerful transmitters with only a short frequency spacing from (weak) neighboring transmitters produce adjacent-channel interference. Other negative factors include ignition spark interference and interference from digital automotive electronic circuits, for example, electronic injection, ABS and on-board computers.

Fig. 8.1 shows a typical block diagram of a car radio.

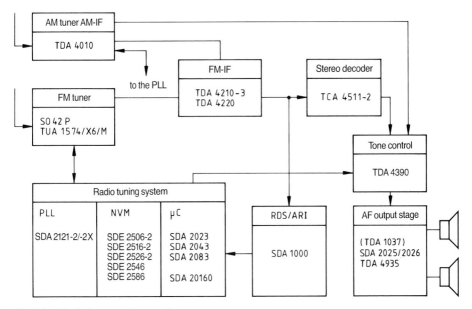

Fig. 8.1   Block diagram of a car radio

We shall briefly discuss the following modules:

TUA 1574/X6/M for the FM tuner
TDA 4210-3 and TDA 4220 as the FM-IF circuit
TDA 4010 as the AM tuner and IF circuit
SDA 2121-2/-2X for PLL
TCA 4511-2 for stereo decoding
TDA 4390 for tone control
TDA 2025/26 and TDA 4935 as AF output stages
SDA 1000 as RDS demodulator

A microcontroller and an NVM (non-volatile memory) of the module family SDA 25XX are used for controlling and storing the transmitter frequency and the security code.

*Tuner IC TUA 1574/X6/M*
Fig. 8.2 shows the block diagram of the TUA 1574/X6/M. It is also suitable for use as a background receiver owing to its large frequency coverage (up to 150 MHz). Its essential characteristics are as follows:
▷ Strictly symmetrical structure in the mixer and in the decoupler stages

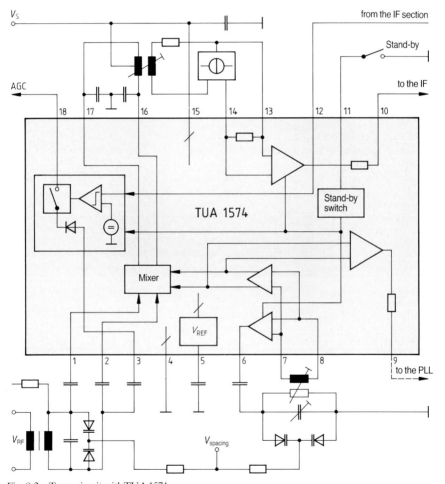

Fig. 8.2   Tuner circuit with TUA 1574

▷ Good large-signal characteristics with low input impedance owing to MOS preselector stage
▷ Low-noise oscillator
▷ IF post-amplifier
▷ Standby circuit with reduced power consumption (not TUA 1574X6)
▷ Output for automatic gain control (AGC)

*IF modules*

The intermediate frequency (IF) module has the task of amplifying and demodulating the IF signal supplied by the tuner. It issues the MPX signal as the output signal.

Circuit TDA 4210-3 contains a 7-stage limiting amplifier with demodulator and uncontrolled AF output. The gain is fixed at approx. 80 dB. When selecting the ratings, importance was attached to ensuring that limiter operation is not dependent upon temperature.

A DC voltage which is proportional to the input signal and which has a slightly steeper rise at low levels, the so-called field-strength voltage, is generated from the IF amplifier train. The derivative is largely free of time constants so that it follows rapid level changes, such as those occurring with multipath interference with no delay. A coincidence demodulator with external phase shifter is used for demodulation of the FM-modulated signals. The required coupling capacitors are integrated. The voltage at the phase shifter circuit should be approx. 200 mV (peak-to-peak).

AFC (automatic frequency control) which coincides with the reference voltage with exact center tuning is obtained from the coincidence demodulator. If the transmitter is mistuned, a voltage (the so-called S-curve) is generated internally, and this can be supplied to a microprocessor for evaluation and precise station centre tuning.

Since the oscillator in a car radio is tuned by a PLL (phase locked loop) without AFC, a clear STS (search tuning stop) criterion is generated by logically combining the AFC zero crossing with the field strength. This switching signal is applied to the STS output at AFC=0 and with adequate field strength.

The AF signal generated in the demodulator passes through a controllable amplifier with gain $v_{max}=0$ dB. The mute depth and mute cut-in point can be set. The maximum gain is achieved at voltages $V_{mute} > 0.7$ V. This permits a reduction in noise at input levels below the limiter cut-in point if the drive exceeds the field strength.

Important characteristics of the TDA 4210 are as follows:

▷ Signal demodulation
▷ Search tuning stop pulse generation for FM and AM
▷ Adjustable mute depth and mute switching threshold
▷ Adjustable reference voltage
▷ 80 dB gain
▷ Limiter operation temperature-stable
▷ Field strength detection signal
▷ Coincidence demodulator with external phase shifter
▷ AFC (automatic frequency control) and STS pulse generation (search tuning stop)

*AM receiver module*

Module TDA 4010 performs the tasks of reception, conversion, demodulation and AF signal conditioning in double-sideband-modulated AM systems. In addition, it contains circuit sections which predestine it for top-quality locators and synthesizers, an internally generated search tuning stop pulse and a controlled oscillator with low amplitude. The module also contains a controller IF output for AM stereo applications.

The signal which is conditioned in the external preselector stage is routed via an impedance transformer stage to the mixer where it is mixed with the oscillator frequency to produce the IF. This is supplied to the three-stage controlled IF amplifier via an external selector. After the control amplifier, the AM-modulated signal is branched off, limited and supplied to an coincidence demodulator.

The AF signal which is produced at this stage is freed of IF residue in active low-pass filters. After passing through an impedance transformer, it is applied to the output and can then be supplied to a tone control. Likewise, the S-curve voltage which can be influenced externally is also applied to the output of the demodulator, thus providing an AFC criterion. This signal is logically combined with the field strength information in such a way, that a switching signal is applied to the station finding stop output only if the input frequency lies within the stop bandwidth close to the intermediate frequency (= required frequency) and if an adequate input signal is available.

*PLL-IC*
Sophisticated car radios tune the tuner with processor-controlled frequency synthesis. This process involves the microcontroller presetting a target frequency as a digital value for the PLL. The PLL generates a tuning voltage for the tuner. A closed control loop constantly compares the frequency generated by the tuner with the required frequency, and readjusts the tuning voltage accordingly.

The PLL module SDA 2121-2 developed for this purpose has the following characteristics:

▷ 50 mV FM and 30 mV AM input sensitivity
▷ Up to 150 MHz FM and 25 MHz AM input frequency
▷ Fast and linearized phase detector output
▷ One phase detector output for FM and one phase detector output for AM
▷ Switchable current yield and polarity of the phase detector
▷ Frequency increment can be set to <1 kHz for AM and <12.5 kHz for FM
▷ Open-drain switching outputs for 10 V

▷ Software-programmable via $I^2C$ interface
▷ Anti-backslash technique
▷ CMOS

The anti-backslash technique suppresses the dead band. This permits phase differences <100 ps to be resolved. The short circuits which normally occur with this technique are suppressed by internal current sources. This means that the VCO voltage remains free of disturbing pulses.

*Stereo decoder*
The demodulated signals supplied by the IF module is disected to the left and right signals, in a stereo unit. The TGA 4511-2 operates on the basis of the switch principle and permits a virtually coil-less circuit. The essential characteristics are as follows:

▷ Controllable base width
▷ PLL circuit for switching frequency conditioning
▷ Correction facility for signal amplitude and phase
▷ Automatic mono and sliding mono-stereo cross-fade adjustable
▷ Lamp output for stereo indicator

*Tone control*
The volume, treble and bass can be set with DC voltage using the $I^2C$-bus controlled audioprocessor TDA 4390.

*AF output stages*
The TDA 2025 is an 18 W bridge amplifier. No clicking noises occur when switching on and off. Integrated protection circuits prevent overload of the speakers. Other characteristics include a low thermal resistance (3 K/W), short-circuit strength and low disortion factor. The TDA 4930/35 modules are stereo bridge amplifiers.

*RDS module*
Since April 1988, the German ARD traffic information broadcasting stations have been broadcasting traffic radio-specific data in digital form (radio data system). Fig. 8.3 shows

Tuning aids

PI   Program Identification Code[1]
PS   Program Service Name[1]
PTY  Program Type Code
TP   Traffic Program Identification Code[1]
AF   Alternative Frequency Code[1]

Switching signals

TA   Traffic Announcement Code[1]
DI   Decoder Identification Code
M/S  Music/Speech Code[1]
PIN  Program Item Number
RT   Radiotext Message
UTC  Coordinated Universal Time
TDC  Transparent Date Channels
IH   In-House Applications

1) Services already available today

Fig. 8.3   RDS information services

the data currently specified. These data are modulated upon a 57 kHz carrier which also conveys the ARI information. A special modulation method prevents mutual interference of the RDS and ARI data. The SDA 1000 module decodes the RDS signal. One TTL output supplies the data information and one TTL output supplies the clock signal. In addition, if ARI is present, the announcement identification code (SK) is available at one output, and a composite signal comprising area identification code (BK) and announcement identification code (DK) is available at a third output. The RDS signals are evaluated by a microcontroller. Fig. 8.4 shows the circuit diagram.

## 8.2 Digital Television

### 8.2.1 Fundamentals

Digital technology started being incorporated in TV receivers and video recorders approx. 10 years ago. At the start, it was only incorporated in the operating controls, station selection and control of analog functions by the $I^2C$-Bus. Since 1983, digital circuits have also been used for processing video signals. The initial aim was color decoding, i.e. dissecting the composite color video signal into its components lumincance (Y) and chrominance (U, V) and both synchronizing and deflecting the electron beam.

Fig. 8.5 shows a block diagram of a digital TV receiver. After A/D conversion, the composite color video signal is supplied to the digital signal processing section which splits the signal into the luminance Y and chrominance (color difference signal) U and V and separates off and regenerates the horizontal and

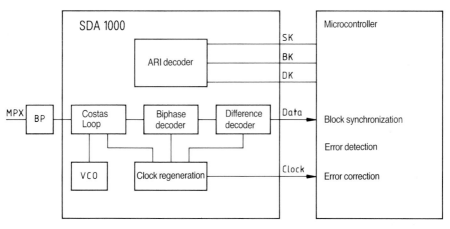

Fig. 8.4   Block diagram of the RDS system

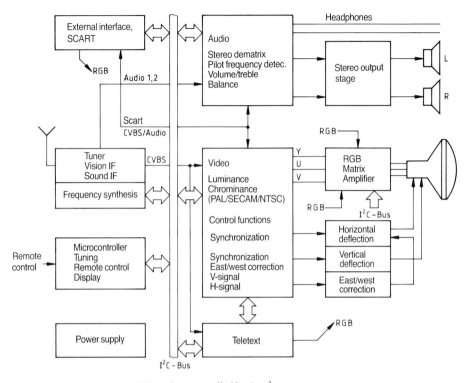

Fig. 8.5   Block diagram of a TV receiver controlled by the I²C-Bus

vertical sync. signals (HS, VS). Subsequent processing covers matrixing and influencing the signals by brightness, contrast and color saturation settings and adaption to the picture tube.

The functions horizontal and vertical deflection, pincushion equalization with digitally adjustable picture geometry and digital stabilization are conducted in a digital deflection section with the horizontal and vertical sync. signals HS and VS.

The picture tube has an analog drive circuit. The D/A conversion can be carried out in the YUV level before the RGB matrix or in the RGB level after a digital RGB matrix and after the analog settings.

The second method makes it more difficult to overlay a further analog RGB source (e.g. from the broadcast videotext decoder). All concepts provide a digital component interface YUV in the signal branch, and this is the starting point for additional signal processing.

It is advantageous if the related sync. signals (HS, VS) are also available since they represent the timebase of the video signal and must be treated together with the video signal for standard conversion etc.

In systems conventional today, the scanning clock is derived from chrominance processing (PAL/NTSC) and is the chrominance subcarrier-coupled, or it is derived from the

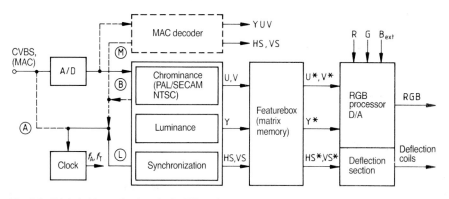

Fig. 8.6   Digital video technology in the TV receiver

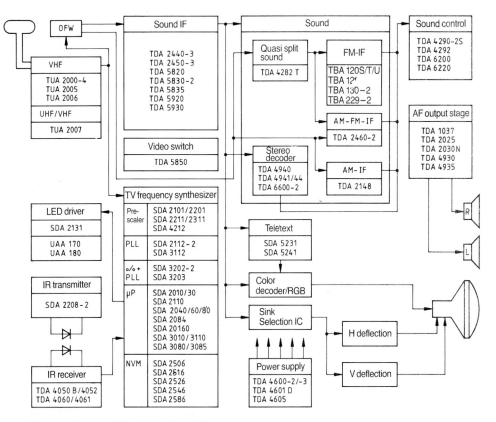

Fig. 8.7   Integrated circuits in a TV receiver

205

sync. signal and is then line-coupled. In principle, asynchronous processing with a freely oscillating crystal oscillator clock is also possible.

When 256 kbit memories became available, this also marked the introduction of matrix memories in TV sets which, in turn, required digitization of the video signal.

New TV standards have now been defined (MAC) or are to be defined (HDMAC, MUSE). Despite analog transmission, they require digital decoding in the receiver. These differing TV standards require receivers which can receive all standards. The digital TV system developed by Siemens essentially consists of three function blocks:

▷ Input section with A/D conversion and color decoding

▷ Featurebox 88 for improving the picture quality and introducing new functions

▷ Output section with recuperations of the analog signals for driving the output stages.

Fig. 8.6 shows a block diagram of the digital video technology in the TV receiver. Fig. 8.7 shows the integrated circuits for a TV set.

Siemens developed the featurebox 88 as an essential component of the digital TV concept. We shall now discuss this featurebox in further detail.

### 8.2.2 Featurebox 88

The essential characteristics of the featurebox 88 are as follows:

▷ Suppression of large-area flicker by doubling the image refresh frequency
▷ Suppression of interline flicker (with restriction)
▷ Suppression of interference stripes when operating VCRs
▷ Noise reduction
▷ Crosscolor reduction

▷ Freeze frame
▷ Picture-in-picture
▷ Nine-unit picture
▷ Tuner scanning
▷ Zoom

The basic circuitry of the featurebox is shown in Fig. 8.8. The central component is the field memory. It has been implemented with nine dual port DRAMs (each 64 kbit × 4). The total memory space required is approx. 2.3 Mbit. In addition to the semiconductor matrix memory, the featurebox consists of three other modules:

▷ Picture processor SDA 9090
▷ Memory output interface SDA 9093
▷ Memory sync controller SDA 9099

*Large-area flicker suppression*
The featurebox 88 produces video signals with 100/120 Hz vertical frequency and 31250/31468 kHz line frequency. This doubling of the field frequency reduces large-area flicker to below the flicker perceptibility of the human eye. Doubling is carried out by directly refreshing the fields (AB→AABB). No disturbing motion artifacts occur during this process. A field memory with a capacity of approx. 2.35 Mbit suffices to implement this system. During normal operation of the featurebox 88, the frame frequency is doubled by directly refreshing each field (AABB with the related deflection raster). This completely eliminates large-area flicker and partially suppresses interline flicker.

Display which is completely flicker-free and free of interline gaps, particularly of broadcast videotext and freeze frame images, is possible by displaying 100/120 Hz frames with 625/525 line normal interlace.

*Interference stripe suppression*
*when using video recorders*
In field mode, it is possible to suppress interference stripes which occur only in every second field. This is of interest in particular as regards video recorder freeze frames if the

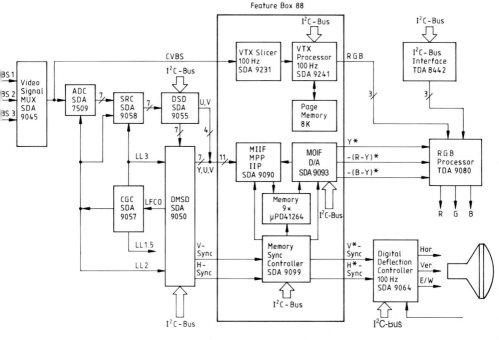

Fig. 8.8  Basic circuit of the featurebox 88

freeze frame of the featurebox 88 cannot be used owing to the fact that there is no frame advance facility. One further advantage is suppression of motion artefacts (double images or ghosting) which occur frequently on video recorder freeze frames.

With specifically synchronized fast search, it is also possible to reduce the numer of interference stripes if individual interference stripes occur alternately in every other field. Not least, a steady picture is obtained during search mode if the interference changes phase from field to field and thus lead to an alternate transient condition of the various horizontal PLLs in the system. In field mode where only every other field is left in the memory, transient condition is always achieved in this case from the same direction and, thus congruently so that all that remains is geometrical distortion.

*Noise reduction*

Picture interference (snow) can be seen to a greater or lesser extent on every TV picture. This interference is frequently already produced in the TV camera, the film scanner or in the film itself (film grain). Further interference is added to this on every transmission path from the transmitter to the receiver (and, in this case, the video recorder frequently serves only as a repeater station). Of course, it is not only interference which impairs the visual impression of the picture. Correlating interference such as the moiré stripes with which anyone who has been cabled will be familiar spoil the pleasure of watching TV. The featurebox is thus equipped with a motion-adaptive interfield noise reduction circuit. The noise reduction may be up to 12 dB in non-moving picture areas. In moving picture areas, the noise reduction is reduced step by step (dependent upon the degree of movement) to zero in order to avoid smearing or lag effects. Noise reduction is performed by recursively weighted, pixel-by-pixel averaging of consecutive fields.

The degree of averaging is rendered dependent upon the strength of the noise added over the transmission path, determined in the vertical blanking interval. Overall, there are three stages (good, moderate and poor signal quality). If the noise is very extensive, the motion detector can no longer distinguish between noise and real movement. In this case, the circuit section responsible for reduction is deactivated.

*Crosscolor reduction*
With conventional color coding methods, crosstalk occurs in the chrominance information if there are very fine luminance line patterns. This produces moving colored patterns which do not belong to the original image. These patterns occur very frequently on finely striped and finely chequered items of clothing and in multiburst test patterns. Since the color patterns change periodically (e.g. at 6.25 Hz) as a function of time on stationary objects in such a way that the mean color value is zero, noise reduction is also ideally suited for simultaneous crosscolor reduction.

*Freeze frame sequence*
In the nine-unit picture mode, the memory is written consecutively with one freeze frame in order to generate a freeze frame sequence, and all freeze frames originate from the same source (Fig. 8.9). The positioning sequence and the time interval can be determined completely freely by means of software. The current nine-unit image can also be shown as a moving image.

*Tuner scanning*
Nine-unit picture mode can be utilized to keep up-to-date of what is happening on 9, 18 or more television channels (Fig. 8.10). The featurebox is synchronized internally in

order to avoid disturbing synchronization process.

The entire matrix memory operates in this case with a crystal oscillator clock from which all display sync. signals are derived. The vertical filter for nine-unit picture decimation serves, in this case, as the clock separating point for the source-circuit coupled picture signals. During the synchronization phase of the tuner, color decoder and memory sync. controller, a freeze frame is displayed. After synchronization, the next picture position can be activated

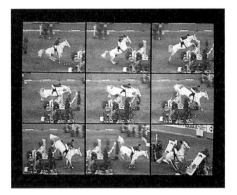

Fig. 8.9
A sequence of freeze frames from the same channel source

Fig. 8.10    Nine-unit picture for featurebox

with the current moving image. Field mode is activated in order to avoid line transpositions on the current moving picture.

*Interference-free station change*
Using the above-mentioned internal synchronization, it is possible to change stations without any transients in deflection and without having to blank the image. This feature can be used not only for the nine-unit picture but also with normal picture size. If we assume a moving picture with external synchronization, the sequence is as follows:

▷ Switchover to freeze frame
▷ Switchover to internal synchronization
▷ Switchover of the tuner
▷ Waiting until the system has reached steady state ( ≅ 200 ms)
▷ Switching over to external synchronization
▷ Waiting until deflection has adapted ( ≅ 300 ms)
▷ Switching back to moving picture

The sequence is as follows for the viewer: Moving picture (station A) – 0.5 s freeze frame – new moving picture (station B).

Other features are the picture-in-picture function and the facility for zooming sections of the picture with 2-fold magnification.

*Broadcast videotext transmission*
*of broadcast videotext data*
A TV picture consists of two fields each with 312/313 lines. 288 of these lines are used for conveying the picture information. The rest is reserved for vertical synchronization and transmission of non-visible data. Transmission of broadcast videotext and VPS (video program system) in these lines is of interest to the user.

Continual transmission of broadcast videotext data is carried out in a specially encoded format at a bit rate of 6.9375 MHz and 360 bits/line. Each transmitted character requires 1 byte with 7 data bits and one parity bit. The quantity of data is thus drastically reduced by comparison with single-pixel transmission.

One broadcast videotext page consists of 24 lines. Transmission of one page takes 240 ms at four lines per field. Since the pages are transmitted cyclically, long waiting times may occur until the required page is found. This situation can be remedied by buffering pages in the TV set.

*Reception and decoding of the*
*broadcast videotext information*
The broadcast videotext decoder receives a composite color video signal from the IF stage of the TV receiver. In the decoder, the TV lines with the broadcast videotext information are detected, and the data are filtered off and edited. As soon as the selected header line is received, the information of this page is stored in a memory (1 kbyte/page). The contents of the page memory are displayed on the TV screen via a character generator.

The broadcast videotext data are edited and displayed in a data slicer and a video processor. The main tasks of the data slicer SDA 5645 are as follows:

▷ Broadcast videotext data clock generation (6.9375 MHz)
▷ Synchronization of the TV set for broadcast videotext mode
▷ Generation of the 6 MHz system clock
▷ Separation and decoding of the VPS and broadcast videotext data
▷ Phase-locked coupling of a 6 MHz oscillator with composite color video signal
▷ Phase-locked coupling of a 24 MHz oscillator with the system scanning frequency (31.25 MHz)

Fig. 8.11 shows the block diagram of a data slicer.

The broadcast videotext processor SDA 5243/SDA 9243 edits the data supplied by the data slicer. The modules have the following main tasks:

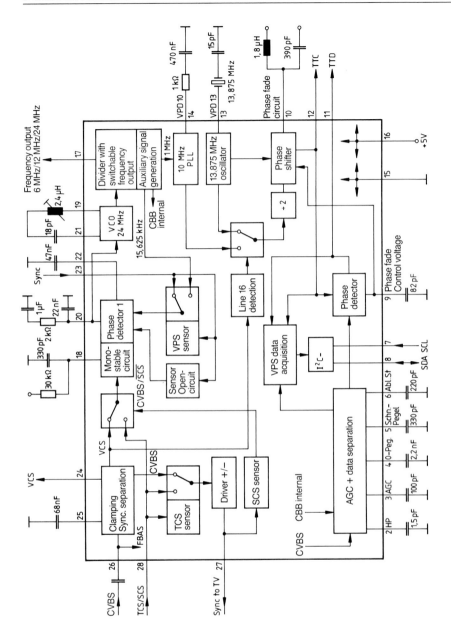

Fig. 8.11  Data slicer SDA 5645

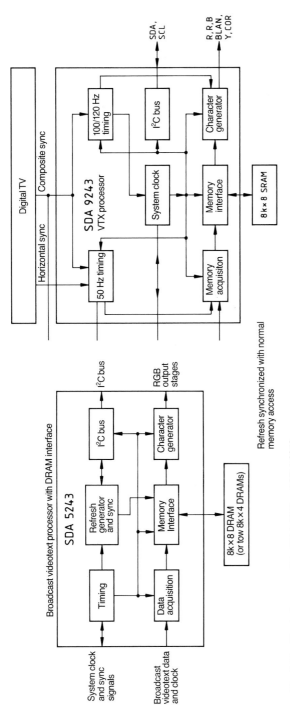

Fig. 8.12    Block diagrams of the SDA 5243 and SDA 9243

211

▷ Processing the information from the data slicer and editing the text data

▷ Receiving additional information (ghost row) for microprocessor data processing

▷ Character generation with 7 different language pages

▷ 25 Hz field detection for overlaying information with no line skips

▷ 12 × 10 matrix for characters and graphics

▷ Controllable character height doubling

▷ Status bit for free-running state detection

By comparison with the SDA 5243, module SDA 9243 also provides flicker-free reproduction with 100 Hz frame frequency synchronization. The signals for this are provided by the featurebox.

Fig. 8.12 shows the block diagrams of the SDA 5243 and SDA 9243.

Future developments in the field of broadcast videotext will be aimed at an efficient single-chip system with large external page memory. This will make it possible to buffer a large number of picture blocks in the set and thus minimize the waiting time for locating a new page.

*Digital sound*

In some countries, digital transmission of sound signals has also been introduced, besides digitization of image processing.

The NICAM 728 method is a digital sound transmission method which is used in addition to the analog FM sound transmission method. The system is thus compatible with existing sound transmission methods. NICAM makes it possible to transmit one stereo signal or two independent mono signals (bilingual). Alternatively, one or both channels can be used to convey data.

Transmission is performed modulated on the basis of the QPSK method (quadrature phase shift keying) with a carrier frequency of 5.85 MHz (B, G-standard) or 6.552 MHz (I-Standard).

*Transmission format*

The transmitted serial data stream is subdivided into 728 bit frames. One frame is transmitted per millisecond (corresponds to 728 bit/s data stream).

704 bits are available per frame for transmission of the wanted information. The remain-

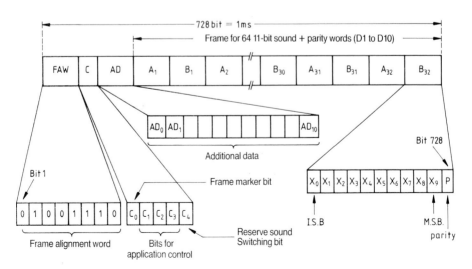

Fig. 8.13 Transmission frame of the NICAM system

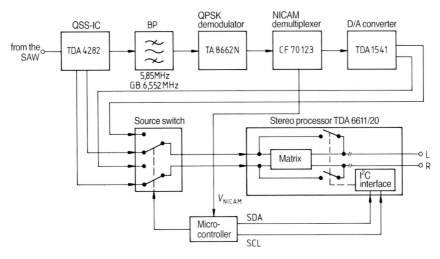

Fig. 8.14    Block diagram of the NICAM decoder

ing 24 bits are used for synchronization and conveying additional and check data.

*Coding the sound information*
The (analog) sound signals are quantized at a sampling frequency of 32 kHz and an initial resolution of 14 bit/sample. This data stream is reduced to 10 bit/sample on the basis of the near instantaneous companding method in order to minimize the data rate.

Bit interleaving is used in order to reduce the effect of transmission errors. In this case, the bits are interleaved on the basis of a stipulated pattern so that no interconnected bits are destroyed in the event of brief interference on the transmission link.

Fig. 8.13 shows the frequency band of the NICAM system.

*NICAM sound receiver*
A NICAM decoder is used in parallel with the existing analog sound processing in the receiver (see Fig. 8.14).

It essentially consists of the QPSK demodulator, the NICAM demultiplexer and a D-to-A converter.

The data stream applied to the output of the QPSK demodulator is decoded in the NICAM demultiplexer, and the samples compressed to 10 bit are converted back to 14 bit-wide words.

## 8.3 Video Recorders

The number of privately owned video recorders is increasing worldwide. In many countries, sales figures for video recorders are, today, even higher than those for TV sets, owing to the fact that the market has become saturated with TV sets.

Requirements made of video recorders are becoming more stringent. Besides higher reliability, better picture and sound quality and easier operation, one further demand is low-price design.

Below, we shall present a video recorder concept developed by Siemens with this aim in mind. Development involved integrating the following components:

▷  Basic functions of the recorder on the mother board:

213

Switched-mode power supply unit
Drive control for the recorder
Control by microcontroller
Tuner
IF receiver circuit
Stereo decoder (optional, otherwise mono)
VPS decoder
Scart connector

▷ VPT decoder which can be plugged into the mother board
▷ Prepared for S-VHS
▷ Economical design

Fig. 8.15 shows the block diagram of a video recorder

*Power supply*
A flyback converter switched-mode power supply unit provides the required voltages of 5V, 12V and 33V. Owing to its low weight, its compact construction and the high reliability, this power supply unit is particularly well suited for video recorders.

*Receive section*
The receive section consists of the tuner, the PLL, the video IF, the two-tone FM-IF, the VPS receive section and the sound processing section. Sound editing is carried out by the VCR sound module TDA 5652. This module performs all essential tasks of sound editing in a video cassette unit.

*VPS*
Inflexible programming of the recording using a timer cannot respond to situations in which TV stations decide to broadcast particular programs at times other than those advertised. This situation is remedied by the TV stations transmitting a signal which indicates the start of the required TV program. Consequently, control information for correctly timed start of recording of video recorders is transmitted in line 16 of the vertical blanking interval. The video recorder switches to record only if the set data in the video recorder (date, time, program source) are identical to the received acutal data. Special cases such

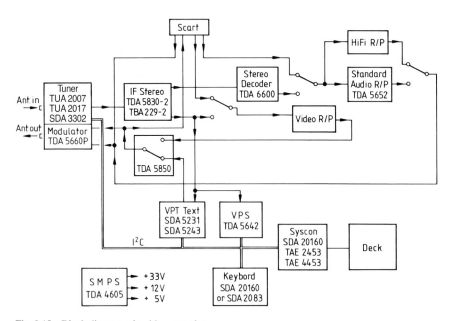

Fig. 8.15   Block diagram of a video recorder

as interruptions (film breaking) are also allowed for by the system.

Siemens supplies the single-chip decoder SDA 5642 for decoding the VPS signals. The task of the decoder is to extract the data transmitted in biphase code from the video signal to make this data available to a microcontroller in suitable form for further processing.

*Modulator*

Many TV sets are now equipped with a direct input for the video recorder via the SCART connector. On TV sets which have only an antenna socket as the input, it is necessary to modulate the video and sound signal with the modulator TDA 5660P.

*Drive control for the recorder*

The drive control system controls all functions of the recorder mechanism. Most of these tasks are performed by the Siemens microcontroller SDA 20160 with the corresponding software. The SDA 20160 is based upon the processor kernel of the 8051. It has been optimized for applications in consumer electronics, see also Chapter "microcontrollers".

*Operator control unit*

The unit is the link between the user and the machine which consists of a microcontroller, the switch for direct control on the unit, the IR receiver for reception of the data from the remote control and the display.

*Software*

Internal communication between individual components of the system is carried out via the I²C bus. Two microcontrollers are responsible for controlling the components. Even if the basic software for initialization and for the basic functions must be present in all machines, the efficiency of the overall system does, however, depend very greatly upon the software written for these microcontrollers.

## 8.4 Tuners

The quality of the tuner essentially determines the quality of a receiver. Owing to the high frequencies, there is a major trend towards even larger-scale integration and, thus also to better RF characteristics. There is also a need to produce receivers for the world market. The different transmission methods in the individual countries should have only a slight effect on production.

Moreover, an extremely diverse range of PTT regulations must be complied with.

*Hyperband tuner*

Fig. 8.16 shows the circuit diagram of a hyperband tuner for the frequency range 50 to 900 MHz, which we shall discuss here by way of example. Nowadays, tuners largely comprise SMDs, not least owing to RF characteristics and the component density. The hyperband tuner circuit has a size of $75 \times 50$ mm$^2$.

The tuner uses the same circuit concept in the RF preselector stages for all three bands:

▷ Highly inductive coupling of the antenna to the tuned input circuit,

▷ Controlled MOS preselector stage with high-amplification, low-noise MOS tetrodes BF 998,

▷ Tuned band-pass filter.

Owing to the broad VHF frequency range, the preselector stage and the tuning diodes have been designed separately for each band. This means that every sub-tuner can be optimized for its frequency range. Three booster diodes which switch the sub-tuners to the input and mutually decouple them are arranged directly at the input of the tuner.

*Tuner IC TUA 2007/2017-X*

The tuner IC is suitable for constructing hyperband tuners, i.e. tuners which cover all television bands from 50 MHz to 860 MHz with no gaps, in three bands, in conjunction with new tuning diodes (BB619, BB620) and which are designed to be operated with the antenna or in cable networks. One special

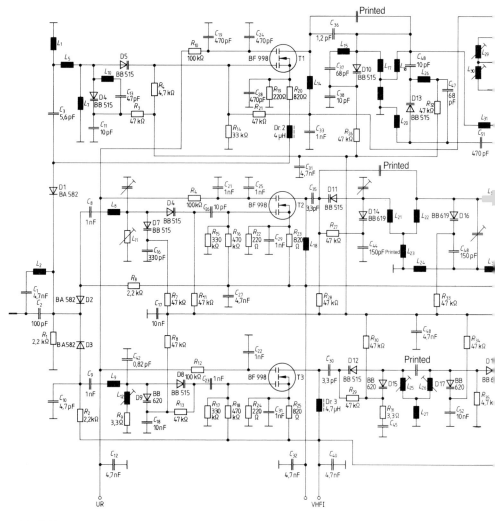

Fig. 8.16
Hyperband tuner with TUA 2007-X and SDA 3302X, VHF 1: 50–170 MHz, VHF 2:
170–470 MHz, UHF: 470–860 MHz

feature is that these tuners are suitable for all TV standards if the ratings of certain components are matched slightly. It is even possible to use them for the French standard by using an IF inverted-position mixer. This dispenses with cost-intensive manufacture of special-purpose tuners for every standard.

The module contains the following stages:

▷ VHF 1 mixer with high-impedance input

▷ VHF 1 oscillator

▷ VHF 2 mixer with low-impedance input

▷ VHF 2 oscillator

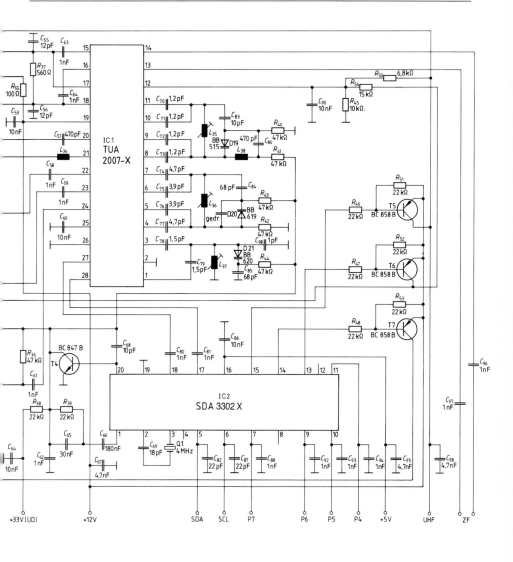

▷ UHF mixer with low-impedance input

▷ UHF oscillator

▷ IF amplifier for low-impedance control of a surface acoustic wave filter

▷ Isolating amplifier for the oscillator signal for driving a PLL or a frequency divider

▷ Switching stage for activating mixer and oscillator of the required band.

The high-deviation tuning diode B620 is used in the VHF band 1. Coupling diodes for compensating for the amplification response are used at the input and at the output of the preselector stage transistor and at the mixer

217

input. The RF band-pass filter is designed as an asymmetrical filter and is also coupled asymmetrically to the mixer. Tuning diode BB619 is used in the VHF band 2 owing to the high quality. The deviation of this diode is adequate for tuning the broad band. Coupling diodes for amplification compensation are used at the input and output of the MOS tetrode. The RF band-pass filter is asymmetrical in the primary circuit and symmetrical in the secondary circuit.

The circuitry of the UHF section largely corresponds to that of the VHF 2 section. Compensating coils are used as balancing elements in the upper frequency band in all tuned circuits. Only one coupling diode of the input of the preselector stage transistor is required in the UHF band. Band switchover is carried out during normal operation of the tuner via the PLL module SDA 3302X. The band switch transistors are integrated in the tuner.

# 9 Surface Mounted Devices (SMDs)

The trend towards smaller circuit configurations with higher component packing density, towards integrated circuits with more and more pins and towards automation in production is leading from through-hole devices to surface mounted devices. It was necessary to develop new types of package for this.

For quite a while now, hybrid technology has offered one possibility of combining components suitable for surface mounting on an insulating substrate material in a very compact format. The knowledge gained from this technique influenced the development and standardization of surface mounted devices.

Surface-mounted devices are abbreviated to SMDs.

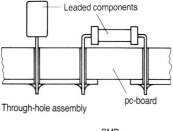

Through-hole assembly

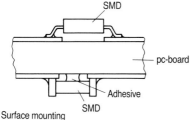

Surface mounting

Fig. 9.1
Throug-hole assembly and surface mounting

The technology for processing SMDs is termed SMT (surface mounted technology).

Fig. 9.1 shows the difference between through-hole assembly and surface mounting.

Certain designs of surface mounted devices are standardized owing to the hybrid technique. Unfortunately, this standardization applies primarily to passive and discrete components. There is still no uniform standard for integrated circuits. However, certain quasi-standards have developed. Frequently, not all components required for a developed circuit can be surface mounted. Consequently, a mixed placement configuration is still generally used today (through-hole assembly and surface mounting). Since surface mounted devices are on the same side as the printed conductor, they can be mounted on both sides of the pc-board.

## 9.1 Advantages of SMDs

SMDs afford the following advantages as regards:

▷ Components
No or short component leads
Smaller dimensions

▷ Pc-board
Simple automatic component placement
High component placement reliability
Good reproducibility
No drill holes for component placement
Use of commercially available pc-boards

▷ Other advantages
Reduction in pc-board size
Can be combined with leaded components

Rational pcb manufacture
Improved RF characteristics
Significant reduction in rework

▷ Overall advantages
Miniaturization
Rationalization
Higher and more uniform quality
and reliability

Proper use of SMDs makes particular requirements of all those involved in development and production. The specific requirements of component placement, soldering, testing and inspection and also repair and maintenance capability must be taken into consideration as early as the development stage. Very stringent requirements are made of positioning accuracy and reliability during component placement. The soldering methods must be very precise owing to the small structures and heating of the components during soldering.

The dimensions of the components must observe close tolerances even at different temperatures.

## 9.2 Components

The most important characteristics of SMDs are as follows:

Small, flat, lightweight
Adapted geometries
Close mechanical tolerances
Suitable solder terminals
Good solderability
High resistance to soldering heat
High reliability
Packaging suitable for automatic machines
Standard processing
Suitable for automatic component placement
Suitable for replacement in the case of repair
Low costs
Standardized

*Types of package*
Fig. 9.2 shows the types of SMD packages manufactured by Siemens. The smallest, flat-

test and most lightweight type for integrated circuits is the MICROPACK. MICROPACK modules are supplied on film (Fig. 9.3).

Almost all discrete semiconductors are available in SMD packages. Preferred types of package are SOD 80, SOT 23, SOT 89 and SOT 143. The most important integrated circuits are available in SO, chip-carrier, VSO, flat-pack, PLCC or MICROPACK packages.

Almost all passive components such as ceramic and tantalum capacitors, NTC and PTC thermistors, varistors, inductors and transformers are available as SMDs. The same applies analogously to many electromechanical component types such as miniature relays, switches, connectors, trimmers, crystal oscillators and potentiometers etc.

*Packaging types*
The components are available in 3 different types of packaging:

▷ loose, bulk
▷ tape
▷ magazines

One type of packaging which is being used more and more is the tape. The tape has recesses to accommodate the component. The tapes are available as cardboard tapes with a width of 8 mm or blister tapes with a width of 8, 12, 16 or 24 mm. Both types of tape are standardized in accordance with IEC. Standardization in accordance with IEC is currently in preparation for wider tapes with a width of 32, 44 or 56 mm. The components in tapes are easier to handle by automatic component placement unit (pick-and-place units) than loose components. There is largely no possibility of damage during storage or handling.

We distinguish between stack and stick magazine and trays. See Fig. 9.4. One special form of tape packaging is the film carrier material for MICROPACK modules.

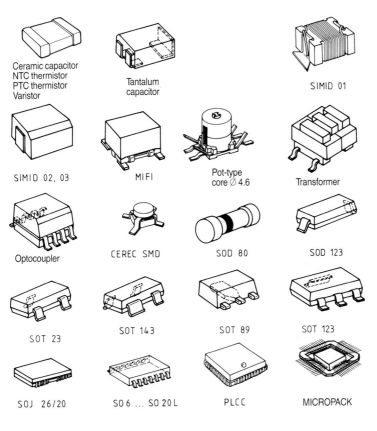

Fig. 9.2
Conventional
SMD packages

Ceramic capacitor
NTC thermistor
PTC thermistor
Varistor

Tantalum
capacitor

SIMID 01

SIMID 02, 03

MIFI

Pot-type
core ⌀ 4.6

Transformer

Optocoupler

CEREC SMD

SOD 80

SOD 123

SOT 23

SOT 143

SOT 89

SOT 123

SOJ 26/20

SO 6 ... SO 20 L

PLCC

MICROPACK

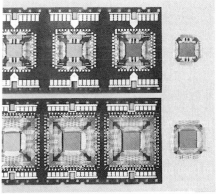

Fig. 9.3   MICROPACK types

221

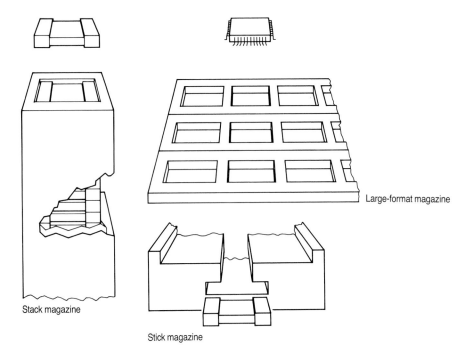

Large-format magazine

Stack magazine

Stick magazine

Fig. 9.4    Types of magazines

## 9.3  SMD Production Techniques

### 9.3.1  PC-Board Layout

The first step towards overall optimization starts with layout of the pc-board. The methods used to manufacture, test, inspect, repair and maintain the pc-board must be taken into consideration at this early stage. Thus, the designer requires information on the permitted arrangement of the components with respect to each other and information on the size and shape of the terminal pads on the pc-board, amongst other things, for layout design. This information, termed layout design rules, reflects the close linkage between all processing steps in surface mounted technology. One other aspect is that components can be placed on both sides of the pc-board with surface mounted technology, as compared with through-hole assembly. The following points must be taken into consideration when designing the layout.

▷ The type and capabilities of the automatic component placement units
▷ Soldering method
▷ Minimum printed conductor track widths
▷ Tolerances (component placement, etching equipment etc.)
   Minimum distances owing to high voltages
▷ Thermal load rating of the components (heat loss)
▷ Testability (test points)

Fig. 9.5 shows a schematic diagram of a CAD-controlled production concept. Post-

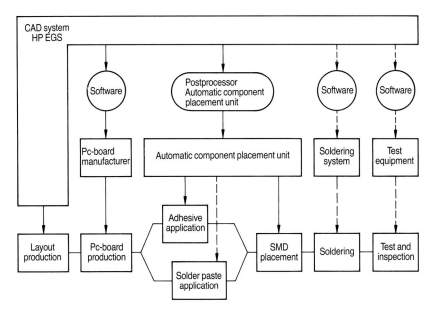

Fig. 9.5 Automatic pc-board design and production

processors control the individual steps in production of a pc-board with components inserted, from a common database.

## 9.3.2 Soldering Techniques

Defective soldered joints are the main cause of pc-board failure with conventional component placement techniques. In view of the small structures of SMDs, soldering defects or irregularities in the soldering process have a particularly serious effect. In the case of through-hole assembly, a form-fit of the connection leads with the pc-board ensures the required retension force and thus mechanically relieves the soldered joint. In the case of SMDs, the soldered joint must also assume this retention function. This necessitates not only new component designs but also, in some cases, new soldering techniques.

When soldering the SMD pc-board, the components are subjected completely to the soldering temperature, dependent upon the actual soldering process. The components must consequently withstand high soldering temperatures without damaging the metallization of the connection leads or electrically damaging the components. The following points which are dependent upon the soldering technique used have a negative influence on the quality of the soldered joint.

▷ Impurities (solder bath, pc-board or components)

▷ Excessive manufacturing tolerances on the components and pc-boards

▷ Wrong soldering temperature

▷ Poor wetting the contacts owing to
solder shadowing
capillary depression
defective adhesive application owing to solder resist
partially masked terminal pads
dewetting in the case of noble metal plating owing to leaching effects
thermal influences (heat sink effect)

▷ Gassing in the case of inadequate expulsion of the solvent in the flux

▷ Bridging owing to
excessively high packing density
pc-board layout not suitable for the method
excessively high transport speed
unsuitable flux
incorrect component position

By comparison with the previous technique (through-hole assembly of the leaded components), the increase in surface size owing to the SMD itself and the capillary interspaces between the underside of the components and the pc-board must be taken into consideration during flux application.

A suitable drying technique must be used in order to achieve adequate expulsion of the solvent from the applied flux.

We distinguish between different methods of fixing in position:

▷ Solder paste (reflow soldering)
▷ Adhesive spot (wave soldering)

*Fixing in position with solder paste*
The solder paste is normally applied to the pc-board at the positions to be soldered using the screen-printing or mask-printing method. But it is also possible to apply the paste by dosing (syringe). When working with solder paste, the terminal pads of the SMDs are simply dipped into the solder paste. After component placement, the soldered joints are heated, thus performing the actual soldering process. Since the solder paste has only a slight adhesive action, the pc-board must not be moved jerkily or turned upside down after component placement and before soldering. Components could otherwise slip or drop out. With this method, the soldered joint is heated by infrared radiation, condensation (vapor phase), hot gas or hot air. One new method is heating the soldered joint with a laser beam.

*Fixing in position with an adhesive spot*
When fixing in position with an adhesive spot, the component is mechanically connected to the pc-board for the subsequent soldering process. The adhesive spot must be applied with precise control. If it is too small, the SMDs will not adhere to the pc-board. If the adhesive spot is too large, the adhesive may spread onto the printed conductors and thus lead to contact faults.

*Wave soldering*
Wave soldering has already been introduced to a great extent in pc-board production. The pc-board is pulled, with the soldering side pointing downwards over a wave of liquid solder. The SMDs are exposed to the maximum temperature occurring, 260 °C, for a few seconds. Consequently, there are limits to wave soldering of SMDs. The components must be able to withstand these high temperatures. Moreover, relatively large clearances must be observed between the components since, otherwise, solder bridges could form and the effect of the capillary depression could mean that insufficient or even no solder at all reaches the soldered joint.

The situation can be improved by introducing a second wave. This dual-wave system is becoming more and more widespread. The first turbulent wave conveys solder to all critical areas of the pc-board (primary wetting). A subsequent second, laminar wave removes the access solder again from the pc-board. Fig. 9.6 shows the principle of the wave-soldering method.

*Reflow soldering*
In the case of reflow soldering, solder which has already been applied is caused to reflow. This interconnects the items to be soldered. The solder is generally applied as solder paste. Reflow soldering differs from wave soldering as follows:

▷ The solder and heat are supplied in 2 process steps

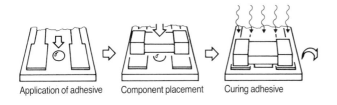

Fig. 9.6
Principle of wave soldering

Application of adhesive    Component placement    Curing adhesive

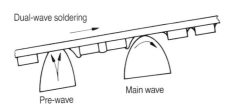

Dual-wave soldering

Main wave

Pre-wave

▷ The quantity of solder at the soldered joint must be applied precisely

▷ Different temperatures and soldering times are possible for the individual solder joints.

The reflow methods with hot gas, hot air, heated platen or infrared radiation are already familiar methods in hybrid technology. Infrared soldering methods are frequently used for SMDs. In the case of infrared soldering, the heat required for soldering is applied by infrared radiation to the soldered joints. But other methods are also used, e.g. condensation soldering (vapor-phase soldering), flat iron soldering and laser beam soldering. Fig. 9.7 outlines the reflow soldering procedure.

*Condensation soldering*
Condensation soldering or vapor-phase soldering is soldering at constant temperature.

The complete pc-board is immersed in the vapor zone of a liquid which has been brought to the boil. The heat of condensation produces the temperature required for soldering within a very short period at the soldered joints and causes the solder paste to melt. Owing to the high heat transfer coefficient, all components can be soldered, regardless of size or position. There is no possibility of overheating owing to excessively high temperature with this method (Fig. 9.8).

Attempts are made to compensate for the disadvantages of the individual methods by selecting different methods. The aim is to thermally stress the components as little as possible and, nevertheless, achieve a good soldered joint. Consequently, attempts are made to set an optimum temperature profile (temperature, time) for every pc-board. This temperature profile is dependent upon the

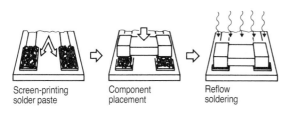

Fig. 9.7    Reflow soldering

Screen-printing    Component    Reflow
solder paste       placement     soldering

225

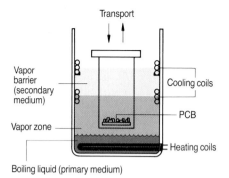

Fig. 9.8    Condensation soldering

thermal capacity, the arrangement and surface of the components and the material of the pc-board.

*Other soldering methods*
In the case of flat iron soldering, the terminal pads of the component are positioned on the pc-board which has been printed with solder paste. A flat iron heated by a current pulse is pressed onto the terminals of the component, thus causing the solder paste to melt. The flat iron must remain pressed against the terminals until the soldered joint has cooled down. Flat iron soldering is frequently used for flat packs (IC packages with leads bent outwards). It is only possible to solder one component after the other.

In the case of laser beam soldering, the terminals are heated individually. This soldering method thermally stresses the components least. This method is still used only very restrictedly since the equipment is relatively expensive and serial soldering methods are slow.

### 9.3.3 Automatic Component Placement Units

The following requirements are made of an automatic component placement unit:

▷ all components, wherever possible, should be capable of being placed with one placement head

▷ high placement rate
▷ short set-up times
▷ precise placing of the components
▷ no placement errors
▷ test capability of the components during placement
▷ low acceleration of the pc-board during placement
▷ capability of being integrated in a production line
▷ a large number of possible feed methods for the various components
▷ no restriction in the layout owing to the automatic component placement unit
▷ acceptance of various packing units
▷ simple programming

In this case, the user must also decide what aspects are of special importance. The actual automatic component placement unit used will primarily depend upon the number of pc-boards in which components are to be placed and the frequency of pc-board change. We distinguish between the pick-and-place and the simultaneous method as regards component placement.

In the case of the pick-and-place method, one component after the other is picked up at the fetch position and lowered (placed) onto the pc-board. In the case of the simultaneous method, several components are picked up simultaneously and placed simultaneously on the pc-board. The performance differences of the various methods are illustrated clearly by the following figures:

▷ Manual component placement: up to several hundred SMDs/h
▷ Sequential automatic units: up to approx. 10,000 SMD/h
▷ Simultaneous automatic units: up to several 100,000 SMDs/h

Simultaneous automatic units require long set-up times if pc-boards are changed. Sequential automatic units are more flexible and have shorter set-up times.

# 10 Quality

Quality is a very crucial and decisive factor as regards the technical and economic success of a product. It is thus an extremely important factor of competition. The subject is in no way trivial and is exceedingly important for the manufacturer and user.

As defined by German Industrial Standard DIN 5530, quality is the "totality of characteristics and features of a product or an activity relating to its suitability of meeting given requirements".

The earlier a defect occurs in the product life cycle and the later its effect comes to light, the more expensive it is to correct. This (statistical) law necessarily leads to the development of procedures for detecting and rectifying defects as early as possible.

All phases of a product life cycle are crucial to product quality. Thus, measuring quality at the development and production stages is an important precondition for verifying and guaranteeing quality. This applies not only to test procedures with which the individual development and production steps are monitored or to checking the product specifications, but also to statements on failure probability, on the product service life and controlling the parameters which influence the mechanisms.

So how important is quality? Let us take a look at a study conducted by the Koblenz Chamber of Industry and Commerce (Fig. 10.1). It illustrates what importance export customers attach to various product characteristics: Quality is the most important characteristic, even more important than experience and delivery time.

Other studies, such as those conducted by the Strategic Planning Institute, Cambridge, Massachusetts, illustrate that quality of products and services also improves the profit situation of a company (measured by "return on investment" or "net earnings per unit of turnover"). Thus, increased expenditure on quality assurance benefits not only the customer but also the company itself. These results apply quite generally to industrial products, regardless of the particular branch of industry. In 1982, the German Institute of the Foundation for Empirical Social Research questioned a representative number of technically interested parties from top and middle management, specifically for the sector of electronic components. An analysis of the results established that "reliability and trouble-free operation" are "number one on the scale of demands" and that "the price or the price/performance ratio" have "no

Fig. 10.1
Importance of quality in export business

paramount importance in relation to reliability and functional reliability".

*Why do our customers attach such great importance to quality?*
The decisive factors are the economic aspects of equipment production. In general, costs incurred when repairing a piece of equipment are far higher than the price of the component which caused the malfunction. In addition, under certain circumstances, a repaired circuit unit or package may be less reliable during operation after it has been repaired than a unit which has no faults right from the very start. Besides, defective components may cause consequential costs (warranty!). Fig. 10.2 shows what costs rectifying defects during the life of a piece of equipment may cause.

The cost factor increases all the more the later a defect becomes noticeable. If equipment is returned under warranty during operation, the repair costs may be more than 1000 times the price of the component. An analogous consideration applies to the component

manufacturer. The aim is high quality at reasonable cost. This can be achieved only by an extremely low reject rate during final inspection. In order to achieve such a situation, components are subjected to tests very early in the manufacturing process.

On the basis of the test results,

▷ the manufacturing process is monitored and optimized constantly and
▷ the (senseless) re-use of defective components is avoided.

The following applies: "Quality is not produced by stringent final inspection. Rather, it must be produced in every manufacturing process!"

Thus, a high component quality benefits both the manufacturer and the customer.

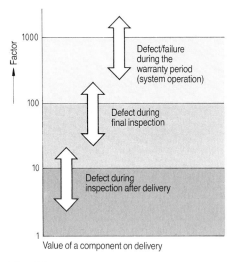

Fig. 10.2
Defect rectification costs in relation to value of a component on delivery

## 10.1  The Arrhenius Equation

In order to obtain realistic statements on the reliability, an attempt is made to simulate the application in a sort of accelerated test. Experiments and analyses of the resultant defects have lead to so-called acceleration methods for determining failure rates. It has been demonstrated that the most important acceleration methods are related to temperature. This is utilized in artificial ageing by heating components and systems (burn-in). This also permits the early failures which occur more frequently in the initial phase of operation to be largely eliminated.

The Arrhenius equation can be used to convert a known failure rate at a higher temperature to a lower temperature:

Failure rate

$$\lambda = e^{-\frac{e_0 V_a}{kT}}$$

For two different temperatures we obtain

Table 10.1
Acceleration factors for various temperatures and activation energies

|        | 0.5 eV | 0.6 eV | 0.7 eV | 0.8 eV |
|--------|--------|--------|--------|--------|
| 25 °C  | 1.0    | 1.0    | 1.0    | 1.0    |
| 55 °C  | 6.0    | 8.0    | 12.0   | 17.0   |
| 75 °C  | 16.0   | 29.0   | 50.0   | 88.0   |
| 100 °C | 50.0   | 109.0  | 239.0  | 522.0  |
| 125 °  | 133.0  | 353.0  | 937.0  | 2491.0 |

the following acceleration factor:

$$\frac{\lambda_1}{\lambda_2} = e^{-\frac{e_0 V_a}{k}\left(\frac{1}{T_2} - \frac{1}{T_1}\right)}$$

$\lambda_1$     Failure rate at temperature 1
$\lambda_2$     Failure rate at temperature 2
$e_0$     Elementary charge
k     Boltzmann constant
$T_1, T_2$     Temperature in K
$V_a$     Activation energy

The activation energy included in this equation differs for various technologies and defect types. Table 10.1 shows acceleration factors which have been calculated for various temperatures and activation energies.

## 10.2 The Bath-Tub Curve of Reliability

Reliability of components is defined as the ability to meet stipulated requirement during a specific period. A failure occurs if a component which was originally free of defects changes to a state in which it no longer meets the requirements.

Reliability characteristics always refer to a large number $N$ of identical components. They make no statement on the behavior of a specific component within this "population". The measure of the average rate at which failures occur successively is the failure rate $\lambda$, defined by the expressing

$\lambda = dN/N \cdot dt$

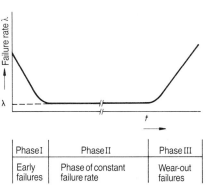

Fig. 10.3    The bath-tub curve

where $dN$ = number of components which fail in time interval $dt$.

The failure rate $\lambda(t)$ is normally specified in "fit" (failures in time). 1 fit = 1 failure/$10^9$ component test hours. Siemens achieves a quality of <50 fit for integrated circuits.

For electronic components $\lambda(t)$ takes the form of a "bath-tub curve" (Fig. 10.3).

The bath-tub curve is subdivided into 3 areas:

*1. Early failures*
There is a phase characterized by a higher failure rate at the start of the components life. This phase lasts approx. 1000 hours at 40 °C with most semiconductor components. This undesirable phase can be substantially shortened by the manufacturer by artificial ageing ("burn-in"). Burn-in means that the goods supplied to the customer are already in phase II of the life cycle when the goods are delivered. For example, the Siemens 256 kbit and 1 Mbit memory chips are always "burnt-in" before delivery.

*2. Phase of constant failure rate*
This phase is characterized by a constant failure rate as a function of time. It is typical of the major part of the component's life, the service phase. The duration of the service phase $t_2 - t_1$ is in the order of magnitude of

decades – in the case of many components, no wear-out failures have been observed at all to date. Should a failure nevertheless occur, the cause is generally wear (leakage of the package).

Consequently, specifying the long-term failure rate $\lambda$ generally suffices for identifying the reliability.

*3. Wear-out failures*
The phase of constant failure rate is terminated by a rise in $\lambda$ resulting from wear-out failures.

Specification of a failure rate $\lambda$ applies in each case to the average production situation during a long production period. The failure rate must consequently be considered as a mean value over a large number of delivery batches of identical components. It is based both on operating experience and on measurement data which may have been obtained under more stringent conditions for the purposes of accelerating tests. The failure rate is thus a statistical value and can, as such, not be guaranteed for legal purposes.

## 10.3 How is Quality Measured?

In order to precisely determine the failure rate, one measures on every component of the "population" the period after which it fails. The accuracy of a knowledge of $\lambda$ is offset by the disadvantage that all components for which $\lambda$ applies will, by that time be defective. The way out of this plight is a compromise: A sampling test provides information on the percentage of defective components of the "fundamental set". This statement is, however, uncertain to an extent. This uncertainty drops with increasing sample size.

The sampling tests are generally a part of a supply contract between the supplier and purchaser. The sampling tests are conducted on the basis of agreed sampling schemes

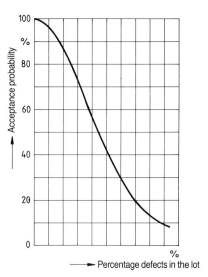

Fig. 10.4  Acceptance characteristic

which, in turn, are based upon the laws of mathematical statistics.

The test and inspection system agreed upon between the supplier and customer also contains risks. Every sampling plan and every sampling instruction has its own particular attributes. It can be represented in the form of a curve, the acceptance characteristic (Fig. 10.4). It provides a visual impression of the selectivity and defect tolerance of the sampling plan.

Sampling tests are conducted on "lots". A lot is a quantity of components which have passed through the manufacturing process jointly. Changes in the manufacturing process consequently effect all components in a lot. If a lot contains no defective components ($= 0\%$), no defective components will be found either in a sample taken components from it. The acceptance probability is 100 %. But, if a lot contains more than 0 % defective parts, it is probable that defective components will also be found in the sample.

The chance of a lot being accepted drops with increasing fraction defective. The shape

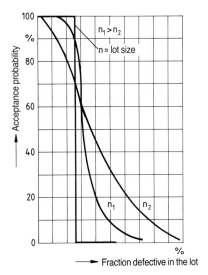

Fig. 10.5   Influence of the sample size $n$

chance of being accepted in a sampling test. This point is termed the "Acceptable Quality Level" $AQL$ (Fig. 10.7):

The $AQL$ can also be termed a supplier's risk since, owing to the random occurrences

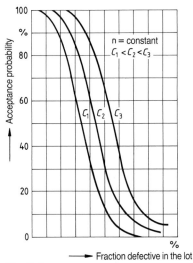

Fig. 10.6
Influence of the permitted number of defects $c$

of the acceptance characteristic is dependent upon two factors:

▷ *The sample size n*

If, in borderline cases, the sample size is equal to the lot size, the acceptance characteristic consists of a step function (Fig. 10.5).

▷ The permitted number of defects c

The maximum permitted share of defective components $c$ at which the lot will still be accepted influences the acceptance characteristic as shown in Fig. 10.6. The lower the permitted number of defects $c$ in the sample, the closer the acceptance characteristic approaches 0 fractions defective in the lot. This means that a sampling plan for instruction is more or less selective, dependent upon the $n-c$ combination.

Various points have been defined on the acceptance characteristic in order to permit clear agreements to be reached between supplier and purchaser. One of the most important points specifies the fraction defective of a lot in % at which this lot still has a 90 %

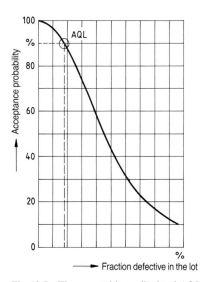

Fig. 10.7   The acceptable quality level $AQL$

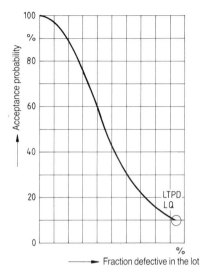

Fig. 10.8   The limiting quality $LQ$

statistically possible, a "good" consignment may be rejected by the customer on the basis of a random test. "Good" consignment means that its fraction defective actually lies below the agreed $AQL$ but an inadmissible fraction defective was established, at random, in the sample. This fact makes it clear that, in this connection, a just assessment of a supplier is possible only on the basis of many consignments. Only a few or only one single consignment do or does not suffice. A reputable manufacturer will maintain his manufacturing quality (also termed $AOQ$ = Average Outgoing Quality) well below the $AQL$ which he has promised. The more he does this, the less complaints he can expect.

Since a mean rejection rate of 10 % is generally intolerable, if an AQL value is agreed, the supplier will endeavor not to exceed a mean fraction defective of $AOQ = AQL/2$. Thus, for instance, the Siemens target is $AOQ < 100$ dpm for integrated circuits (dpm = defectives per million), i.e. $AOQ < 0.01\%$ fraction defective per consignment.

The second important point on the acceptance characteristic is "limiting quality" $LQ$.

It states the fraction defective in percent of a supplied quantity at which it will still be accepted with 10 % acceptance probability (Fig. 10.8). The $LQ$ can also be designated the customer's risk since, in this case, a "bad" consignment of the sample could, accidentally, be accepted (i.e. the reverse case to that with $AQL$).

"Bad" consignment means that it actually contains a fraction defective which lies above the agreed $AQL$ but, by change, a lower fraction defective than that just permitted has been found in the sample.

## 10.4   Semiconductor Quality at Siemens

### 10.4.1   Fundamentals

What is quality assurance in practice like at Siemens? Every product group in the company division has its own quality assurance system which allows for the special features of the manufacturing process. Taking SQA-IC (Siemens quality assurance for integrated circuits) as an example, we shall now illustrate how the quality of the integrated circuits is produced, checked and assured at Siemens from the incoming inspection through to final acceptance.

▷ The objective of the SQA-IC is to ensure that

▷ the delivery quality and reliability of the integrated circuits meet the requirements and quality targets and

▷ defects established are remedied by corrective action.

Quality assurance covers

▷ qualification and approval of new technologies, production lines and products,

▷ quality monitoring in production with tests and inspections in the incoming goods department and after important production steps

▷ and quality and reliability surveillance on finished products.

A product/process/manufacturer is considered as "qualified/approved" if the product/process/manufacturer comply with specific, precisely defined quality requirements. The verification of these characteristics is termed "qualification". When the product/process/manufacturer attains qualification, the product/process/manufacturer is granted "approval" by the quality department. All departments of the plant are responsible for meeting the quality and reliability requirements within the framework of their scope of duties. The central quality department coordinates and monitors all quality-assurance measures. A documentation department which approves and distributes the technical information, documents, directives and instructions is affiliated to the central quality department.

The effectiveness of quality assurance is checked continually.

The following data is used for this purpose:

▷ Process monitoring data obtained during production
▷ Test and inspection results
▷ The results of reliability surveillance and the
▷ Field data from users

The experience gained increases component quality and reliability and improves the quality assurance measures. The heads of the organizational units responsible for quality of products and process make sure that quality assurance is being applied effectively in their divisions and sectors by conducting quality audits on site.

The most recent editions of the following specifications, standards and books etc. are used for quality assurance:

▷ Data books
▷ Quality specifications
▷ Siemens standards and
▷ External reference specifications

Table 10.2 contains an overview of how the external reference specifications are used in internal instructions for various requirements.

The reference specifications and Siemens standards are applied to the extent stipulated in this document and in the internal specifications for quality tests and inspections. The European reference specifications CECC90000 and 90100 correspond to DIN 45940, Parts 1 and 11.

Failure analyses are conducted, where required, on the failures from various tests and inspections. This process involves localizing the defect source in the integrated circuit and determining the failure or defect mechanism. A frequent occurrence of the

Table 10.2
Applied reference specifications

| Internal specifications for quality tests and inspections | Reference specifications for quality tests and inspections | | | | | | | | |
|---|---|---|---|---|---|---|---|---|---|
| Requirements made of: | MIL-M-38510 | MIL-STD-883 | MIL-STD-202 | UL 94 | CECC 90000/100 | IEC 68: IEC 147 | MIL-STD-105D | MIL-S-19500 | JEDEC JC 40.2 |
| Quality assurance system | ● | | | | ● | | | | |
| Incoming inspection | | | | | | | ● | | |
| Process quality | ● | | | | | | | | |
| In-process tests and inspections | ● | ● | ● | | ● | ● | ● | ● | |
| Electrical final test and inspection; type sampling | | ● | | ● | | ● | ● | | |
| Reliability | ● | ● | | | ● | ● | ● | | |
| Qualifications | | ● | ● | ● | ● | ● | ● | ● | ● |

same failure or defect mechanism leads to specific defect remedial action. Failures may, amongst other things be attributable to design or production errors or use beyond the maximum ratings or electrostatic discharge. The failure analysis is represented by the failure analysis triangle (Fig. 10.9).

The triangle emphasizes the importance of the statistical background of failures and their loading conditions for the degree of information obtained from each failure analysis. A failure analysis on a few failures of unknown origin is less helpful. The triangular form is also intended to indicate that, as failure analysis steps progress, smaller and smaller quantities are investigated but, nevertheless, they are investigated in greater detail. The aids and auxiliary equipment used are listed at the right-hand edge of the triangle. These include:

▷ computer controlled automatic testers
▷ analytical test benches
▷ light-optical microscopes
▷ scanning-electron microscopes (SEM)

▷ EDX (electronic dispersive X-ray microscope)
▷ Auger electron microprobe for analyzing thin surface coatings and platings.

A shmoo plot provides information on the dependence of a failure or defect mechanism upon temperature for instance. Other aids are used for chemical and metallurgical examinations. Defect localization by electrical, physical, optical, chemical and metallurgical defect analyzes is indicated at the left hand edge of the triangle. Initially, an attempt is made to obtain as many findings as possible from the non-destructive tests. A thorough knowledge of the interrelationships between the defect symptoms and the failure or defect mechanism is necessary for effective defect analyzes. Remedial action is taken is the same defect or failure causes occur frequently.

Integrated circuits in the laboratory and pre-production stage are identified by a three-digit date code: The first digit specifies the last digit of the year and the two last digits

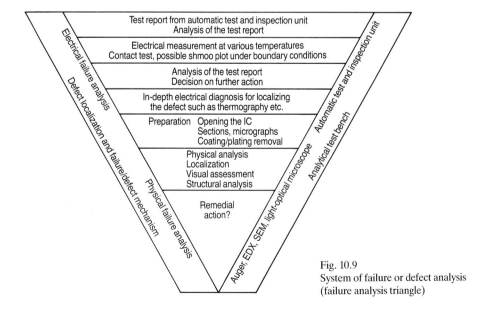

Fig. 10.9
System of failure or defect analysis
(failure analysis triangle)

specify the calendar week number of production (example: 1988, 3rd calendar week has code 803).

A four-digit date code is used for integrated circuits in the production stage: The two first digits specify the last digits of the year and the two last digits specify the calendar week number (example: 1988, 3rd calendar week has code 8803).

In order to permit the production and test lots to be traced back, codes with date information from wafer production and final inspection are attached to the modules or chips, provided space permits, but, at all events, on the packaging boxes.

The documents relevant to quality are kept for five years. The retention period starts on the date on which the document was issued.

## 10.4.2 Qualifications and Releases of Integrated Circuits

Mechanical, climatic and electrical tests and inspections for qualifications and release surveillance are conducted on representative products from the production lines, so-called "master products". The master products are selected such that they represent the entire product spectrum of the line, including the rules for "structural similarity" (Table 10.3).

Every master product thus represents a product family of structurally similar products.

Remarks further to Table 10.3:

1. If a feature identified with ● is identical on two different products, these two products are considered to be structural similar as regards the identified stress type and the feature.

Table 10.3   Definition of structural similarity

| Features | Stress types | | | |
| --- | --- | --- | --- | --- |
| | Package-specific | Climate | Electrical operation | Electro-static strength |
| Test categories | 0, 1, 2, 3, 4, 5, 6, 11 | 7, 10 | 8, 12 | 9 |
| Wafer production line and technology | – | ● | ● | ● |
| Passivation | ● | ● | ● | – |
| Electrical function (digital/analog) | – | – | ● | – |
| Chip resist | ● | ● | – | – |
| Chip size Length Width | <1.5× <1.5× | <1.5× <1.5× | <1.5× <1.5× | <1.5× <1.5× |
| Package type, number of pin groups | ● | ● | – | ● |
| Package material | ● | ● | – | ● |
| Chip mounting | ● | ● | – | – |

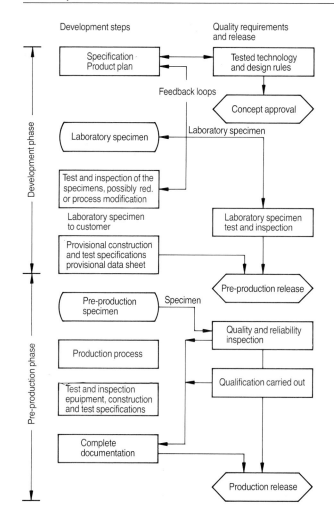

Fig. 10.10
Development steps and quality releases

2. As regards electrostatic discharge strength (ESD strength), the protection structures must also be identical on structurally similar products.
3. The chip sides of the structurally similar products are smaller than 1.5 chip sides of the master product.
4. Semicustom chips/ASICs must originate from the same gate array master family with the same library. Even in the case of cell design, the chips must originate from the same library. They must meet the conditions in respect of structural similarity of the master product family in both cases.
5. Integrated circuits in similar packages are combined to form structurally similar groups, dependent upon the number of pins. In the case of dual-in-line plastic packages, the following structural similar groups are formed for instance: 4 to 8, 14 to 20, 22, 24 to 48 and >48 pins.

Planning and development of new products and the related manufacturing processes and test and inspection methods are carried out on the basis of stipulated directives, allowing for the internal and external regulations and specifications by the relevant, responsible development departments for products and processes. This planning process is carried out in cooperation with the marketing division, the commercial departments, the production department and the quality department. Assuring the quality of products and processes during development is based on a complete and binding definition of the requirements, subdivision of the tasks into sections with defined requirements, complete documentation of the development results and the approvals on the basis of verified compliance with the requirements (Fig. 10.10).

Before new products or products from new processes are released for delivery, processes and products and the related documents are carefully checked in order to ensure that they comply with the requirements. Qualification starts at an early point and is carried out section-by-section in line with progress in development work, in order to permit quality-assurance and remedial action to be taken in good time. Releases are granted step-by-step for limited quantities until compliance with the requirements can be verified completely.

If samples have to be supplied at an early time of the new products, laboratory and pre-production specimens can already be forwarded to the customer.

Table 10.4   Types of specimen and sample

| | Works designation | | |
|---|---|---|---|
| | Laboratory specimen | Pre-production specimen | Production specimen |
| Used for the following on the customer's premises | Used for approximate function tests | | |
| | | Used for epuipment development | |
| | | | Used for equipment development and statistical tolerancing |
| | | | Used for reliability tests |
| Status of the specimens/ samples | Not yet fully developed. Possibly still defective. Not fully characterized, series production not ensured. | Specimens/samples comply with electrical specification. Means of production have been stipulated. Production is monitored by QA. | |
| | | Reliability data are not yet available. Limited production quantity. | Reliability results are availabe. All requirements of our quality standard are met. |
| Identification | No manufacturer's identification, "Engineering sample" or "ES" product designation. | With manufacturer's identification, company symbol or monogram and product designation | |
| | 3-digit date code | | 4-digit date code |

Table 10.5   Tests, inspections and types of defect

| Test category | Test/inspection | Defect type | Layout of the chip | Chip fracture | Silicon crystal defect | Oxidation, insulating layer | Soiling | Passivation | Plating | Corrosion | Chip mounting | Contact strength | Wire breakage | Wire routing | Leakage | Thermal matching | Stamping | Leads/pins | Plastic compound, material |
|---|---|---|---|---|---|---|---|---|---|---|---|---|---|---|---|---|---|---|---|
| | | | | | | Chip | | | | | Assembly | | | | Package | | | | |
| 0.1 | Electrical measured values | | • | • | • | • | • | • | • | • | • | • | • | | | | | | |
| 0.2 | Dimensions | | | | | | | | | | | | | | | | | • | |
| 1.1 | Visual inspection | | | | | | | | | | | | | | | • | | • | • |
| 1.2 | Solvent resistance | | | | | | | | | | | | | | | • | | | • |
| 1.3 | Internal visual inspection | | | • | | | • | • | • | • | • | • | • | • | | | | | |
| 1.4 | X-ray inspection | | | | | | | | | | • | • | • | | | | | | |
| 2 | Solderability | | | | | | | | | | | | | | | | | • | |
| 3 | Thermal stressing | | | • | | | | | | • | • | • | • | | • | • | | | • |
| 4 | Mechanical stressing | | | • | | | | | | | • | • | • | | • | | | | |
| 5 | Strength of the leads/pins | | | | | | | | | | | | • | | | | | • | |
| 6 | Salt atmosphere | | | | | | | | | | | | | | | | | • | |
| 7.1 | 85/85 test | | | | | | • | • | • | • | | | | | | | | | • |
| 7.3 | Water pressure test | | | | | | • | • | • | • | | • | | | | | | | • |
| 8.1 | Electrical operation | | • | • | • | • | • | • | • | | • | • | • | | | • | | | |
| 8.3 | Soft-error test | | • | | | | | | | | | | | | | | | | • |
| 9 | Electrostatic discharge | | • | | | • | | | | | | | | | | | | | |
| 10 | Temperature storage | | | • | • | • | • | | • | | | • | | | | • | | • | • |
| 11 | Photosensitivity | | | | | | | | | | | | | | | | | | • |
| 12 | Latch-up test | | • | | | | | | | | | | | | | | | | |
| 13 | Flammability | | | | | | | | | | | | | | | | | | • |
| 14 | Contact strength | | | | | | | | | | • | • | | | • | | | | |

Table 10.4 provides a description of how the specimens and samples are used, their stage of development and the identification of the individual types of specimen and sample.

New processes, packages and products are qualified before production approval. Requalification is carried out in the case of major modifications in the design, processes, packages and products or if wafer production is relocated to other locations. Observance of the quality and reliability requirements is ensured with the qualification and subsequent reliability monitoring.

Table 10.5 shows the interrelationship between testing/inspection and types of defect.

The plant carries out comprehensive quality assurance measures in order to ensure that modifications in the design, process and testing/inspection system or relocation to another location or another subcontractor do not have disadvantageous effects on delivery quality and reliability.

The customers are informed of modifications which could become noticeable in the majority of applications in respect of the specified characteristics before delivery of the modified products.

Some examples of such modifications are as follows:

▷ Mechanical dimensions;
▷ Plastic material of the package;
▷ Material and surface of the leads/pins;
▷ Packaging.

After packaging, the quality department ensures that the final inspection has been conducted correctly by taking samples from the tested quantity and subjecting them to an independent type test.

Every integrated circuit which does not comply with the data sheet is defective by definition.

The following features are checked in the type test:

▷ Visual inspection of external features
▷ Electrical ratings

▷ Static ratings and function at 25 °C and at the maximum operating temperature
▷ Dynamic ratings

Temperature correlations are also frequently used to check the electrical ratings and high and low temperatures. The *AQL* and *AOQ* values are available on request.

The quality features which are particularly expensive and complex or time-consuming to test or which can only be tested destructively (reliability, ambient stressing) are monitored every week or every four weeks on samples of the master products. The samples are taken after packaging or are taken from the sales warehouse. This reliability surveillance is conducted on the basis of a relevant combination of tests and inspections. The packaging of the products is designed to avoid a reduction in quality owing to transportation in-house and to the customer.

*Activities after delivery*
Integrated circuits about which complaints have been received are precisely analyzed if required. Valuable results and information from these analyses are collected and evaluated. This results in an improvement of the products and services.

A correlation of the testing and inspection system with failure analysis and remedial action on the premises of the manufacturer and on the premises of the customer is frequently required in order to coordinate testing, inspection, quality and application questions.

# 11 Glossary

**Adaptive echo cancellation:** The echo response of the line is simulated and the echo characteristic of the transmitted signals is determined with transversal filters. The resultant cancellation signal is subtracted from the received signal at the receive end so that the receive signal, with cancelled echo, is then available.

**AM stereo:** A method used particularly in the USA for transmitting stereo broadcasts in the medium-frequency band and thus utilize the longer range by comparison with the VHF band.

*AOQ:* Average outgoing quality. Expressed in %.

*AQL:* Acceptable quality level. Specifies the fraction defective of a lot in %, at which this lot still has a 90% chance of being accepted in a sampling test.

**ASIC:** Application specific integrated circuit. Whilst standard ICs such as memory chips, microcontrollers, microprocessors or peripheral chips are developed using the classic design methods at transistor level, rationalized design methods are used for ASICs.

**ASIC libraries:** They contain wiring specifications on higher-organized functions such as logic gates, counters, multiplexers etc.

**Avalanche effect:** If, in the case of PN junctions, very high voltages drop across the space charge region, this region loses its insulating property. The high voltage accelerates the charge carriers in the space charge region so strongly that new charge carriers are produced, in the manner of an avalanche, by collision or impact ionization. The avalanche effect is one of the high-field effects in the semiconductor.

**4B3T code (MMS 43 code):** 4B3T coding involves combining sets of 4 bits of the binary signal and converting them to a ternary signal.

**B-channel:** Speech/data channel in the ISDN

**BA:** Basic access. The BA serves to connect individual subscribers and small private branch exchanges.

**BORSCHT:** Battery feed – overvoltage protection – ringing-signaling – coding – hybrid – testing

**Bus arbiter:** An arbiter which coordinates access of several processors to one bus.

**Cache memories:** High-speed buffers for the commands, instructions and data required directly by the CPU.

**CCITT:** Comité Consultatif International Télégraphique et Téléphonique; the most important international standardization commission in the field of telecommunications engineering.

**Cell design:** Design technique for developing customized semiconductor circuits with predefined macros (standard cells).

**CEPT:** Conférence Européene des Administrations des Postes et des Télécommunications. This conference drafted concepts on implementing the ISDN.

**CEPT concept:** Based on the PCM 30-system.

**Channeled-gate array technique:** A technique for connecting the gates via the intermediate wiring channels.

**CISC:** Complex instruction set computer

**CML:** Current mode logic. Bipolar wiring technique.

**CMOS:** Complementary metal oxide semiconductor. On the CMOS, one basic unit consists of an N-channel transistor and a P-channel transistor. N or P-substrate is used. In the case of N-substrate, the N-channel transistor must be accommodated in a P-type substrate and, in the case of P-substrate, the P-channel transistor must be accommodated in a N-type substrate. Since, during operation, one of the two transistors is always forward-biased and the other is reverse-biased, very little current indeed flows in steady state. The current consumption is essentially caused by dynamic charge reversal of the switching capacitances when the transistors switch.

**Coercive field strength:** $H_c$ is the field strength to be applied in order to reduce the flux density $B$ or the magnetization $J$ to zero again.

**Compiler:** A program which translates a program formulated in a high-level programming language to machine language. RISC compilers also order the commands of the machine code so that the pipeline of the RISC is supplied optimally.

**Condensation soldering:** Also designated vapor-phase soldering. With this soldering method under constant temperature, the complete pc-board is immersed into the vapor zone of a liquid which has been brought to the boil.

**Coprocessor:** Specialized processor which, in conjunction with the central microprocessor, assumes special tasks, for example floating-point arithmetic operations.

**cpi:** Clock cycles per average instruction.

**CPU:** Central processing unit

**CRC method:** Cyclic redundancy check

**D-channel:** Signaling channel in the ISDN

**Datex-L network:** Data transmission with circuit switching.

**Datex-P network:** Data transmission with packet switching.

**Dhrystones:** Synthetic program for computer comparisons. There is an ADA version, a C version and a Pascal version.

**Digital network:** Signifies digital transmission and switching of information between the subscriber terminal equipment.

**DMA:** Direct memory access. In the case of DMA, the DMA module controls the system bus and transfers memory contents within the memory or to or from the periphery far faster than the processor could.

**dpm:** Defectives per million.

**DRAM:** Dynamic memory. The information is stored as a charge in a capacitor which must be cyclically refreshed.

**ECL:** Emitter coupled logic. Bipolar logic module family.

**EEPROM:** Electrically erasable programmable read-only memory. This is a non-volatile memory which retains its memory contents if the power supply is switched off. The information can be erased electrically.

**Energy density:** The absolute products of the $B$-$H$ values obtained from demagnetization of a permanent magnet are formed in each case. The energy density $BH_{max}$ designates the efficiency of the permanent magnet.

**EPROM:** Erasable programmable read-only memory. A non-volatile memory which retains its memory contents if the power supply is switched off. The information can be erased with ultraviolet light.

**Failure rate** $\lambda$ **(*T*):** Usually specified in "fit" (failures in time). 1 fit = 1 failure/$10^9$ component test hours.

**fit:** Failures in time. 1 fit = 1 failure/$10^9$ hours

**FREDFET-SIPMOS transistors with integrated free-wheeling diode:** Transistors for controlled three-phase drives, with simple structure, in the kilowatt range.

**Free-wheeling diode:** This compensates for voltage peaks within the supply voltages.

**Frequency diversity system:** A system for automatically changing the receive frequency if reception conditions worsen. The receiver must have stored all transmission frequencies of the corresponding transmitter for this purpose.

**Fullcustom IC:** Individualized integrated circuits developed at the transistor level. Fullcustom ICs are normally developed by the semiconductor manufacturer.

**Gate:** Basic structure of the gate arrays consisting of transistors. A gate consists of 2 to 8 transistors. An equivalent gate function corresponds to four transistors.

**Gate array:** Consists of so-called gates and wiring channels in between.

**Graded-index fiber:** An optical waveguide with predominantly parabolic refractive index profile. This reduces multimode dispersion.

**Hall effect:** If a current is passed through a strip conductor and if there is a magnetic field perpendicular to this, the electrons are deflected to the side owing to the Lorentz (electrodynamic) force. This produces an electric field at right angles to the current di-

rection, the force of which just cancels the Lorentz force in equilibrium. The Hall voltage which is thus produced is dependent upon the electron mobility in the conductor.

**Hall sensor:** A silicon semiconductor based on the Hall effect.

**HDLC:** High-level data link control.

**I$^2$L:** Integrated injection logic. Bipolar logic module family.

**Integrated services network:** All services for voice, text and data communication are provided in one communication network with one network access.

**Interrupt:** An interrupt synchronizes the processor with events which occur at unpredictable times, for example an entry from the keyboard. The program currently running is interrupted by the interrupt and branches to an address (vector) scheduled for the interrupt. After the interrupt routine has been run, the program continues at the point at which it was previously interrupted.

**IOM interface:** ISDN-oriented modular interface. It permits the user to compile the optimum configuration for his application.

**ISDN:** Integrated services digital network.

**LAN: Local area network.** Such a network can span distances up to maximum 10 kilometers.

**LAPD:** Link access procedure for D-channel.

**Latch-up:** The CMOS structure contains parasitic thyristors which may fire when the voltage levels at the inputs or outputs of a CMOS chip lie outside the supply voltage range. This means that high currents can then flow between the supply voltage terminals, thus destroying the chip. Firing can be interrupted only by turning off the supply voltage. The latch-up effect may occur in particular as the result of disturbances on the signal line resulting from turn-on or turn-off processes. Attempts are made to minimize the latch-up sensitivity.

**Line interface:** Subscriber line in the telephone network. It starts in the ISDN exchange at the line termination LT and terminates at the subscriber equipment in the network termination NT.

**Lot:** A quantity of components which have passed through the manufacturing process together. Changes in the manufacturing process effect all components in a lot.

**LQ:** Limiting quality. This specifies the fraction defective in % of a supplied quantity at which it will still be accepted with 10 % acceptance probability.

**LT:** Line termination. A line termination in the ISDN.

**Magnetic field concentrator:** Since soft iron (mild steel) has a low magnetic resistance (reluctance), it can be used as a magnetic field concentrator.

**Master:** Silicon slice prefabricated for production of gate arrays.

**Maximum ratings:** Exceeding even only one of these ratings may destroy the module or chip. A corresponding safety margin with respect to the maximum rating must always be incorporated when developing the system.

**MFLOPS:** Million floating point operations per second.

**Microcontrollers:** Microcontrollers provide an operable computer system with only one chip with minimum configuration. All systems components absolutely necessary are integrated in the microcontroller.

**Microprocessors:** Programmable chips modelled on mainframes. They contain the arithmetic logic unit (ALU) as the section which performs the arithmetic operations, the instruction decoder and the executive sequencer. More and more peripheral functions are being integrated on one silicon chip.

**MIPS:** Million instructions per second. In order to obtain this, one mixes the instructions which occur statistically most frequently. The lack of standardization restricts the informative content of this statement. MIPS is an expression suitable only for assessment of computers of one family or with comparable architecture.

**Monomode fiber:** Only one mode is guided in the fiber, i.e. multimode dispersion is zero. These fibers can transmit even higher frequencies than graded-index fibers.

**MOS-GTO:** Gate-turn-off thyristor. Today, the thyristor principle is still indispensable for switching currents of over 1000 A and, at the same time, blocking voltages of several thousand volts. A thyristor, once turned on, can be turned off only by interrupting the current which flows. The GTO turns off with a negative gate current which is approximately one fifth of the load current. Siemens supplies a family of wafer GTOs for a voltage range covering 1.8 to 4.5 kV and currents up to 3000 A.

**Multiprocessor system:** Two or more processors work together more or less closely (fixed or loose coupling) in such a system. Synchronization of this cooperation, generally via semaphore mechanisms (semaphore = traffic light control) is of particular importance in this respect. The purpose of multiprocessor systems is the higher achievable system power thanks to delegation of tasks and parallel operation.

**N-channel transistors:** N-channel types are controlled with a positive gate-source voltage and block positive drain-source voltages.

**Near instantaneous companding method:** In biphase code, every data bit is represented by two mutually complementary elements, a logical 1 by the element string 1,0 and a logical zero by the element string 0,1.

**NMOS:** N-channel metal oxide semiconductor. MOS technology with N-channel transistors of a P-doped substrate. The designation channel refers to the inverted polarity of the P-doped zone between source and drain with the transistor switched.

**NT:** Network termination in the ISDN.

**P-channel transistors:** P-channel types are controlled with a negative gate-source voltage and block negative drain-source voltages.

**p-data:** Packet-oriented data

**PA:** Primary access. Large private branch exchanges.

**PBX:** Private branch exchange.

**Peripheral functions:** This means all peripheral functions, i.e. everything related to control of external functions.

**Personalization:** The master is converted to the customized semiconductor circuit by intra and inter-cell wiring.

**Piezoresistive effect:** A change in the electrical resistance of a metal or semiconductor under the influence of a mechanical stress or strain. In the case of semiconductors, the cause lies in the band structure and, in the case of metals, in the Fermi surface which is deformed by the mechanical strain or stress. This changes the conductivity.

**Pipelining:** Simultaneous instruction execution for speeding up the program run. Instruction execution is dissected into five time slots on the SAB R3000. With a filled pipeline, an instruction is completed after each time slot.

**PROFET®:** SIPMOS transistors of the Smart family with integrated protection functions and check-back signals to the control logic.

**PROM:** Programmable read only memory. PROMs are programmed by the user himself. There are electrically erasable PROMs and PROMs which can be erased with ultraviolet light (EEPROMs and EPROMs).

**RAM:** Random access memory.

**Reactive load:** This means capacitive and inductive loads. When driving reactive loads, the load line (in the case of resistive load) degenerates to form an ellipse. This means that there are high power losses in the power operational amplifier.

**Reflow soldering:** Solder which is already applied to the pc-board is caused to reflow, thus joining the pc-board and components. The solder is generally applied in the form of solder paste.

**Reluctance:** See magnetic resistance.

**Remanence:** $B_r$ is a measure of the magnitude of the residual magnetic flux density after full magnetization in the closed circuit.

**RISC:** Reduced instruction set computer.

**ROM: Read only memory.** The memory contents are written in mechanically or electrically as early as the production stage.

**S-interface:** The interface of the subscriber line area. It is located between the network termination NT and the terminal equipment TE.

**$S_0$ interface:** A passive 4-wire bus, the S-bus. Up to 8 terminals can be connected simultaneously to the S-bus.

**Sea-of-gates technique:** Gates are connected not via the wiring channels but directly via the gate-array cells (logic cells). This technique reduces the silicon area required.

**Semicustom IC:** These are developed on the basis of prefabricated gate arrays or standard cells. Semicustoms ICs can be developed by the user himself with assistance from the semiconductor manufacturer.

**Series gating:** It is possible to minimize the space requirement and power loss and achieve a substantial reduction in propagation delay by multiple utilization of the cross current (up to 3 difference amplifier stages).

**SIPMOS®:** MOS transistor product family manufactured by Siemens for switching high current and voltages, which can be biased directly with TTL/CMOS levels.

**SIRET®:** Siemens-ring-emitter-transistor for high switching rates in the voltage range 500 to 1200 V. It permits construction of power converters in the power range of several hundred kilowatts at frequencies over 10 kHz, such as those required for low-noise drives.

**SITAC®:** Optically coupled triac for electrical and high-voltage strength isolation of the control circuit from the output circuit (at mains voltages of 220 V).

**SLMA:** Subscriber line module analog. The functions of the SLMA are summarized under the term BORSCHT.

**SLMD:** Subscriber line module digital.

**SMD:** Surface mounted device.

**SMT:** Surface mounted technology.

**SOA:** Safe operating area. A power operational amplifier may be operated only in this area.

**Speed Power Programming:** Facility for programming individual gates for high speed or low power loss.

**Splicing:** Connection technique. Fibre-optic cables for instance are fused together under an arc.

**SRAM:** Static random access memory. SRAMs store the information in two inverters connected with feedback (bistable element).

**Stack:** Subroutine and interrupt return addresses are reserved using this technique. Moreover, parameters can be transferred between the subroutine and main program in the stack. The stack is managed via the stack pointer. Its contents are an address which points to the next free position in the stack. With each read operation (POP) or each write operation (PUSH) on the stack, the stack pointer is incremented or decremented by one address respectively.

**Standard cells:** Pre-developed functions blocks such as counters, memories and computer kernels etc. They can be called and assembled as macros of a CAD system.

**Surface mounting:** Printed conductors and components are located on the same side of the pc-board. No drillholes are required.

**TE:** Terminal equipment

**TEAG:** Total effective air gap. It must be kept as small as possible. This permits generation of a relatively large magnetic stroke with small magnets.

**TEMPFET®:** SIPMOS transistors of the Smart family with temperature sensor.

**Through-hole assembly:** The components are plugged into holes on the pc-board.

**Trade-off:** The circuit developer can decide on the required ratio of short gate propagation delay to low power loss individually for each individual cell.

**Translation lookaside buffer:** Fully associative memory which contains a translation table with the virtual addresses and the corresponding physical addresses.

**Translation mechanism:** This consists of the alternative functions modes frontal approximation and lateral lead-past.

**TTL:** Transistor-transistor-logic. Bipolar logic chip family.

$U_{K0}$ **interface:** Two-wire interface, i.e. the digital signals are transmitted bidirectionally simultaneously on the existing twin copper wire.

**Vapor-phase soldering:** See condensation soldering.

**Wafer:** Silicon wafer which forms the basis for semiconductor manufacture.

**Wait states:** Wait cycles which are inserted in the machine instruction cycle in order to adapt a fast processor to slower memories or peripheral processors.

**Wave soldering:** The pc-board is pulled over a wave of liquid solder with the soldering side pointing downwards.

**Whetstone:** Synthetic program for computer comparisons. It was developed in Whetstone, England, and is based upon ALGOL, but is generally used in FORTRAN. There is one version with single precision (32 bit) and one with double precision (64 bit).

# 12 Literature

## Literature for Chapter 3

Bechteler, M.: GTO-Thyristoren: Leistungsschalter für heute und morgen. Siemens Components (1988) Special − Schaltungen und Bauelemente der Leistungselektronik, Pages 10 to 13

Becker, K.; Binder, J.; Ehrler, G.; Hagen, H.; Frantisek, M.: Silizium-Drucksensoren für den Bereich 2 kPa to 40 MPa. Siemens Components 23 (1985) Issues 2 and 3

Binder, J.; Ehrler, G.; Wetzel, K.: Mikroelektronik. Kraft- und Drucksensoren. BMFT-Forschungsbericht T83-100 (1983)

Bisio, G.R. et al.: Structure and Electrical Characteristics on High Power GTO: Criteria for Optimum Design. Proc. PCI MOTORCON. Sept. 1983. Pages 238 to 252

Data book: SIPMOS-Kleinsignal- und Leistungstransistoren. Ordering code B3-B3209

Diagnoseverfahren zur Auswertung des PROFET-Statusausganges. Design & Elektronik. Issue 9, 2.5.1989, Pages 148 to 150

Ehrler, G.; Nagy, G.: Drucksachen. Elektronikpraxis 18 (1983) Issue 9, Pages 30 to 33

Freundel, P.; Dobray, E.: FREDFET, ein neuer Leistungs-Mosfet mit schneller Inversdiode. Siemens Components 23 (1985) Issue 2, Pages 58 to 63

Hesse, J.: Fachberichte Messen, Steuern, Regeln. Interkama-Kongreß 1983. Published by M. Syrbe and M. Thoma

Kanada, Y.: Piezoeffekt in Halbleitern. Festkörperprobleme II. Braunschweig: Vieweg 1963, Pages 188 to 202

Magnetic Sensors Databook. Ordering code B359-B6033-X-X-7600

Nakagawa, A.; Ohashi, H.: A study on GTO Turn-off Failure Mechanism. A time and temperature dependent 1-D-model analysis. IEEE Trans. on ED, Vol. ED 31., No. 3. March 84, Pages 273 to 279

Schaltbeispiele: DC/DC-Wandler von 12 V auf +25 V/180 W. Ordering code B1-B3191

Schaltbeispiele: Durchflußwandler-SNT. Ordering code B/3030

Schaltbeispiel: Einsatz von Temperatursensoren KTY und Mikrocomputer SLE43215P in energiesparenden Heizungsreglern. Ordering code B1-B3078

Schaltbeispiele: Induktiver Näherungsschalter. Ordering code B/3093

Schaltbeispiel: Kostengünstige Temperaturmeßschaltung für MC-Systemlösungen mit KTY-Temperatursensoren und Ein-Chip-Mikrocomputer SAB80215. Ordering code B1-B3079

Schaltbeispiele: Schaltnetzteil. Ordering code B/3031

Schaltbeispiele: Sperrwandler-SNT. Ordering code B/3032

Schaltbeispiele: Tiefsetzsteller. Ordering code B/2987

Schaltbeispiele: Umrichterschaltungen für Drehstrommotoren. Ordering code B/2906

Schaltbeispiele: Batteriebetriebenes 100-kHz-Lampenvorschaltgerät. Odering code B1-B3192

Schumbrutzki, W.: FREDFET-Leistungshalbbrücke kurzschlußfest durch Lichtleiterelemente. Siemens Components 25 (1987) Issue 2, Pages 59 to 61

Schutzmaßnahmen gegen elektrostatische Aufladungen. Ordering code B/2909

Siemens Components Special: Schaltungen und Bauelemente der Leistungselektronik (1988). Ordering code A19100-L524-U887

SIPMOS Leistungstransistoren: Technologie. Schaltverhalten, Schutzschaltungen, Anwendungsbeispiele, Technische Beschreibung 1985. Ordering code B3-B3129

SIPMOS-Transistoren: Lieferprogramm. Ordering code B3-B3336

Stoisiek, M.; Patalon, H.: Power devices with MOS controlled emitter shorts. Siemens Forschungs- und Entwicklungsberichte Vol. 14 (1985) Issue 2, Page 2, Pages 45 to 49

Tufte, O.N.; Chapman, P.W.; Long, D.: Silicon Diffused-Element Piezoresistive Diaphragms. J. Appl. Phys. 33, No. 11, 3322 (1962)

Wetzel, K.: Von 110 auf 220 V: Automatische Spannungsumschaltung mit SITAC. Leistungselek-

tronik. Siemens Components (1988) Special –
Schaltungen und Bauelemente der Leistungselektronik

Zerbst, M.: Piezoeffekt in Halbleitern. Festkörperprobleme II, Braunschweig: Vieweg. Pages
188 to 202

Zuverlässigkeit von SIPMOS-Transistoren. Ordering code B/2910

*Literature for Chapter 4*

Acht Beine für Megabits: Optokoppler-Lieferpro-
gramm. Ordering code B3-B3880

Aman, M.C.; Mettler, K.; Rolf, H.: Laserdioden-
Sendebauelemente hoher Lichtleistung für die
optische Nachrichtenübertragung. telcom report 6 (1983) Special – Nachrichtenübertragung
mit Licht, Pages 84 to 89

Baberg, F.; Luft, J.: GaAlAs-Halbleiterlaser für
hohe Leistungen. Siemens Components 26
(1988) Issue 4, Pages 154 to 159

Böckl, R.: Lichtleiter-Bauelemente regeln Hoch-
frequenz-Schaltnetzteile. Siemens Components
25 (1987) Issue 6, Pages 238 to 234

Druminski, M.; Gessner, R.; Kappeler, F.; Wester-
meier, H.; Wolf, D.; Zschauer, K.: MOVPE
(AlGa)As/Ga/As 870 nm Oxide Strip Lasers
with Highly Uniform Laser Characteristics. Jap.
J. appl. Phys. 25 (1986) No. 1, Pages L17/20

Frankenberg, H. v.: Qualitätsaspekte bei der
Kopplerherstellung. Siemens Components 22
(1984) Issue 5, Pages 216 to 219

Haas, H.; Karsten, W.; Schellhorn, F.: Optische Signalübertragung mit neuen Lichtleiterelemen-
ten. Siemens Components 25 (1987) Issue 1, Pages 62 to 64

Halbleiterbauelemente für die LWL-Technik und
Laserarrays: Lieferprogramm 1988/89. Ordering code B3-B3829

Heinen, J.: Optoelektronische Sender und Emp-
fänger. telcom report 10 (1987) Special – Multi-
plex- und Leitungseinrichtungen, Pages 156 to
159

Hirschmann, G.: Schneller Lichtleiter-Optokopp-
ler. Elektronik-Entwicklung 5 (1987). Pages 8 to
10

Huba, G.: Anwendungsbeispiel: Verkürzung der
Schaltzeiten von Standard-Optokopplern. Siemens Components 24 (1986) Issue 5, Pages 179
to 183

Kappeler, F.: Monolitic Phase-Locked GaAlAs
Laserarrays, Siemens Forschungs- und Entwicklungsberichte 14 (1985) No. 6, Pages 289 to 294

Kneubühl, F.K.; Sigrist, M.W.: Laser. Stuttgart:
Teubner 1988

Neue Bauelemente für die Signalübertragung mit
Kunststoff-LWL. Laser Magazin 4 (1986), Pages
5.30 to 32

Schumbrutzki, W.: FREDFET-Leistungshalbbrücke kurzschlußfest durch Lichtleiterbauele-
mente. Siemens Components 25 (1987) Issue 2,
Pages 59 to 61

Stürzer, H.: Motorsteuerung mit galvanischer
Trennung von Bedienermodul und Leistungsteil. Siemens Components 25 (1987) Issue 5. Pages 196 to 198

Tannenbaum, A.: Implication of Structured Programming for Machine Architecture. Commun.
ACM. March 1978

Wayrich, C.; Zschauer, K.: Grundlagen der elek-
trooptischen Signalwandlung. telecom report 6
(1984) Special – Nachrichtenübertragung mit
Licht. Pages 15 to 20

*Literature for Chapter 5*

Bauer, P.; Feger, O.: Impulse definierter Dauer
(Compare-Capture-Einheit im SAB80C517).
IEEE-Steuerungstechnik. No. 24. 29. Novem-
ber 1988, Pages 12 to 14

Blaser, L.; Franco, H.: Push Pull Class-AB Trans-
formerless Power Amplifiers. IEEE Transac-
tions on Audio. January 1963

Burr-brown International GmbH: Leistungsopera-
tionsverstärker-Spezifikationen richtig interpre-
tiert. Elektronik-Industrie 3 (1984). Pages 45 to
48

Caroll, E.: International Rectifier. Definition des
Sperrerholverhaltens von Dioden. Design und
Elektronik 16, 5. 8. 1986

Feger, O.: Applikationen zur 8051-Mikrocontrol-
ler-Familie. Haar bei München: Markt & Technik 1988

Feger, O.: Die 8051-Mikrocontroller-Familie.
Haar bei München: Markt & Technik 1988

Feger, O.: Fahrstuhlregelung mit dem Mikrocontroller SAB80C517. Elektronik-Informationen
10 (1988), Pages 138 to 141

Feger, O.: Motorsteuerungen mit dem Mikrocontroller SAB80C517. Elektronik-Entwicklung 10
(1988), Pages 31 to 33

Hellberg, A. v.; Feger, O.: Rasches Entwickeln
von Mikrocontroller-Systemen mit Experimen-
tierplatinen. Elektronik (1988) Issue 23, Pages
71 to 74

Kaiffler, E.; Möller, F.; Tihanyi, J.: Grundschaltungen mit SIPMOS-FET-Treibern – neue Optokoppler erschließen neue Schaltungsvarianten. Siemens Components 27 (1988) Issue 1, Pages 8 to 23

Kane, G.: MIPS R2000 RISC Architecture. Englewood Cliffs, NJ: Prentice Hall 1987

Lenz, M.: Der Leistungsoperationsverstärker TCA1365B. Elektroniker 12 (1988), Pages 28 to 35. Siemens Ordering code of the reprint B100-B6022

Lenz, M.: Leistungsoperationsverstärker mit integrierter Freilaufdiode. Design & Elektronik (1988) Issue 9, Pages 76 to 88. Siemens Ordering code NI-B3930

Patterson, D.; Sequin, C.: A VLSI RISC. Computer, Sept. 1982. SAB80515 Data Sheet: Ordering code B2-B3353-X-X-7600

SAB80515/80535 Single-Chip Microcontroller, User's Manual 10.88. Ordering code B2-B3343-X-X-7600

SAB80C515 Data Sheet: Ordering code B2-B3814-X-X-7600

Schumbrutzki, W.: FREDFET-Leistungshalbbrücke kurzschlußfest durch Lichtleiterelemente. Siemens Components 25 (1987) Issue 2, Pages 59 to 61

Schwager, B.: Leistungsoperationsverstärker TCA 365. Siemens Components 19 (1982)

Storandt, S.; Feger, O.: Sichere und fehlertolerante Mikrocontroller-Systeme. Elektronik (1989) Issue 10, Pages 88 to 90

Storandt, S.; Feger, O.: Wie macht man Prozessor- und Controller-Systeme ausfallsicherer? Grundlagen und praktische Hinweise zum Thema „Verfügbarkeit". Elektronik (1988) Issue 17, Pages 72 to 76

Stürzer, H.: Motorsteuerung mit galvanischer Trennung von Bedienermodul und Leistungsteil. Siemens Components 25 (1987) Issue 5, Pages 196 to 198

Tannenbaum, A.: Implication of Structured Programming for Machine Architecture. Commun. ACM, March 1978

Wildar, R.; Yamatake, M.: High-power op amp provides diverse circuit functions. EDN 29. 5. 1986, Pages 185 to 200

## Literature for Chapter 6

Arsac, M.; Kugelstadt, T.: SICOFI: eine Lösung für jeden SLIC. Siemens Components 26 (1988) Issue 1, Pages 8 to 13

Kaul, P.: ISDN. Heidelberg: R. v. Deckers 1986

Kuhn, R.: IC-Komfort fürs Telefon. Siemens Components 26 (1988) Issue 1, Pages 13 to 17

Schollmeier, G.: Teilnehmeranschlußtechnik im ISDN. telcom report special issue ISDN (1985), Pages 23 to 28

Suckfüll, H.: ISDN – das Universalnetz für alle Individualkommunikationsdienste. telcom report special issue ISDN (1985), Pages 4 to 10

## Literature for Chapter 7

Brauschke, P.; Sommer, P.: Leistungstransistor mit integriertem Temperatursensor. Design & Elektronik (1987) Issue 9

Brauschke, P.; Sommer, P.: Relais mit eingebauter Sicherung. Elektronik-Applikation (1987) Issue 46

Dannhäuser, F.; Storandt, S.: Anwendungsbeispiel Klimaregelung im Kfz mit dem Mikrocontroller SAB80515. Elektronik Informationen 11 (1986), Pages 62 to 66

Fenzl, H.: Smart-Power-Bauelemente auf der Basis der SIPMOS-Technologie. Siemens Components 25 (1987) Issue 4

## Literature for Chapter 9

Bauelemente für Oberflächenmontage: Lieferprogramm. Ordering code B3-B3264

Diskrete Halbleiter für die Oberflächenmontage: Datenbuch. Ordering code B3-B3235

Mikropack, eine kompakte IC-Bauform für die Oberflächenmontage: Product info. Ordering code B1-B3166

## Literature for Chapter 10

Ausgewählte Qualitätsbegriffe leicht verständlich. Ordering code B/2271

Bauelemente, gesicherte Qualität zum Nutzen für den Anwender. Ordering code B9-B3583

Qualitätsbegriffe für elektronische Bauelemente. Ordering code B9-B3466

Qualitätsordnung. Ordering code B9-B3616

Rahmenbedingungen für Zuverlässigkeitsangaben bei elektronischen Bauelementen. Ordering code B9-B3812

SQS-IS. Ordering code B1-B3859

Statistische Kontrolle von Prozeßlinien – Vorgehensweise zur Herstellung von Kontrollkarten. Ordering code B9-B3689